Earth's Grandest Rivers

Books by Ferdinand C. Lane

EARTH'S GRANDEST RIVERS

THE WORLD'S GREAT LAKES

THE MYSTERIOUS SEA

EARTH'S GRANDEST RIVERS

Ferdinand C. Lane

DOUBLEDAY & COMPANY, INC.

Garden City, New York, 1949

*To my wife, whose aid in preparing
my books on global geography
has been invaluable.*

EARTH'S GRANDEST RIVERS ALPHABETICALLY ARRANGED

	RIVER	CONTINENT	LENGTH in Miles	AREA Square Miles	DISCHARGE Cubic Feet per Second
1.	Amazon	South America	4,000	2,772,000	7,200,000
2.	Amur	Asia	2,900	787,000	
3.	Brahmaputra	Asia	1,680	361,000	500,000
4.	Churchill	North America	1,000	140,000	
5.	Colorado	North America	1,450	244,000	23,300
6.	Columbia	North America	1,270	259,000	280,000
7.	Congo	Africa	2,900	1,425,000	2,000,000
8.	Danube	Europe	1,760	347,000	315,000
9.	Dnieper	Europe	1,410	202,000	
10.	Euphrates	Asia	1,700	430,000	
11.	Ganges	Asia	1,540	432,000	270,000
12.	Hwang Ho	Asia	2,700	400,000	116,000
13.	Indus	Asia	1,700	372,000	300,000
14.	Irrawaddy	Asia	1,250	158,000	
15.	Jaxartes	Asia	1,700	320,000	
16.	La Plata-Paraná	South America	2,450	1,198,000	2,800,000
17.	Lena	Asia	3,000	1,169,000	325,000
18.	Mackenzie	North America	2,525	682,000	450,000
19.	Mekong	Asia	2,600	350,000	600,000
20.	Mississippi-Missouri	North America	3,986	1,243,000	513,000
21.	Murray-Darling	Australia	2,345	414,000	13,000
22.	Nelson-Saskatchewan	North America	1,660	360,000	
23.	Niger	Africa	2,600	584,000	
24.	Nile	Africa	4,053	1,293,000	420,000
25.	Ob	Asia	2,800	1,000,000	
26.	Orange	Africa	1,300	400,000	
27.	Orinoco	South America	1,700	570,000	
28.	Oxus	Asia	1,500	115,000	
29.	Rhine	Europe	800	86,000	
30.	Rio Grande	North America	1,800	232,000	5,180
31.	St. Lawrence	North America	2,100	565,000	400,000
32.	Salween	Asia	1,770	62,700	
33.	São Francisco	South America	1,811	252,000	
34.	Volga	Europe	2,325	592,000	
35.	Yangtze Kiang	Asia	3,400	750,000	770,000
36.	Yenisei	Asia	3,553	1,000,000	
37.	Yukon	North America	2,300	330,000	
38.	Zambezi	Africa	2,200	513,000	

Global geography is still in a formative period. River discharges as measured in cubic feet per second are somewhat conjectural, while authorities also differ on certain river lengths and drainage areas. The above table, however, is a painstaking effort to sift out and select from a mass of conflicting data the most accurate figures now obtainable.

Contents

PART FOUR

The Great Rivers of Asia

PART FIVE

The Great Rivers of Africa

Earth's Grandest Rivers

PART ONE

Introduction

~~~~~~

FOREWORD

RIVERS, so Homer sang, "are heaven sent," a poetic flight echoed by many a wayfarer in a thirsty land. To the ancient Hebrews "green pastures . . . beside the still waters" marked the height of earthly felicity. Four rivers compassed their fabled Eden, while the rhapsodist who penned the Book of Revelations saw "a pure river of water of life, clear as crystal." In gloomy contrast, ebon currents coursed through the Underworld. The Greeks thought that Souls were ferried to the realm of Shades across the Styx, while that dark fantasy the River of Death finds frequent repetition in our literature.

Drinking water is only the first gift of flowing streams. In river valleys nomads found pasturage for their flocks and later, with the growth of agriculture, developed settled communities. Marginal fields were broadened by irrigation ditches. The canals of Chaldea are older than history. Rivers also provided fertilizing silt, so that after thousands of years of intensive cultivation Egypt's thin ribbon of cultivated land remains one of the garden spots of the world.

River valleys were the cradles of early civilization. From Nilotic mud were erected the walls of fellahs' huts, and bricks of similar nature builded Babylon the Great. Clay was the raw material of the potter's craft, and with broken potsherds the archeologist delves into a forgotten past. River reeds provided thatch for humble homes, mats for earthen floors, baskets for storing grain.

The crested papyrus of the Nile gave the world its earliest paper, a medium for magic formulae, religious incantations, and eventually literature.

Man's halting footsteps and the donkeys, oxen, and camels he later broke to bear his burdens were surpassed when the first rude raft, or balsa, of bundled reeds embarked upon the neighboring stream. Rude coracles of wattlework and hides swirled down the Euphrates long before the days of Hammurabi, and boats sketched upon the walls of crumbling Egyptian tombs differ little from picturesque craft that float down the Nile today.

New worlds of hope and promise have always beckoned from beyond intervening rivers. For centuries hordes of barbarians surged against the ramparts of the Danube and the Rhine, eager to share the luxury of Rome. From many a Nebo across many a Jordan the human race has surveyed its lands "flowing with milk and honey."

Rivers have always provided avenues of exploration. French *voyageurs* invaded the great Northwest through forest-shaded streams. Orellana, drifting down an unknown current, gave the world its first authentic information of the Amazon. From branch to branch of the huge Siberian rivers Cossack adventurers traversed six thousand miles of wilderness to the far-off Pacific. Mackenzie, seeking a new route to the Indies, followed the great river which bears his name to the frozen Arctic. Stanley, fighting his way through hostile natives and foaming rapids, sketched geography's second largest river, the Congo.

But the picture has its somber side. Among nature's demoniac outbursts none transcends a flood. Millions of Chinese have perished in the swollen torrents of the Hwang Ho or succumbed to the famine which stalked the subsiding waters. No wonder this great river, yellow with the dust of Asian deserts, has been called "the scourge of the Sons of Han." The biblical Deluge was perhaps the memory, preserved in Sumerian legends, of some fearsome inundation of the Tigris or the Euphrates.

And so, partly in gratitude, partly from fear, rivers have become objects of veneration. Millions of devout Hindus believe themselves cleansed from sin in the muddy current of the Ganges and ask no richer favor than to yield their parting breath beside its shores. And how indelibly is the Jordan woven into the very fabric of Jewish and Christian faith.

From such traditions, clothed in poetic imagery, rivers emerge into the field of science as the great transformers of our global surfaces. Like pliant fingers stretching out from the sea, they sculpture our valleys, smooth down our mountains, and continually remodel our landscape. At the present rate of erosion it has been estimated that all the continents and islands of the world would be reduced to sea level in something over six million years. That seems long to the feverish tempo of the present, but it is scarcely a week in our planet's two billion years! No vestige of the dry land which first rose above the primordial seas remains. It was obliterated long ago by rivers that have disappeared and left no other trace. The wastage of ancient uplands was collected on the floors of shallow seas to be pressed into rock once more, layer upon layer of the limestone and sandstone and shale which covers at least three quarters of the land surface of the globe.

The more practical materialist sees rivers as highways of commerce, or unfailing reservoirs to supply great cities and equip irrigation projects, or as sinews of that power which starts the whirring of huge dynamos.

The biologist recognizes in rivers those convenient avenues through which life, awakening from ocean slime, first invaded the fresh waters and then crawled out upon dry land to proliferate into the numberless species we know today.

And to the meteorologist rivers appear as the pulsing arteries in that great circulatory system of global moisture which sustains and nourishes all life. Up from the sea in vapor that moisture rises, to be borne inland by the winds and fall in showers until the surplus sluices away in river channels to return to the sea once more.

Yes, Homer was right, rivers are "heaven sent," for they have their origin not in the too obvious spring or lake or melting glacier, but in the clouds.

DEFINITION AND CLASSIFICATION

Webster tells us that a river is "a natural stream of water larger than a brook or a creek."

According to the Encyclopedia Britannica, a river is "any natural stream of fresh water, larger than a brook or creek, which flows in a well-defined channel." But there are salt rivers also, the Chelif in Algiers being nearly half as saline as the Caspian, while no river is absolutely fresh, since its waters contain some mineral matter in solution.

The word river comes from the French *rivière*, and that in turn from the Latin *rivus*—"a stream or river"—which survives in the diminutive rivulet. The root has also given us "rive" and "riven," a splitting asunder, so suggestive of a river's erosive power.

We might classify rivers in a variety of ways. There is, for example, commercial activity which makes the Thames more important than the huge Lena coursing the vacant forests and tundras of Siberia. And there are political implications such as give the Rhine a prominence quite out of proportion to its length or drainage area and make the Danube a breeder of international ill will.

There are historical associations, for the Meander in Asia Minor, though of little consequence, flows by the "topless towers of Ilium" where Homer's demigods strove long ago upon the Plains of Troy. Religious veneration has conferred a prominence upon certain rivers. From the Lake of Gennesaret to the Dead Sea is only sixty-five miles, but the Jordan is of greater significance to more people than the Amazon. And the Ganges is nearer to the heart of the average Hindu than the particular form his government may assume.

Global considerations suggest a separation of rivers that flow into the sea from others, like the Volga or the Oxus that empty into isolated drainage basins. Even the oceans offer natural divisions, for most of the world's great rivers empty into the Atlantic, including that Arctic Mediterranean which geographers assign to it, rather than into the Indian or the much vaster Pacific.

Dependability varies from the steady current of the St. Lawrence, regulated by the overflow of the Great Lakes, to the capricious antics of some wadi in an arid land, one day a raging torrent, the next a sun-baked gully. Or the mineral content of the waters might provide an index ranging, let us say, from the souplike Yellow River to some mountain stream that glints with the diamond sparkle of flawless purity.

Yes, there are various angles of approach, but the dominant one appears in the very name river—*"larger* than a rivulet or brook." Size, in a survey of global topography, is the chief consideration, so earth's grandest rivers are its largest rivers also.

Since each trade and craft and science develops its own vocabulary, the study of rivers presents a few characteristic terms. Most of these are common knowledge, such as a river's source and mouth—the beginning and the end. The source may be a spring, a lake, a glacier, or a swamp; the mouth may broaden into an "estuary" or divide into a "delta."

The river "bed" is that excavated trough which contains the normal volume; the "channel" the deepest part of that bed, sometimes difficult to find where it zigzags across surface waters twenty miles wide, as in the Yenesei, or is hidden beneath mantling vegetation like the mid-Nile. The river "valley" or "basin" may be no broader than the river "bed," as in the Grand Canyon, but usually it slopes gradually upward from both banks to the distant ramparts of the worn-down uplands. Still larger is the drainage area, the entire territory upon whose surplus waters a river levies tribute.

A transverse profile or cross section of the river bed and valley may vary from a gash thousands of feet deep, as in the upper Yangtze Kiang, to a plain hundreds of miles broad near that same river's exit into the China Sea. The longitudinal profile is usually concave—a definite slope from the headwaters, a more gradual declivity in the mid-section, a nearly level plain approaching the sea. For it is the mission of every river to reduce the uplands to a flat base or peneplain that never quite reaches sea level.

The right and left banks of a river are determined by facing away from its source and toward the mouth. Hence St. Louis is on the right bank of the Mississippi. The velocity of the current varies with slope and sometimes with volume, as we shall observe later. The "load" is mineral matter borne onward by the current, the wastage of the uplands. For convenience, this is divided into three parts: matter in *solution*, such as the salts that make the oceans ever saltier; matter in *suspension*, the characteristic silt or mud which builds up deltas and flood plains; and *traction* material, too heavy to float but dragged along the bottom by the current, each particle an edged tool rasping out a deeper, broader channel.

Other more technical terms are of interest only to the student of hydraulics or geology.

GLOBAL DISTRIBUTION

The domain of rivers is strictly limited. First of all, more than 71 per cent of the global surface is covered by the oceans. True, the fifty-six million square miles that remain seem spacious enough, but Professor C. B. Fawcett reminds us that no less than 40 per cent of this residue is desert where rivers are either alien or unknown.

Much of this territory is made sterile, not from lack of moisture, but by the severe cold. Some ten million square miles comprise the polar regions or mountain heights where bare rock protrudes above the timber line. Here there is no failure of water supply, but rather an unproductive excess. Mountain climbers on Everest report a single blinding storm where the snow accumulated to a depth of twenty-four feet! Greenland and Antarctica groan beneath a weight of ice that would, were it to melt, swell the oceans and drown every seaport in the world.

In addition to this frozen waste are some twelve million square miles too arid for rivers of any size or permanence, such as the Gobi or Kalahari deserts. The rivers of the frigid zones are mainly glaciers, those of the "thirst lands" mere gullies flushed for a few hours by erratic downpours to blister in the heat for months on end.

To be sure, a few streams course Arctic tundras like Baffin Island or dry areas like Turkestan, but the rivers of the world are largely confined to some 60 per cent of the total land surface, or about thirty-four million square miles.

Even this reduced figure, more than twice the size of all Asia, offers ample scope for river development, and streams do appear literally by the thousands. But the largest are much more restricted both by topography and climate.

The great rivers of southern Asia, for example, are warped and twisted by giant mountain ranges which not only direct their course but limit their drainage areas. Only a few, like the Mississippi or the Amazon, can sweep grandly across continental vastness, meeting no formidable obstruction on their progress to the sea.

Climate is even more determinant. As Dr. Albrecht Penck observes, "Large rivers can never originate in arid regions," for there are no surplus waters to be carried away. To be sure, rivers like the Nile or the Colorado may penetrate deserts, but if so, their volumes are replenished by distant lakes or melting snows.

Rain clouds are the great purveyors of moisture, the natural "river feeders," and rainfall is amazingly capricious. In Iquique in Chile not a drop of rain fell for four successive years, while Cherrapunji in India has reported a twelve-month downpour of 905 inches with a 41-inch deluge in a period of twenty-four hours!

But *rainfall* is no accurate gauge of river volumes. For rivers are born not of mere moisture, but of its *excess*, and it is their province to carry away only surplus water that is not absorbed by the atmosphere or soaks into the soil or is sucked up by growing vegetation. An annual rainfall of slightly more than thirty inches maintains the Great Lakes and the St. Lawrence River. An equal rainfall would be swallowed up by the burning climate of Arabia with no appreciable result, for there the annual rate of evaporation mounts to 160 inches!

All rivers, then, are evidence of an excess of moisture over local requirements, be the latter irrigation ditches or an insatiable atmosphere. Where the water surplus is temporary, floods result; where it is continuous, a permanent stream. And that surplusage or the lack of it is largely governed by the winds and the temperature. The winds and their vagaries we shall discuss a little later; the temperature is confined more readily within definite zones. Cold regions, it has been said, show a moisture deficiency where the annual precipitation falls below 8 inches; temperate lands, below 12 inches; hot countries, below 18. Conversely, precipitation becomes excessive in cold lands where it exceeds 50 inches, in temperate lands 80, in the tropics 100. Hence Siberian rivers thrive upon a water surplus that would disappear in equatorial regions, while their "runoff" is proportionately greater because the subsoil remains frozen to profound depths.

The ideal environment for great rivers is a drainage area of continental width stretching across an equatorial rain belt clothed with forests. And that is precisely the locus of earth's grandest of all rivers—the Amazon and the Congo.

Geographically great rivers are most unevenly distributed. Antarctica has none; Australia but one, the Murray-Darling, which makes a brave showing upon the map, although it has a meager outflow to the sea. Asia, hugest of continents, has many notable rivers, though none of the first rank. Her rivers are sustained by the snows and glaciers of tremendous mountain ranges, for much of the interior is an arid waste. In Europe the Volga and the Danube are impressive, but rivers of lesser magnitude are noteworthy mainly because of historic associations or commercial activity.

Much African territory is occupied by the most extensive deserts in the world, but from the lofty interior plateau four great rivers flow toward the four points of the compass—the Nile to the north, the Niger south, the Zambezi east, the Congo west. And they are among the most interesting of all rivers.

North America is well represented, with the Mississippi in the foremost rank. But South America is pre-eminently the continent of great rivers. Its peculiar topography, with the Andean backbone along the western edge, leaves much "elbowroom" across well-watered lowlands. Here is best illustrated that water surplus which is the very lifeblood of rivers. The La Plata-Paraná ranks among the leading three or four super rivers, while the Amazon is unrivaled. Nor should we wonder at its almost oceanic volume when we realize that its drainage area comprises nearly one tenth of productive "river territory" in which is concentrated probably one fifth of all the moving surplus fresh waters of the globe.

PART TWO

Our Changing Landscape

~~~~~~

THE ANCIENT EARTH

ACROSS our land surfaces rivers have scrawled in giant characters the high lights of global history. Some of these runic inscriptions have been deciphered so that we may read, as from a mutilated Assyrian monument, fragmentary details of the past billion years or more. Often the text, repeatedly erased and rewritten, is quite illegible. Great areas have sunk beneath the sea to emerge smeared with primordial slime and the sweepings of the uplands; vast lavas have welled up from the molten interior through the cracked and faulted crust, while the script has been further defaced by fire-spitting volcanoes. The Columbia River plateau, which covers some 250,000 square miles of Oregon, Washington, and Idaho, was formed by just such an incandescent overflow.

Geologists recognize three types of rock—igneous, sedimentary, and metamorphic; the first forged in elemental fires, the others reorganized and molded anew in a drama of never-ceasing change. All rock was once igneous. As the glowing planet developed a stony crust, granitic rock of lighter texture bulged up into continents; basaltic rock, denser and heavier, sank to form the ocean floors. Petrologists catalogue no fewer than seven hundred kinds of igneous rock. But the agents of erosion have so blurred the original design that three quarters, or it may be four fifths, of all land surfaces are now covered with sedimentary rock piled layer upon layer like the pages of a colossal book, much of it, as well as igneous rock, greatly metamorphosed.

Sedimentary layers, dated by the fossil remains of once living organisms, have been assigned to definite periods. Thus the Carboniferous Age saw vast forests of fernlike trees and other lush vegetation provide the basis of our coal beds, while the Devonian Age ushered in shoals of fishes from the lower invertebrates. Such rock strata, variously named, are being correlated so that science may now identify similar formations in Europe or Africa.

No portion of the original continental surfaces remain. If they did not subside beneath the sea to be coated with sediment, or receive a veneer of fiery lavas, their very texture has been altered by weathering and chemical action in that transforming process known as metamorphosis. The Archean, oldest of surface rocks, have been changed the most because they have been exposed the longest.

Aside from minor outcroppings, such as the Balkan region in Europe and the Deccan plateau in India, six great areas of semi-continental size are recognized as the most ancient of all land surfaces. In North America the Canadian shield overspreads some two million square miles; in Europe the corresponding Baltic shield covers Finland, northern Scotland, the Scandinavian peninsula, and projects toward the south; in Asia the Angara shield overlaps southern Siberia. Similar ancient rock formations appear in Africa in the southern and mid-African plateau and overspread the South American highlands of Brazil and Guiana. Regions in central and western Australia belong to the same remote era. Of Antarctica we know but little, as that lonely continent lies buried beneath the ice.

Geologists are not always in agreement as they pore over the blotted and tattered pages of global history, but a passing glance at one of them—the great Canadian shield—is revealing. Perhaps the most ancient sedimentary rock known is there exposed in the Coutchiching deposits nearly a mile in thickness, composed of mica schists and dolomites derived from metamorphic shales. Far more extensive are the Keewatin formations—from an Indian name meaning the Great Northwest. Originally lava outcroppings now much deformed and mingled with sedimentary rock, they are sometimes four miles in thickness.

Overlaying the older Keewatin are Temiskaming strata of basalt, conglomerate, sandstone, shale, and limestone to a maximum thickness of twenty thousand feet. Younger but immeasurably old are the Huronian strata, also of a maximum thickness of twenty thousand feet, while superimposed in turn are the Keweenawan lavas and red beds of northern Michigan with an extreme depth of fifty thousand feet. All these, be it remembered, are among the most ancient of rock surfaces; most land areas are covered with much later deposits. Could all known strata be collected in one place, their estimated depth would approximate a hundred miles!

Such, in brief, are some of the changes and revisions, the erasures and the corrections Time has made upon the once blank pages of the ancient earth.

THE PAGEANT OF DECAY

All exposed rock surfaces decay. This decay is twofold: physical disintegration, or the breaking up into ever-smaller fragments, terminating in rock flour or clay, and chemical decomposition, in which the very elements of the rocks are rearranged. Both processes are usually in operation at the same time.

We may observe their action upon a monument in a cemetery. The gloss upon new-placed marble or granite is soon clouded, while year by year the inscription becomes more blurred and indistinct. Lichens also etch the surface with their acid secretions, until the resistant rock, wracked by alternate frosts and heats and pelting rains, crumbles slowly above a sunken grave. It seems as though nature had conspired to consign both to oblivion.

The story of a neglected tomb is magnified upon all the rock surfaces of the globe in that process known as weathering. Unhurried, but never tiring, it wears down the hardest stone. Its tools, like those of the sculptor, are keen-edged. First of all are temperature variations. Long-range transitions from summer to winter are less disturbing because less abrupt than the sudden drop from noonday heat to midnight chill. Alternate expansions and contractions loosen the mineral framework, as mountaineers realize when they scan the precipice above for rock slides dislodged by the morning sun. Water permeates surface rocks and freezing splits them asunder. So do trees lodged in convenient clefts, and even lightnings upon a minor but spectacular scale.

Winds, clothed in clouds of dust or sand, scour endlessly as we shall presently observe, while water is so important a factor in erosion that a single phase of its activities, river action, is the theme of this volume. Such agents of global wear and tear are called mechanical.

Chemical changes, though less apparent, are even more far-reaching. Here again water plays a major role. It leaches away certain rock constituents, leaving the residue completely altered. In caves it transforms dull limestone into fantastically colored stalactites and stalagmites. More subtle are its workings in the deeper recesses of the earth crust. Some geologists believe that juvenile water, newly created in the heated laboratory of the rocks by the union of those gases oxygen and hydrogen, seeps upward through crack and crevice, bearing in solution the heavier metals, copper and iron, and flakes of gold and silver. If this theory be correct, the sweating gnomes that German fancy pictured as toiling in subterranean galleries were drops of water.

We do not think of rocks as growing, yet in a sense they do, by a certain rearrangement or substitution of constituent parts. What geologists call concretions are really rocks formed in the substance of other rocks. To the layman this process is perhaps best revealed in petrified wood. Here rock elements, evicting those of vegetable growth, retain the original form and texture.

Magnesium limestones known as dolomites were developed mainly by metamorphism. Great accumulations of this rock have given their name to the Dolomite Alps. The oldest of all sedimentary rocks were formed by the breaking down of still more ancient formations.

One result of rock decay is the creation of soil, that fertile mantle in which are rooted our pastures and our wheat fields, our flower beds and our forests. These thrive upon a continuing decay, beginning in the rotting of the rocks and sustained through an endless cycle by the further decomposition of plants and animals. Truly, as Hindu sages remind us, life draws sustenance from death.

In fact, all life, as we know it, has been pictured as a fungus growth upon a dying world, with its ultimate survivor a lichen clinging to a frozen stone as earth succumbs at last to the dead chill of outer space.

THE WARFARE OF THE WINDS

The winds! How they whistle about the eaves, dash rain against the windows, and whirl clouds of dust across the roadway. Winds are like rivers in the air, but how profoundly they remodel our global surfaces.

Rocks, as we have observed, disintegrate from weathering. Derby noted the decay of shales at a depth of 394 feet. Berg believes that even loess deposits, usually wind-driven, may develop locally from prolonged weathering and chemical action. But winds and waters and, to a lesser degree, lava flows are the great distributors. Weathering softens and pulverizes rock surfaces; winds scatter the fragments broadcast.

In arid regions winds rather than waters are the abrasive agents. Winds have groined the arches and columns and cathedral spires of Utah's scenic wonderland—the Garden of the Gods. Winds have scooped out such tremendous depressions as the weird Seistan lake region of Persia and the Qattara Sink in Egypt. Winds heap the sand in giant drifts that we call dunes. Winds erected Kill Devil Hill in North Carolina, from whose steep slopes the Wright brothers first launched their frail-winged craft upon the ocean of the atmosphere. When I visited the region some years ago the entire hill had moved bodily away from the monument placed there to commemorate the event. At Sandy Neck on Cape Cod, I once observed a sprig of wild cherries ripening above the surface of a twenty-foot dune which had swallowed the tree. Dunes sometimes threaten entire communities. To arrest their devastating progress their slopes have been clothed with beach grass and scrub pines. Dunes form the skirmish line of expanding deserts. In the Sahara, where they are called *ergs*, they have already blighted great areas of the once fertile Chad region. According to A. B. Grabau, 380,000 square miles of the Sahara is shifting sand; while Arabia shows 320,000 square miles of similar unstable surfaces.

Violent winds transport sand grains bodily; winds less aggressive bounce them along. Accumulating in drifts, they roll onward, each individual grain gradually wearing down into a finer dust. A single storm of wind-driven sand may permanently cloud the windowpanes of beach cottages.

In desert regions sandstorms are a terrifying phenomenon. Whole caravans fling themselves upon the ground and bury their faces in protective clothing. Arab dhows, yawing clumsily across the Arabian Sea, encounter inky clouds whirling like colossal genii from beyond the horizon to deluge their decks with sand.

Fine dust is still more the sport of the "wanton winds." Many a farmer in the Dust Bowl beyond the Mississippi has seen his corn lands disappear in clouds, leaving only dilapidated trees and buildings banked with smothering drifts. Winds transport dust to incredible distances. Dust from the Sahara has been observed in England. Walther reports that the destructive storm of March 9–12, 1901, scattered dust over 300,000 square miles of Europe and 170,000 square miles of sea to an average depth of .239 millimeters. He estimated the total weight at 1,650,000 tons, yet some of it was borne a distance of twenty-five hundred miles! According to J. A. Udden, the windstorm of March 9, 1918, bore dust two thousand miles from Arizona to Wisconsin. An instructive table has been worked out showing the carrying loads of the winds:

Rock fragments under 8 millimeters in diameter are borne
. . . . *a few feet*
Coarse sand less than a millimeter . . . . *under a mile*
Fine sand . . . . *several miles*
Coarse silt—$\frac{1}{16}$–$\frac{1}{32}$ millimeters . . . . *200 miles*
Medium silt—$\frac{1}{32}$–$\frac{1}{64}$ millimeters . . . . *1,000 miles*
Fine silt or clay less than $\frac{1}{64}$ millimeters . . . *around the world!*

In glacial times wind-blown dust girdled the globe in a broad band between 40 and 45 degrees north latitude. It has even been said that every square mile of land surface may be sprinkled with dust from every other square mile!

In volcanic eruptions winds become violent torrents. When Katmai in Alaska deluged the heavens, volcanic dust at a distance of ten miles had accumulated in less than two days to a depth of four feet. When Krakatoa exploded in the Straits of Sunda, with appalling loss of life on neighboring Java, the finer dust circled the globe and remained suspended for months in the upper stratosphere.

Yet such tremendous erosion is not wholly destructive. Sir Aurel Stein observed wind-driven loess on the flanks of the Kunlun Mountains, twelve thousand feet above the sea. In the Mississippi Valley are loess deposits a hundred feet thick, rock flour ground by the continental icecap and distributed by the winds. Across northern China loess has accumulated to a maximum depth of a thousand feet. Such sediments are called aeolian. Millions of peasants carve out homes in the claylike substance and cultivate gardens enriched by the sweepings of the Gobi. Volcanic dust is so fertile that farms ascend far up the slopes of still-smoldering volcanoes. Dust particles in the atmosphere provide the "core" for raindrops. By breaking up the light rays they give the sky its delicate and beautiful blue. For months the dust of Krakatoa dyed the sunsets a richer gold.

But the direct action of the winds is less important than their indirect action in the great pageant of erosion. The waters of the earth are largely directed by the winds. These guide the ocean currents which so affect our global climate, dry up vast areas with a parching evaporation, and deluge other areas with torrential downpours. How biased they are and how capricious! They bring too much moisture to northeastern India, to the Malay region, and the valley of the Amazon, while all but ignoring such regions as the Kalahari Desert and interior Australia. As E. J. Wayland reminds us, "The great arid wastes lie . . . in the track of desiccating winds which pass equatorwards" across the "thirst lands of intermittent showers." Water, to be sure, is the major factor in global erosion, but its distribution is largely determined by the winds.

GLOBAL FRESH WATERS

Water dissolves some rocks, disintegrates others, then sweeps them away, tearing down mountains, filling up valleys, smoothing the harsher landscape features to gentle slopes and plains.

The Vedic poem wonders "how the sparkling waters of all rivers flow into one ocean without ever filling it," a query that the writer of Ecclesiastes echoes in the plaint, "All the rivers run into the sea; yet the sea is not full." Evaporation is, of course, the answer: clouds born of the sea fall upon the earth in showers and return in rivers. Li Po expressed it all when he wrote, "The water that flows into the distant sea return anon in the shallows of the transparent pool," then asks somewhat wearily, "Who can tell the end of the endless changes of things?"

The sun is the celestial motor, and temperature the gauge of evaporation. At zero (Fahrenheit) a cubic foot of air can support less than half a grain of water; at 50 degrees it can support about 4 grains; at 100 degrees nearly 20. For this reason the snowfall in the Arctic is lighter than that in Scotland, and the volume of Siberian rivers far less than their magnitude would warrant. Conversely, the thirst of desert regions is insatiable. In Arabia the moisture from infrequent showers does little to appease a fiery evaporation. Yet there is always some water vapor in the air except over such parched regions as Death Valley, where it occasionally disappears.

Half the annual rainfall over the United States is absorbed by evaporation in an endless cycle of sunlight, cloud, and recurring showers. One sixth either gives drink to thirsty plant life or sinks into the earth to sustain that hidden ocean of fresh waters known as the water table. One third runs off in rivers.

Vegetation soaks up moisture like a sponge. In the sudd region of the Nile equatic vegetation not only chokes that great river but absorbs so much water that the current is reduced to a mere trickle. The process, however, is a balance between profit and loss. True, vegetation absorbs rainfall, but it moistens the atmosphere in that curious process known as transpiration. Growing leaves give off moisture much as animal surfaces perspire, and for much the same reason: to reduce or equalize temperature. By transpiration an oak of average size, during a five-month season, gives off no less than twenty-eight thousand gallons of water. No wonder the forests of the Amazon drip with moisture as does the atmosphere. Forests everywhere are great stabilizers of river volumes. In Malaya torrential rains that drain from cleared areas within twenty-four hours are conserved in forested regions for weeks.

Even more interesting, because concealed from the view, are "the waters under the earth" which so intrigued the writer of the Book of Genesis. To be sure, the Hebrews thought the flat earth floated upon an underground ocean and the Deluge ensued when the "windows of heaven were opened" and the "fountains of the great deep broken up." Plato believed that rivers had their source in subterranean reservoirs, a theory that Aristotle ridiculed. Yet there was some basis for Plato's opinion. Certain rivers, rising in springs, do gush out of the very earth. This is the mere overflow of the underlying water table which sustains the levels of most lakes and ponds. O. E. Meinzer, of the United States Geological Survey, lists sixty-five springs within the territorial limits of the United States, each with a flow of at least fifty thousand gallons a minute. One of these gushers, Silver Springs in Florida, has an estimated volume of four hundred thousand gallons. This is almost one sixth the average outflow of the Rio Grande!

Long ago the ancients learned to tap the "waters under the earth." Wells in the valley of the Indus date back to the third millennium B.C. Pilgrims in Palestine pause at Jacob's Well, laboriously chipped out of solid rock. Egyptian paintings of thirteen hundred years B.C. depict wells with rude sweeps, while Rameses II boasted of a well 202 feet deep which he completed in the desert to supply miners working there. The Romans were past masters in constructing wells, reservoirs, and great aqueducts for transporting water.

Rain water, sinking into the ground, is slowly diffused, depending upon the porosity of soil and underlying rock strata. From irrigation ditches the lateral spread is sometimes fifty feet a day. Mine shafts in Arizona have recorded a diffusion of about a mile in a year; in the sandstones of Wisconsin it is about half a mile.

Much of the alternate soaking and drying-out process upon global land surfaces is relatively local; rivers, as we have already noted, merely bear away the surplus. Sir John Murray estimated that 1,213 cubic miles of water fell annually over the drainage area of the Congo in Africa and that rather more than a third, or 419 cubic miles, flowed back into the sea through that vast river. The Po in Italy and the Magdalena in Colombia bear away more than half of their valley rainfall; the Darling in Australia scarcely a tenth. Less than 10 per cent of the rainfall in the Victoria Basin in Africa seems to drain into the lake. In mountain streams the runoff may approach 100 per cent; in desert wadis it may sink to zero. The Britannica gives a range from 15 to 75 per cent, but from a quarter to a third is a conservative estimate.

PART THREE

River Characteristics and Activities

~~~~~~

HOW RIVERS REMODEL THE LANDSCAPE

"THE HISTORY of the land," as John Hodgdon Bradley reminds us, "has been written very largely in water." This is shown upon a major scale by those far-reaching oscillations of the earth crust which saw the continents emerge and then subside to emerge anew in endless conflicts with the ocean. Much of our sandstone has solidified along ancient beaches; much of our limestone once carpeted shallow seas. Li Po painted a clear picture when he wrote, "The tiger leaps in the valley where once the mang fish floated, and a carpet of coral covers the ravine where in other days the violet bloomed." In more prosaic vein, Eratosthenes mentioned "Inland, two or three thousand stadia from the sea, vast numbers of oyster and scallop shells," which he surmised were relics of former seas.

In such basic changes even the mightiest of rivers are overwhelmed. The Rhine once extended hundreds of miles farther to the north and west; Chesapeake Bay is the drowned valley of a greater Susquehanna; the Gulf of St. Lawrence marks a deep invasion of the sea at the expense of the river. Conversely, much of the drainage basin of the Amazon was once a gulf of the Pacific, while the main valley of the Mississippi was an extension of the Gulf of Mexico. When this subsidence was most pronounced, a quarter of all North America sank beneath the waves.

Temperature changes disintegrate rock surfaces; the winds, dust-laden, rasp and wear, but water is the great agent of erosion, and rivers its unwearying toilers. The rise and fall of continental masses is marked by passing aeons; the life history of rivers is expressed in millions of years, sometimes mere millenniums. Yet there is probably no single square mile of land surface that has not been changed by water action. Monadnock, in New Hampshire, is a solitary relic of a former plateau. The uplands of the West were denuded long before the Colorado began to excavate the Grand Canyon; the beds of the Great Lakes were scooped out by forgotten rivers; even the Sahara is crisscrossed by the beds of vanished streams.

As already observed, erosion, if continued at the present rate, would reduce all land surfaces to near sea level in something over six million years. To be sure, so monotonous a landscape will not result, for erosion will not continue at the present rate, while land surfaces are built up as well as torn down. But it is true that rivers tend to smooth out and flatten the virile uplands to senile peneplains. Such plains occur even in lofty tablelands which have been elevated only to be ground down anew. Unless the map of Asia is distorted by some as yet undreamed of convulsion, the Ganges will one day conquer Everest.

The rate of river excavation varies widely. It has been estimated that the Danube lowers its drainage basin one foot in 5,134 years; the Mississippi in 4,500 years; the Ganges in 617. In mountain streams abrasion is terrific; in quiet channels approaching the sea it may sink to the vanishing point. The rivers of England lower the entire land surface one foot in a little under thirteen thousand years. Such intervals, long to us, are but moments in the life history of our planet.

Water action breaks up rock surfaces in a variety of ways, but rivers not only etch the uplands but transport the material elsewhere. River erosion is of two kinds: *mechanical* and *chemical*, known respectively as *corrasion* and *corrosion*. The former, which rasps and scours, outranks the latter, which dissolves and bears away, in the ratio of roughly two to one.

Scouring action, or corrasion, assumes two forms—traction and suspension. In traction the currents drag along the bottom particles too heavy to support. In suspension lighter particles float. The size of traction debris varies directly as the square of the velocity of the current. A current flowing at a speed of three inches per second can drag along only particles of fine mud; at six inches, fine sand; at one foot, coarse gravel half an inch in diameter; at four feet, cobblestones four inches across. The traction power of mountain streams swollen by freshets is prodigious. In a gorge of the upper Euphrates, Ellsworth Huntington noted a boulder thirty feet in diameter that had been rolled some distance downstream by gravity plus the current. River sorting or selective action is well illustrated by the Po in northern Italy. The upper channel, where the current is rapid, is carpeted with pebbles and coarse gravel. Some two hundred miles from the sea these give place to sand, and this in turn to fine mud and silt. Although the traction load of rivers is usually far less bulky than the suspension load, some 11 per cent in the case of the Mississippi, according to Humphreys and Abbot, it accounts for an annual transportation by that great river of forty-four million tons! Yet Gilbert found traction and suspension roughly equal at the mouth of the Colorado.

The suspension load swirled seaward by the muddy rivers of the world is called silt. It comprises the fine sweepings of the uplands, the continental dust. Every year the rivers of the United States carry out to sea an estimated 513,000,000 tons of silt. Since the days of Lewis and Clark the Mississippi River alone has filched from millions of acres of fertile farm and pasture land some ten cubic miles of silt. According to R. D. Salisbury, all the rivers of the world bear an annual silt burden of sixteen billion tons.

Corrosion, or the chemical breaking down of rock and soil, comprises another staggering contribution from the continents to the oceans. Though not so bulky as the products of corrasion, such dissolved mineral matter sometimes accounts for one third the total wear and tear of the uplands. F. W. Clarke estimates that the annual load of soluble material in all the rivers in the world totals 2,700,000,000 tons. No wonder the oceans are such inexhaustible mines of valuable minerals.

But rivers, though destructive, are colossal builders also. River sediments, usually yellow, red, or brown, carpet the neighboring shallow seas. The debris of the Grand Canyon has been strewn by the Colorado River over the floor of the Gulf of California for hundreds of miles. The Mississippi has added fifty square miles to the area of Lousiana in the past century. The shallow Persian Gulf is filling up with the silt of the Euphrates as its shore line recedes seventy-two feet a year. Much of eastern China is an alluvial plain eroded from the giant ranges of Asia by the Hwang Ho and Yangtze rivers. Here we may observe sterile mountains worn down to provide farm lands for millions of toiling peasants.

Among European rivers, the Rhone, the Ebro, and the Po have been most active in building up the coast line within recorded time. The city of Arles in France is said to be twice as far from the sea as it was in the late days of the Roman Empire. The tower of St. Louis, erected on the seacoast in 1737, is now four miles inland. In places the coast advances seven feet annually.

In Italy, Ravenna, once insular like Venice, is now separated by a wide area of pine barrens. Aquileia, one of the great seaports of the Adriatic in the early Christian era, is now seven miles from sea, and Adria, which gave its name to that sea, is thirteen miles inland. Deposits from the Vistula cover 615 square miles formerly part of the Gulf of Danzig. River valleys are proverbially fertile. The silt of the Nile has enriched Egypt for thousands of years.

Many of our oldest sedimentary rocks were laid down by river action. In some cases the rate of accumulation has been estimated with what is probably fair accuracy. Shales are the characteristic deposits of lakes and estuaries. Six million five hundred thousand years were required to form shales twenty-six hundred feet deep in the Green River Valley of Colorado and Wyoming.

In the terse and "flinty" verbiage that geologists prefer, the work of rivers is threefold—*erosional*, or wearing down; *transportational*, or bearing away; and *depositional*, or building up. And this perpetual mingling of creation and destruction was recognized by the Prophet Isaiah when he wrote, "Every valley shall be exalted, and every mountain and hill shall be made low."

A RIVER'S LIFE—AND DEATH

Rivers have a definite birth, display the energy of youth, the fullness of maturity, then enter upon a tranquil old age.

This panorama is often enacted in the course of a normal river from its source to its mouth. Emerging from some mountain spring or melting glacier, it goes cascading down the heights, rending, gouging, and grinding its pathway to lower levels, widening its valley until far-off borders blend with the horizon, then meanders across a nearly level plain partly eroded from the worn-down terrain, partly built up by the freightage of silt and gravel from remoter uplands. In this manner the Ganges, one of the most impetuous of mountain streams, shows a gradient of scarcely two inches a mile during the final hundred miles of its course, and the Yangtze, battling like an imprisoned titan with some of the most rugged ranges in the world, approaches a dead level across a broad plain to the sea.

How old are rivers? No one knows. The ancients wondered as we do now. Herodotus thought that the Nile must have required some thousands of years to build up its extensive delta; and Pliny noted that an ancient seaport of the Persian Gulf had been stranded many miles inland by the silt of the Euphrates. Such speculations, however, break down for lack of an adequate gauge, as though one tried to measure the Pacific with a foot rule. A few rivers (we shall glance at one or two later) are comparatively recent phenomena dating from the glacial period, so that Cro-Magnon cave dwellers could have witnessed their birth. But the life history of most great rivers cannot be written in mere millenniums. The Amazon, for example, must be millions of years old, and he would be a bold geologist, indeed, who set definite limits upon the age of most great rivers.

Rivers are really watery empires, rising and falling, perhaps to rise again, their life a struggle with climate, the terrain, and with one another; their boundaries alternately expanding and contracting, sometimes rejuvenated by an earth upheaval to begin life anew. The surplus of the Great Lakes once drained into the Mississippi. Gravel beaches two hundred feet higher than present levels mark its shores above St. Louis. And such momentous changes are not mere incidents of the past but are going on all the time so slowly as to be unperceived. Delicate measurements indicate that the Great Lakes region is tilting westward at the rate of nine inches per century. Should this continue, Lake Michigan would flow once more into the Mississippi, to be followed in turn by all the other Great Lakes, except Ontario. The Mississippi, formerly a much greater river, has lost ground not only to the St. Lawrence but to the Saskatchewan, which now drains the remnants of fossil Lake Agassiz. Should the lower valley subside five hundred feet as it has done in past ages, the Gulf of Mexico would probe far into the continent of North America and St. Louis might become a seaport.

A river's active life is spent in eroding the uplands and bearing denuded material to the sea. At first, as we have briefly noted, these uplands control its course. The Indus, the Ganges, and the Brahmaputra rise within fifty miles of one another in a tangled mass of snow-covered peaks. A single mountain spur separates the Colorado and the Missouri. Nor are mountains the sole determining factor. The Congo and the Zambezi, flowing across Africa to separate oceans, drain a common swampland on the high plateau. In the jungle interior of South America two mighty river systems, the Amazon and the Paraguay, approach within less than a mile.

As time progresses rivers increase in length. By eroding the uplands their headwaters eat deeper into the hinterland; by building up deltas and alluvial coastal plains they encroach upon the sea; while on their course across the smoothed and flattened lowlands they tend to meander in those sinuous loops which gave the landscape artist Hogarth his "curves of beauty." River warfare may be heightened by disturbances of earth levels, as noted in the case of the Mississippi, but rivers tend to develop their own battlegrounds and compete fiercely with one another for available water supplies. The Amazon, not content with the most spacious basin in the world and the greatest volume of waters, has reached northward through a giant tributary, the Negro, to tap the headwaters of the Orinoco, as we shall observe in a study of that river. The Niger in Africa is losing out to the

Senegal on the west but recouping lost territory at the expense of the Lake Chad area. The Mohawk River once flowed into the St. Lawrence until the Hudson captured it. But examples of such "beheading of rivers" or "river piracy" might be indefinitely prolonged.

Rivers also battle the sea. In examining certain African and Asiatic rivers, I was impressed with the distinct outline traced by their waters upon the vaster canvas of the ocean. Fresh water has been dipped up from the surface more than a hundred miles off the mouth of the Amazon, while some indication of that tremendous influx has been reported six hundred miles from shore! River channels often extend below the sea to the verge of the continental slope, like the submerged gorges of the Congo, the Indus, the St. Lawrence, and the Hudson. River bars and shoals, expanding deltas and alluvial plains, mark the advance battalions of the silt deposits the rivers of the world are continually thrusting out into the sea.

In a sense rivers tend to commit suicide. Their beds fill up with silt so that they sometimes rise above the surface of the surrounding country, like the lower Mississippi. Rivers also change their channels, winding through successive oxbow loops and cutoffs, or leaping bodily from their beds to gouge out a new route to the sea, as the Indus and the Hwang Ho have done within comparatively recent years.

Eventually, when their sculpturing of the landscape has been completed, rivers enter upon a prolonged senility. The lilting "Song of the Chattahoochee" then dies down to the plea of the now pulseless stream, "May there be no moaning of the bar when I put out to sea."

Some rivers linger indefinitely, little better than tidal appendages of the sea. Others choke with silt and vegetation, break up into stagnant pools and swamps. Death, though delayed, seems inevitable. Those serpentine ridges known as eskers mark the beds of glacial streams. All the desert areas of the world are crossed by the trails of vanished rivers. E. H. L. Schwartz noted in the Sahara vacant stone huts beside dry gorges, relics of human settlements that withered with the water supply.

And so, from aspects of a riotous youth to senile age, we may trace a river's progress from source to exit, while a somewhat similar trail marks its career across the passing centuries.

RIVER MAGNITUDES

In discussing rivers, geographers have always stressed comparative size. This is implicit in the very definition *"larger* than a rivulet or brook."* Strabo wrote, "It is sufficiently agreed that the Ganges is the largest of known rivers on the three continents, and after it the Indus, and third and fourth the Ister [Danube] and the Nile." Of the New World, with its Amazon, its Paraná, and its Mississippi, he knew nothing, while beyond his horizons lay the Congo, the Zambezi, and the giant rivers of Siberia, China, and Malaya. Even in familiar territory Strabo's observations were inaccurate. Although he had ascended the Nile beyond the first cataract, he gave that great river less prominence than several remoter streams, so great is the deference paid to the unknown.

From the earliest antiquity claims similar to Strabo's have been made. The Hebrews of King Solomon's day referred to the Euphrates as "the great river"; Herodotus thought the Ister [Danube] was the world's largest, while Marco Polo placed the Yangtze Kiang at the head of the list.

There were no surveys then, for geography was in its swaddling clothes. But even now the investigator who scans the atlases, the dictionaries, the encyclopedias, and the scientific journals will be astonished at the maze of contradictory reports. True, unlike the ancients, we know that the Amazon is the King of Rivers, and the Congo in second place, but the picture soon becomes blurred and indistinct.

Much confusion is due to insufficient data. The sources of several great rivers are unknown or in dispute; their length estimates, their drainage areas, and still more their volumes, mere guesswork. An attempt to tabulate them soon becomes an excursion into the unknown.

An absurd chauvinism adds to the bewilderment of the fact-finder. North Americans are proud of their great river, the Mississippi-Missouri. But this is poor excuse for the gradual "stretching" of that river to 4,221 miles, which recent authorities announce makes it the longest river in the world. Possibly it is the longest, though that contention is debatable, but the Corps of Engineers of the Mississippi River Commission give its extreme length as "approximately 3,986 miles."

Difficulties in measurement are complicated by capricious river action. Some rivers coil and uncoil through their final course in alternate oxbow loops and cutoffs, while others leave their ancient beds entirely to wander off across the countryside. Over the longer range they may add to their length by pirating less virile neighbor streams or be themselves beheaded by successful rivals. Rivers, as we have also observed, tend to become longer by reaching out into more remote hinterlands, at the same time encroaching upon the sea by delta formations.

Drainage areas, though also fluctuating because of a changing terrain and aggressive river action, are a fairer gauge of "size" than mere length and have become the accepted standard of comparison. Other considerations would make the Amazon the chief of rivers, but its supremacy is soundly based upon a drainage area almost as large as the United States and nearly double that of the next biggest river, the Congo.

Strabo was excusable for refusing to head his list of great rivers with the Nile, for it flowed for hundreds of miles through a desert without receiving a single tributary. Even now, while it is probably somewhat longer than the Mississippi and perhaps the longest of all rivers, it resembles an alimentary canal with no body to justify its attenuated length. In contrast with its slender, palmlike trunk, the Volga suggests a shaggy oak sprawling over a wide terrain. Length, after all, is but one dimension. Among lakes, shallow, twisting Balkhash is longer than Superior, but there all comparison ends.

Drainage areas, however, though more informative than length, remain indifferent criteria. Such areas are computed by connecting the extremities of all tributaries by a perimeter of lines from the river's mouth to its source and back again on the other side. Where the branches of other streams intrude like the cogs in meshing wheels, a fair division is attempted between conflicting watersheds. The error arises in treating all drainage basins alike when they are quite dissimilar. Much of the drainage area of the St. Lawrence system is actual water, the surface of the Great Lakes and many lesser lakes. Some of the drainage area of the Niger is the Sahara, which is no drainage area at all. Rivers of noteworthy size, like the Murray-Darling in Australia and the Rio Grande, accumulate less water than many a tropic stream one tenth their dimensions. The Orinoco, upon the map, looks decidedly secondary to the Mississippi, but it probably pours a greater volume of water into the sea.

And so a third and perhaps fairer method of river comparison is expressed in volume. The length of an irrigation ditch or the area it traverses are minor considerations in contrast with the water it carries. The observer cannot see a river's length or its drainage basin, but he can be impressed with its width and volume. The size of a tree is determined not so much by its height or the area shaded by its branches as by the diameter of its trunk. Since it is the work of rivers to carry off surplus water, why shouldn't the river that carries the most be considered the largest?

RIVER VOLUMES

River length and drainage area can be surveyed, for both are relatively fixed. River volumes, on the contrary, may vary from flooded valleys to empty channels. Even the largest rivers show startling extremes. On April 28, 1927, the Mississippi poured an estimated 1,557,000 cubic feet a second into the Gulf of Mexico; on November 1, 1939, that discharge was only 49,200. The maximum volume of the Father of Waters was nearly thirty-two times its minimum, while tributaries show even wider fluctuations. On January 12, 1940, the volume of the Missouri was only 4,200 cubic feet a second, less than one per cent of its 676,000 cubic feet discharge on June 7, 1903. Such examples show some of the difficulties in determining a river's *average* volume.

The Mississippi has been charted through all its branches, its volume checked and rechecked for flood control. Few other rivers have been subjected to such exhaustive study. The Indus River Commission has learned much about that turbulent stream, while the Nile River Commission is a modern "carrying on" of ancient measurements inaugurated by priests of Egypt thousands of years ago. Herodotus, who made a personal tour of the Nile, preferred the Danube because of its steadier current, for he wrote of it, "The Ister, which is the greatest of all the rivers we know, flows always with an equal stream summer and winter." He recognized the fact that a river's average outflow is a more reliable index of volume than its temporary floodwaters.

Certain standards of measurement have been adopted for water volumes. In reservoirs or lakes that volume is expressed in "acre-feet"—a watery surface an acre in extent, a foot in depth. That unit has been applied to many a city reservoir; it has also recorded the capacity of Lake Superior.

But as rivers are water in motion, *velocity* becomes a factor. Hence a river's outflow is usually expressed in cubic feet per second.

The underlying principle of such measurement is simple, its application extremely difficult. In theory a cross section of a river need only be multiplied by the velocity of its current. Unfortunately, cross sections vary with the locality. Even the mighty Amazon is constricted to a width of little more than a mile at Obidos, Brazil; the Zambezi below Victoria Falls is squeezed into a strait jacket scarcely sixty feet wide, while the Nile at Murchison's Falls slips through a rocky cleft in the earth crust but eighteen feet across! In such cases rivers strive to maintain an even current by increasing their velocity or dredging deeper channels. The Congo boils through the final gorge of the African plateau at a speed of thirteen knots; the Orinoco at Ciudad Bolívar has excavated a channel 335 feet deep. Cross sections present their problems.

Quite as difficult is an accurate appraisal of velocity. First of all, this varies with volume as floodwaters go swirling seaward, while a current depleted by drought becomes sluggish and in some rivers may cease altogether. River velocities and volumes have been studied by such investigators as Ganguillet, Kutter, Folse, and others. To understand all their conclusions would require a course in hydraulics at some technical school. For the layman a much simplified picture will suffice. *Friction* is important. Experiments on the Mississippi show that velocity increases *outward* from the shores, *upward* from the bottom. Velocity, however, is not greatest at the surface, but at about three fifths of the depth. Surface velocities are disturbed by winds. Gales may accelerate or retard them. Surface ice slows the water immediately beneath; anchor ice, coating the bottom, decreases friction and increases velocity. The friction of shores or bottom contours, however, is minimized by the velocity, as in mountain streams, or by the sheer impetus of waters, as in the Amazon.

There are other complications. River volumes do not necessarily increase all the way to the sea. The volume of the Nile sixteen hundred miles upstream exceeds that at the delta; the volume of the Oxus is greater near its source than at its mouth. The pattern of global river volumes is enormously complex.

To a degree such volumes are interwoven with river lengths and drainage areas. Dr. Albrecht Penck has estimated that in Turkestan an increased flow of two cubic meters per second would double the length of a river one hundred kilometers long and fifty meters wide. But there evaporation is paramount.

Velocity measurements have evolved from crude beginnings. The Indus River Commission spanned that stream with floating flags a hundred feet apart and calculated their downstream drift. The current of the Danube was measured from a platform supported by pontoons anchored to upstream moorings. Permanent gauges have since been established along some rivers and their recordings noted perhaps twice a year. Current meters have been devised for open channels. Torpedo-shaped and weighted so as to sink vertically, these mechanisms involve a spinneret whose revolutions per minute automatically record on shore the current movement.

River velocities are important, for they largely determine the rate of erosion and the traction load of silt and gravel. We need to supplement our knowledge of length and drainage area with more information about volume.

That this is a problem for the future, however, is made clear in a letter received from the office of the Chief of Engineers of the War Department at Washington. "Unfortunately none of the reference books either technical or nontechnical in the extensive library of the Corps of Engineers attempts to give the discharge in cubic feet per second of any foreign river. The chief librarian is unable to suggest a source for the data you desire."

Although puzzling problems, from the records of foreign river commissions, from standard encyclopedias, and from reports of various visiting scientists the following river volumes have been gleaned—inaccurate, no doubt, but presenting at least a rough approximation of facts.

River	Continent	Discharge in cubic feet per second
Amazon	South America	7,200,000
La Plata-Paraná	South America	2,800,000
Congo	Africa	2,000,000
Yangtze Kiang	Asia	770,000
Ganges-Brahmaputra	Asia	707,000
Mekong	Asia	600,000
Mississippi-Missouri	North America	513,000
Mackenzie	North America	450,000
Nile	Africa	420,000
St. Lawrence	North America	400,000
Volga	Europe	350,000
Danube	Europe	315,000
Indus	Asia	300,000
Columbia	North America	280,000
Hwang Ho	Asia	116,000
Colorado	North America	23,300
Murray-Darling	Australia	13,000
Rio Grande	North America	5,180

WHERE HISTORY AND GEOGRAPHY CLASH

The blunders of history are written large on all the maps of the world in the delineation of great rivers.

A river, with its branches, is a geographic unit, but it is seldom so regarded. It was natural for Admiral Sir Thomas Button, cruising desolate Hudson Bay, to name a great river the Nelson in memory of his mate who died and was buried by its lonely shores, but it seems unnecessary to continue that name as a portion of the greater Saskatchewan system well known to the Indians before Admiral Button was ever heard of. In any case, the two form a single river and should be called either Nelson or Saskatchewan.

Primitive peoples may be excused for such river dissection, for their horizons are limited. Joseph F. Rock, exploring the country of the Tibbus in the provinces of Kansu and Szechwan, found a tributary of the Yangtze River known locally under no fewer than eleven names. Stanley, drifting down the Congo, observed that the name of that great river changed with each of the many savage tribes along its shores. Occasionally there is some merit in such arbitrary division. The African natives in the valleys of the Joliba and Quorra rivers never suspected a connection between the two, which flow in opposite directions, and geologists are inclined to believe that they were once separate rivers until they united to create the Niger. But there is no similar excuse for calling the Amazon the Solimões beyond its juncture with the Negro or the Marañón in the Peruvian highlands. And why should New Yorkers persist in designating the mouth of the Hudson as the North River, a verbal hangover from colonial times when the Delaware was the "South River"?

In some cases lakes obscure the picture. The Detroit and Niagara rivers seem separate entities, though both are fragments in the greater St. Lawrence design. But it is unfortunate that the Mackenzie should be mutilated like a dissevered serpent by calling one part of the main stream the Great Slave River and another the Athabaska.

The historic approach has caused many an error of the map maker. The Murray River of Australia was explored before the much lengthier Darling, and so the shorter was recognized as the major stream, the longer a mere tributary. But we need not journey halfway around the world to observe a parallel case. The Mississippi-Missouri is a classic example of faulty nomenclature. The length of the upper Mississippi is 1,205 miles, the length of the Missouri 2,807, while from that point to the sea the channel is common to both, yet the Mississippi tail has continued to wag the Missouri dog ever since the first rude sketch was plotted

by French explorers. Because Marquette and Joliet and later
La Salle sailed down a river that the Indians called the Mississippi, the much longer Missouri from an unknown hinterland
was regarded as a tributary. Had North America been explored
by envoys of a Manchu emperor from beyond the Pacific, the
legend of Mississippi supremacy would never have arisen. Nor
is it enough to exclude the Big Muddy because of its erratic
current, for the Ohio in flood has poured more water into the
Mississippi than that river empties into the Gulf of Mexico. On
February 1, 1937, it swirled past Cairo, Illinois, at a rate of
1,850,000 cubic feet a second, a volume that nearly rivaled that
of the Congo.

The Yenesei in Asia has suffered from the same approach. Its
western branch was known to Cossack adventurers before the
much longer Angara-Selenga connecting with cavernous Lake
Baikal. Yet atlases continue to announce the shorter of the two
branches as the main channel.

The Volga is neither so long nor probably so voluminous as
the Kama tributary winding down from the Ural Mountains, but
because the western drainage area was better known to early
Russians and became the seat of their capital, Moscow, while
the valley of the Kama long remained under Tartar control, the
great river of Europe has followed the course of history rather
than geography.

On many rivers information has been lacking. The Chinese
thought the Sungari was the main channel of the mightier Amur,
for it had its source in their familiar Ever-white Mountains and
often flooded the plains of Manchuria; while even now geographers are undecided whether the vast Ob River of Siberia has its
true headwaters in the so-called upper Ob branch or in another
known as the Irtysh.

Sometimes religious motives have determined the choice of
names. The Hindus, regarding the Ganges as sacred, had it
spring from the icy Himalayas, the throne room of the gods,
ignoring the fact that the Chambal branch of the tributary Jumna,
issuing from the Deccan plateau, was considerably longer.

While geography was slowly emerging from a mist of legend

such errors came about naturally and unavoidably. Yet it seems unfortunate, with increasing knowledge, that names so carelessly bestowed should prove so resistant to revision. Biologists continually reclassify species of the living world, but river names, however faulty, seem inscribed upon the map in indelible ink.

PART FOUR

The Great Rivers of Asia

~~~~~~

THE GREAT RIVERS OF ASIA

ACROSS an arc of sixty-five hundred miles, one quarter the circumference of the globe, sprawls the huge continent of Asia. Its more than sixteen million square miles of area nearly equal the entire Western Hemisphere.

Ancient land surfaces appear in outcroppings of pre-Cambrian rock. Most extensive are the Angara shield along southern Siberia and the gnarled plateau of the Deccan in India. Great mountain ranges stretch east and west, the Himalayas, the Tien Shan, the Kunlun, and others, impassable barriers to modifying winds, so that the northern continent freezes while the southern swelters in unnatural temperatures. Caught up in this upsurging of the earth crust are lofty plateaus, the Pamir, or the "World's White Roof Tree," and the huge tableland of Tibet. According to Philip Lake, in the *Royal Geographical Journal*, this upsurging may have brought molten material to the surface from a depth of forty miles! As the crust crumpled and folded, underthrusts from the Pacific met overthrusts from the land much as one ice sheet on a frozen river is shoved above another. These lateral movements are evident in semicircular arcs like the Kurile and Aleutian chains of islands. At the edges of over- or under-thrust the earth crust sagged in gulfs like the Japan Trough and the Mindanao Deep, which are quite close to the land.

Between the northerly and southerly transverse ranges a vast area of nearly five million square miles is shut off from the sea to form the most extensive interior drainage basin in the world. This area is arid and much of it is desert. At least 380,000 square miles are uninhabited, 1,000,000 nearly so. Water is always scarce and when found is often made nauseous by the roots of tamarisk trees. The nomad inhabitants seem driven hither and thither like the sands before the winds which sweep clean the very horizons. Across this region the Gobi Desert stretches from the confines of China to merge into the arid steppes of Turkestan and the areas about those inland seas, the Aral and the Caspian. The latter territory extends into Europe to embrace the valley of the Volga and all central Russia. Scattered here and there are lesser isolated basins such as occupy fully one half of Persia.

Asia well illustrates the three divisions into which geographers divide continental land masses: the Arcic—with no runoff—such as the deserts of Arabia; the Endoreic—with internal drainage—like that of the Caspian; and the Exoreic—with a normal runoff to the sea, the continental border areas.

Asia then is a hollow shell, its largest rivers crossing only the outer segments of the continent. Moreover, as it lies north of the equator, there are no such regions of tropic downpour as swell the current of the Congo or the Amazon. Yet the continent is so vast that it presents a notable array of great rivers sustained by coastal rain belts or the melting glaciers of the world's most extensive mountain ranges.

These rivers fall into well-marked divisions. Three, the Ob, the Yenesei, and the Lena, which provide the great commercial avenues of Siberia, flow generally northward into the Arctic. Although the rainfall is scanty, often under ten inches and seldom exceeding twenty, the peculiar nature of both terrain and climate sustain a considerable runoff.

Across the whole breadth of the continent and extending through northern Europe to the Atlantic stretches the greatest coniferous forest in the world. In Asia it is called the taiga, a wilderness of swamp and upland. Inhabitants are few in number, summer breeds innumerable swarms of mosquitoes, the boles of the trees are often marked by the claws of bears, the tusks of savage wild boars. This forest conserves the limited moisture while the frozen subsoil permits an almost total runoff of rain-

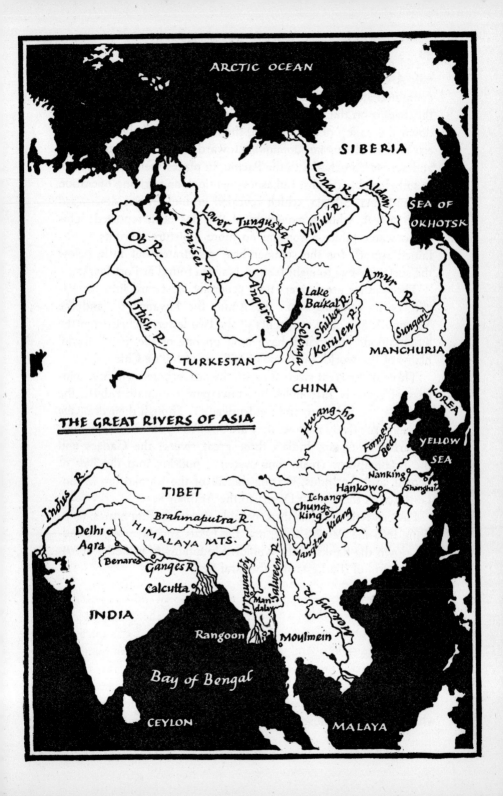

fall. A subterranean region of perpetual frost underlies an area computed at 3,728,000 square miles. According to K. I. Lukashev, this begins on the shores of Russia's White Sea, turns southward down the valley of the Yenesei, then follows roughly the southern border of Russian dominions toward the mouth of the Amur and across Kamchatka to the Pacific. In places the earth is frozen to unbelievable depths. Lukashev mentions one drilling operation at Amderma, Siberia, which revealed ground frozen downward for 815 feet, while a maximum of 890 has been reported! This static water table, absorbing no more moisture, permits a sustained runoff, for the summer heat penetrates but little below the surface—five to eight feet, so Nansen found at Port Igarka.

Three other great rivers flow generally westward into the Pacific or its outlying seas: the Amur, the Hwang Ho, and the Yangtze Kiang. The sediments of the two latter, filched from the mountainous hinterland, have built up one of the great alluvial plains of the world, the home of millions of toiling Chinese.

Three other great rivers flow southward, gripped within a compass of scarcely fifty miles by converging mountain ridges: the Mekong, the Salween, and the Irrawaddy. Though their drainage areas are relatively narrow, they are swollen by torrential rainfalls.

Farther west are India's three great rivers: the Ganges and the Brahmaputra (really one system), pouring into the Bay of Bengal, and the Indus, bearing the silt of the Karakorum Mountains across the Punjab Desert to the Arabian Sea.

Eastern Asia also has three notable rivers: the Euphrates, emptying into the Persian Gulf, and the Oxus and Jaxartes, cascading down the flanks of the Kunlun Mountains to meander across the deserts of Turkestan to the Aral Sea.

I

The Siberian Group

THE LENA—RIVER OF GRIEF AND GOLD

Length—3,000 miles. Drainage area—1,169,000 square miles

MANY RIVERS rising in the highlands of Asia flow northward across Siberia into the Polar Sea. To most of us their names are only a jumble of barbaric syllables. How many have even heard of the Khatanga, the Olenek, the Yana, the Indigirka, or the Kolyma? Yet each of these is longer and drains more territory than the Rhine. To such oblivion does remoteness and arctic cold condemn otherwise important streams.

Three Siberian rivers, however, force recognition by their sheer size: the Lena, the Ob, and the Yenisei.

The Lena, rising in mountainous terrain at an elevation of 2,855 feet not far from huge Lake Baikal, winds for some three thousand miles through a drainage basin of 1,169,000 square miles, nearly equal to that of the Mississippi. Its course resembles the sickle of the Soviet flag. At first it trends eastward through the oldest rocks of the continent, where gnarled and eroded uplands still present such peaks as Tentorgo, 6,336 feet in height. Sometimes called the river of a thousand tributaries, the Lena collects from the south, among lesser streams, the Karenga, the Vitim with its gold-bearing sands, and the Olekma, fully a thousand miles long, that sweeps downward from the rugged Yablonovy Mountains not far from that other giant Asian river, the Amur.

Curving northward around the sickle's arc, the Lena receives from the east the many-branched Aldan, fifteen hundred miles in length, which rises within fifty miles of the fog-cursed Okhotsk Sea, while the Vilyui, quite as long, bears the overflow from vast lowlands to the west. The Lena crosses the Siberian plain at a gradient of little more than two inches per mile, a slow-moving flood of Amazonian vastness from four to twenty miles in width, to empty by several mouths into the shallow Arctic.

The upper river traverses a mountainous country of wild and varied scenery. In one place it has gouged out a canyon twenty-five miles long flanked by precipices two thousand feet high. Here are the colorful *stolbi*, or columns, formed of alternate layers of red and green limestone, each layer less than two feet in thickness.

Emerging from the highlands, the river crosses the lonely taiga, the most extensive forest on earth. Though interrupted at intervals, this spreads its evergreen mantle over two continents, for it is a continuation of the coniferous forests of Scandinavia to the shores of Bering Sea. Though it lacks the cloistered gloom of those tropic forests that bury the valleys of the Congo and the Amazon, the taiga is overwhelming in its oceanic vastness. No wonder Norse mythology venerated Vidar, who presided over the primeval wilderness. Thor, the wielder of thunderbolts, was destined to perish in the twilight of the gods, but Vidar would survive to restore a greener, newer world.

Some ninety miles from the sea the taiga merges into the tundra, a swampy lowland matted with clumps of moss into which the sojourner sinks nearly to the knee. Here only willow shrubs persist, but they too die out some thirty-five miles from the Arctic. Few regions save the lifeless deserts of Africa or Arabia can be so forlorn. In summer the tundra is well-nigh impassable; in winter it becomes a world of snow, swept by the fearful purgas, or blizzards, when all life must seek temporary shelter or perish.

The great delta of the Lena is a geological curiosity. Its area, some twelve thousand square miles, is exceeded only by that of the Ganges and the Niger. Of the several outlets, the most considerable is the Bylovski, swerving farthest to the east. Ice chokes the innumerable cross channels from mid-October to the following July, while in severe seasons they do not open at all. The low-lying mossy islands are in part "rock ice" covered with earth, which would dissolve beneath the sea if subjected to the tropic heat of the Ganges. Nonetheless, the sluggish river, though choked and shackled, discharges every second into the Arctic an estimated 325,000 cubic feet of water, so that Borchia Bay is brackish rather than salt, while the sea for miles offshore is shallow with accumulated silt.

The forest resources of the Lena Valley are well-nigh inexhaustible and await only an available market. The river abounds with fish which the natives formerly caught in nets made of horsehair. The muksun, a species of salmon held in particular esteem, is often eaten raw. In summer hunters voyage to the delta in clumsy canoes to fish and slaughter the innumerable aquatic birds that nest there. Wild geese, helpless when molting, are driven into netlike cages. Fifteen men in a day thus captured forty-five hundred. These are buried for dog food, but when provisions run low the natives devour the half-decayed bodies themselves. Snowy owls, half blinded by continuous sunlight, may be readily approached. Fox traps are constructed from driftwood, while nomadic Tungus drive their reindeer into the tundra to escape the stinging hell of the mosquitoes farther south.

Stranger game than sables or wild fowl is sometimes found, for this was once a favorite range of the hairy mammoth (*Elephas primigenius*). Bodies sunk in the mud and frozen have been preserved for thousands of years, to be exposed by the eroding river. One nearly complete carcass, its veins filled with coagulated blood, was partially devoured by dogs. Even the natives sampled the flesh of this grotesque creature that became extinct millenniums ago. The tusks, abnormally long and curved, are an article of commerce. Middendorff estimated that during the two centuries prior to 1840 no fewer than twenty thousand mammoth tusks had been exported from Sibera. Such fossil ivory is even mentioned by the Roman writer, Pliny.

The Lena Valley holds a wide diversity of mineral wealth. Sulphur springs bubble up in various places and curative mud baths. There is coal of rather poor quality, and native Yakuts smelt iron. Amber is sometimes found, and emeralds and platinum. But most noteworthy are the gold fields of the Vitim and Olekma, with their history of stark brutality.

Here miners, many of them convicts, have toiled since 1840, wading in icy water up to their knees, tormented by insect pests, sleeping in rude barracks, scourged by pulmonary and other diseases. Then comes a periodic debauch in the town of Vitim, with scanty savings wasted in an aura of vodka, and, penniless once more, back they troop to the pitiless Lena. No wonder mortality among them has been staggering.

Climate is the curse of the lower river and winter its nemesis. The brief summer thaws the ground to the depth of a few feet at most. Beneath lies the Kingdom of Perpetual Cold. The icy temperature, penetrating deeper century after century, has frozen the ground in places to the incredible depth of more than eight hundred feet! Toward the delta region winter's rigors are increased by the darkness as the sun dips below the horizon. Barometric pressures seem to conspire with other unfavorable features to harass the valley. A vast blanket of cold air settles over it like an incubus, so entrenched that even gales rebound from its elastic walls. This stagnant atmospheric eddy remains for months. Verkhoyansk, in the valley of the Yana, east of the Lena, has long been called the coldest spot on earth. Although this dubious distinction has been challenged, the lowest temperature on record was recorded there—94 degrees below zero. George Kennan in his classic *Tent Life in Siberia* describes the effects of such cold. Steaming soup, lifted from the fire, froze before it could be consumed a few feet away; steel axes split as they rebounded from trees frozen to the very heart, while exercise that caused the feet to perspire invited crippling injury and possible death. Most terrifying of all are the blasts that sweep down from the Arctic. In these chill smothers one cannot see five feet, in fact can scarcely breathe. The winds sweep him off his feet, the cold probes every crevice of his clothing. Stifled and half blinded, he must seek instant shelter, if only beneath an overturned sledge, to shiver for hours or even days until the atmospheric frenzy subsides. For such hardships the northern lights offer an insufficient recompense, although they blaze across the dark sky in a splendor that defies description. Not until March, as the Yakuts say, do "the horns of the bull of winter begin to break."

Simple-minded Russian peasants call their great river "Mother Lena," but she has proved a cruel stepmother. Convicts once left Russia in chains to be buried alive in remote settlements along her shores. Vladimir Zenzinov has made public some memoirs of his exile at Bulun on the lower Lena. This tiny hamlet on the rim of the habitable globe suggests that dismal region of the Hyperboreans that Homer mentions. Life under such circumstances becomes a bitter struggle for existence in an environment of almost unendurable hardships. Not the least of these is the utter loneliness, the sense of being lost to the world, swallowed up in a chaos of furious winds and swirling waters, of silence and darkness and cold.

Yet the Lena Valley has always been sparsely settled. Nomadic Tungus of Mongolian and Yakuts of Turkish origin have eked out a meager living by hunting, fishing, and trapping, or from their herds of domesticated reindeer. Marco Polo evidently came in contact with these wild Tungus, for he speaks of "regions where darkness prevails . . . of wagons drawn by dogs," the sledges which still speed over the frozen snow, and of "men who rode upon stags," i.e., reindeer. They still ride them, seated high upon the animal's shoulders.

When Cossack outlaws, many of them with a price upon their heads, fled from Russia into Siberia they passed readily from one great river system to another. True, these rivers flowed north rather than east or west, but their tributaries approached closely enough to provide transportation. The westernmost or Ob River bends within six miles of the Yenisei, which in turn makes a near contact with the Lena, while the Aldan branch of the latter river bore poineering boatmen to within a few leagues of the Pacific. Hence the six-thousand-mile expanse of Siberia was crossed by hardy adventurers in a surprisingly brief time. In 1637 the Cossack Elisei Busa followed the Lena to the delta. A hundred years later the Russian Lieutenant Prontschischev sailed down the river seeking to round the northern tip of the continent only to perish of privation and be buried with his young wife in a single grave.

The De Long expedition, attempting to sail around northern Asia from Bering Sea, came to grief off the mouth of the Lena. When their ship, the *Jeannette*, was crushed in the ice the party tried to reach the shore in the three boats. One foundered with all on board, a second managed to gain safety, the third under

De Long himself also made the shore, the party wading through the shallow waters when their boat could advance no farther. Two members of this party were ultimately rescued, but De Long and eleven others merely exchanged a sudden death by drowning for one of prolonged suffering. A hill some seven miles from the main outlet of the Lena is crowned with a monument inscribed with the words, "In memory of twelve of the officers and men of the U. S. Arctic steamer *Jeannette* who died of starvation on the Lena Delta in 1881." Many others have fallen victim to that river's savage temper. A loftier hill a thousand feet high near the head of the delta is also crowned by the tombs of three shamans, and no one knows how many lie in unmarked graves.

The natives commonly enclose their dead in hollow logs aboveground. The shamans believe that underground is the abode of malignant spirits which manifest their presence in the hideous sounds of cracking ice and frozen soil. Like the priests of other faiths, they consign the souls of evil men to gloomy deeps where, arraigned before the throne of Erlik Khan, they are purged of sin by being boiled in kettles of burning tar.

The coming of the white man was no unmixed blessing, for he also brought his vodka, his vices, and his diseases. Smallpox in particular has been a terrible scourge, added to malnutrition, cold, and sore eyes caused by the smoke of unventilated lodges. Most terrifying of maladies, however, is the Arctic hysteria, a madness born of sheer vastness, darkness, and cold.

The main city of the Lena basin is Yakutsk, near the easternmost point of the sickle curve. Cattle are bred in that vicinity, barley and rye are grown, while potatoes, cabbages, turnips, and other crops mature in the brief but almost continuous summer sunshine.

Native dugout canoes have been largely replaced by *pausks*, scowlike flatboats with rounded roofs. These provide floating variety stores to scattered settlements along the banks. Kitchen and sleeping quarters for the crew are in the after part, while forward are the shops and inevitable saloon.

Still ruder are the *pauzoks*, or freight barges, but steamers, in-

resembling the Gulf of St. Lawrence. Were it situated in the latitude of Puget Sound, it would doubtless be a center of important
cities; instead, lying mostly beyond the Arctic Circle, flanked
by dreary tundra and facing the Polar Sea, it is ice-choked most
of the year. The Ob, which enters the western branch of this
capacious gulf through a considerable delta, freezes over in October to remain a sheet of ice until the following June, so brief is
the open season in northern Siberia.

The balance of world power turned from Asia to Europe in
the valley of the Ob. Europe had been guarded on the southeast
by the Mediterranean and the Black Sea, together with the impassable Caucasus Mountains and the Caspian; but northward
the Ural Mountains were an insecure barrier, while the Ural
River was no barrier at all. Across this river swarmed not only
conquering armies, but whole nations emerging from the profound recesses of the mother continent pressed ever westward toward the Atlantic. Such were the Celts, the Germans,
the Huns, the Avars, and Bulgarians and other lesser peoples;
followed in turn by the devastating hordes of the Mongols. From
the south came the Persians, who once threatened to absorb all
Greece, the Saracens, who swept across Africa to conquer Spain
and menace France, while the Turks, later pouring over the
Balkans and southern Russia, still retain a foothold upon the
narrow straits. Since the dawn of history Europe has been darkened by storm clouds rolling up out of Asia; has been repeatedly
desolated and great areas permanently vanquished.

But the tide definitely turned in 1580, and subsequent conflicts between huge Asia and little Europe have proved an unbroken series of triumphs for the latter. In that year, into the
valley of the Kama in eastern Russia fled the Cossack outlaw
Yermak Timofeyevitch, with a price upon his head. Collecting
a band of several hundred kindred spirits, he yearned to lead
his little army beyond the mountains into the valley of the Ob,
where stood the stockaded town of Sibir, seat of a Mohammedan
khanate, a fragment of the once mighty Mongol Empire. Yermak
was playing with fire, for the Lord of Muscovy, who had assumed the imperial title of Czar, was no other than that formidable character, Ivan the Terrible. To him Yermak appealed for

permission to wage war upon Sibir, a permission which the Czar, who had just cast off the Tartar yoke, was graciously pleased to grant. Before the furious Cossack onslaught Sibir fell like a house of cards and Yermak pursued the disorganized enemy up the valley of the Ob.

Sibir, only a rude settlement in the wilderness, gave its name to all Siberia; Yermak, a brigand who never commanded more than a few hundred men, turned the tide of conquest from Europe to Asia. Other adventurers penetrating the northern wilderness were not even halted by the Pacific but swept into North America, adding Alaska to the dominions of the czars. No other conquests, save that of the Saracens following Mohammed, or the Mongols under Genghis Khan and his successors, ever involved so vast a territory or were so speedily consummated.

In reward for services rendered, Yermak was not only pardoned by Ivan but presented with a cuirass inlaid with gold. This proved a fatal gift, for the Cossack, fleeing an outlaw band that thirsted for his blood, tried to swim the Irtysh encumbered by his armor, only to sink beneath the current. Four brief years had elapsed since he set out on his warlike expedition, but they were fateful years which banished for all time the threat of future Asiatic aggression and laid the foundation for the Soviet Empire of today.

The Ob has always been a great watery highway through a sparsely settled region. Tobolsk and Omsk upon the Irtysh long ago became important trade centers, while on the eastern branch Tomsk and Novosibirsk are the principal cities. Steamers were introduced in 1845, and in 1915 numbered no fewer than 350, together with hundreds of barges. Since that date commerce has greatly increased as cattle raising, agriculture, mining, lumbering, and many other industries multiply and prosper.

Giant icebreakers now struggle to keep river channels open, and hydroplanes equipped with skis patrol the coast. One native, who had never seen an automobile, when shown a picture said it was probably an airplane without wings. Potatoes are grown beyond the Arctic Circle, which prompted a disgruntled kulak to remark, "If you put a university professor behind each potato . . . you can probably raise them at the North Pole."

And still the great river rolls on through mountain, desert, swamp, and forest, itself unchanged, while all about is changing. For if the ghost of Yermak, clad in the glittering armor which dragged him to his death, could emerge above its icy current, he would doubtless be amazed at the feverish activity throughout its vast drainage basin.

THE ICE-CHOKED YENISEI

Length—3,553 miles. Drainage area—1,000,000 square miles

Halfway across the continent of Asia and into the ice-choked Arctic flows the Yenisei. In the language of Tungus nomads its name, which is divided into four syllables and means "Great River," is richly deserved. Fridtjof Nansen, sailing upstream from the sea, called it the fifth longest river in the world and thought it ranked seventh in drainage area. Both figures as they appear in encyclopedias and atlases are varying estimates, but the most recent appraisal gives the length as 3,553 miles, the basin a round one million.

The Yenisei, like the Mississippi, has suffered at the hands of the map makers. Just as La Salle, tracing the latter river from what is now Illinois, ignored the much longer Missouri, so Russian explorers, approaching from the west, followed the Yenisei to what they assumed to be its mountain source and called the much lengthier Angara-Baikal-Selenga combination a tributary.

The Selenga, however, marks the true headwaters of the Yenisei. Its many branches, coursing among the mountains of Mongolia which attain a height of five thousand feet, penetrate far into that remote country. Some seven hundred miles in length, this river empties into the colossal trough called Baikal, which contains more fresh water than any other lake on earth. Although this lake plumbs abysses more than a mile in depth, the delta of the Selenga continually encroaches upon broadening shallows. From the opposite shore issues the Angara, or upper Tunguska, a river so purified of silt that Nansen found the bottom at a depth of several fathoms plainly visible. The Angara makes a vast right angle for some fifteen hundred miles, first north then west, to unite with the shorter western branch, and then proceeds on its leisurely course through forest and tundra to that deep indentation of the seacoast known as the Gulf of Yenisei.

If the Yenisei is not the major river of Siberia, a claim that might be challenged by the Ob or Lena, it makes the most imposing appearance upon the map. Immensely long, its drainage basin, like that of the Nile, is relatively narrow. Like the Nile also, it issues from a tableland but recently explored and draws much volume from lacustrine overflow. The Nile drains several lakes, including Victoria Nyanza, next to Superior the most extensive body of fresh water in the world; the Yenisei drains only one, but that lake, Baikal, could swallow all the Nilotic lakes with much room to spare, so capacious is its volume.

Like the Lena, the Yenisei is a marginal stream along an ancient highland which once formed the core of Asia. Although its worn-down mountains seem relatively minor, they are far older than the snowy Kunlun, the Karakorum, or the Himalayas, which boast the loftiest summits in the world.

Among lesser tributaries of the Yenisei two great branches approach from the east through mingled forests and swamplands. Of these, the Stony Tunguska is a good thousand miles in length, the Lower Tunguska nearly two thousand. The latter approaches within six miles of the Vilnui, a prominent affluent of the Lena.

The Selenga River and the Angara, where it issues from Baikal, are essentially mountain streams. Arid Central Asia here yields to the vast taiga, or timbered region, of Eurasia, where seemingly endless coniferous forests are interspersed with other trees, particularly yellow birch.

The Yenisei is seldom less than a mile and a half in width. Above its juncture with the Stony Tunguska lie the perilous reefs known as the Seventy Isles. Beyond latitude 70 the great river, here six miles wide, enters the dreary tundra, broadening into an island-choked estuary. The final two or three hundred miles is a moving tide. Nansen wrote, "The land on the west side of the river we could only just see, far away across the water. It might have been about twenty miles off . . . one of the great water arteries of the world."

The riverbanks are in striking contrast: the western low, the water shallow, the eastern steep and continually being undermined by the deeper channel. This river action, which partially accounts for the great width (sometimes thirty miles), is caused by the rotation of the earth. Other far-northern rivers emptying into the Arctic show the same tendency to veer eastward in a continuous global whirl.

Belugas, or white whales, mistaking the estuary of the Yenisei for a gulf of the sea, swim far up the channel where they are harpooned and their tough hides sold to Samoyed tribesmen to make harnesses for their sled dogs or reindeer. Small whales also invade the river. Sidorov, writing in 1859, mentions the killing of twenty-five of these huge mammals together with a much greater number of belugas and dolphins. Sturgeon and other fish abound, particularly a species of salmon which is caught in rudely constructed nets.

The retarding influence of the Arctic chill is well illustrated in the life of the lower river. Nansen mentions a larch ten feet high whose age he estimated at 150 years, while a fish 21½ inches long revealed by the rings upon its scales an age of sixteen years. Such is the sluggish tempo of life in the darkness and cold of the prolonged winter.

The mouth of the river and neighboring gulf freeze about October 20 and do not thaw out until the longest day of the year, about June 22. Meanwhile great ice masses, driven in sheets one above another to a height of fifty feet, gouge the riverbanks in a turmoil of current, ocean tides, and polar gales. Huge rocks are sometimes borne along on the ice.

The frozen surface presents an inviting speedway for native dog teams, but death lurks beneath. When the giant river, awakened by the summer sun, struggles to break its fetters there is continuous cracking and growling which almost justifies the native belief that demons are imprisoned below. One branch of the Yenisei has thus gained the evil name of the River of the Devil.

The natives of the Yenisei Valley are often a confused mixture of racial stocks. Urga, the capital of Mongolia, is situated in the valley of the Tola, a tributary of the Selenga. Like Lhasa in Tibet, it was the seat of a living Buddha surrounded by all the revolting rites of devil worship. The city was also a trade center and gained a sinister reputation for the most terrible prisons in the world. These were stout boxes with a single opening, so constructed that the manacled prisoner within could neither sit up nor stretch out. Shelterless in temperatures which fell to thirty below zero, a single sheepskin cover was permitted the wretched inmate, who nevertheless sometimes survived months of torment. But imagination falters at the barbarities practiced by man upon his fellows in the savage hinterlands of Central Asia.

Farther down the valley the prevalent Mongolian strain shows an infiltration of Turkish and other racial groups. Most numerous, however, are the Tungus, definitely Mongolian, with square skulls, slant eyes, and wiry bodies seldom over five feet four inches in height. Many are trappers; others have domesticated herds of reindeer. Their name has been bestowed upon the several Tunguska branches of the Yenisei.

The Yakuts, also widely scattered over northern Siberia, speak a language of Turkish origin. Among other tribes are the Ostiaks of Finno-Ugric descent, and the Samoyeds, whose nomadic settlements mark the bleak seacoast from the Yenisei to northern Russia.

To Cossack adventurers who visited the Yenisei in 1616 the hospitable natives lent their wives, with a resultant half-breed population. Like other primitive races, they followed a crude logic of their own. One Samoyed arraigned before a Russian court on the charge of having killed and eaten his wife during a famine admitted the act but obligingly explained that he had bought her, adding that he "paid a good price for her too."

One native dining on birds' eggs nearly ready to hatch carefully removed the feathers, a refinement of table manners which his less cultured neighbors ridiculed. Another, lacking a knife, bit off chunks of reindeer meat which he offered to his European guests. A true delicacy of the region, however, when prepared without its usual accompaniment of dirt and dog hairs, is sturgeon stew.

Religion with these people is an endless effort to placate the demons of cold and darkness and sheer starvation. Rude altars made of wood smoke with sacrificial reindeer blood, while native priests or shamans seek to guarantee good health, good weather, and good fishing. Missionaries are viewed with tolerant skepticism. One venerable Samoyed admitted that the Christian God might do for white men but doubted if He understood reindeer.

Much of the Yenisei basin is described by travelers as "an endless, flat forest country." Siberian spruce and cedar are the prevalent trees. Cedar nuts are eaten and widely marketed. Furs have always been a valued product, particularly foxes, ermines, and sables, whose glossy skins are called "living gold."

There is much mineral wealth. Rich seams of coal crop out in the river basin, while there are extensive deposits of iron, graphite, magnesium, asbestos, and gold. That rarer metal, platinum, is also reported.

From immemorial times the Yenisei has provided a highway through an almost trackless wilderness. Ostiak tribesmen, like North American Indians, learned to construct birch-bark canoes; while even simpler are the rafts which still float down the broad current. Early Cossack explorers were expert boatmen as well as horsemen. Steamships were introduced long ago by the Russians and are now numerous. Within recent years icebreakers have kept the main channel open much longer than formerly, while a considerable coastal commerce follows the Arctic seaboard from northern Russian ports. Irkutsk, not far from Lake Baikal, was founded in 1652. The great Trans-Siberian Railway, which once paused on the shores of this lake for freight cars to be transshipped to waiting barges, now follows the southern shore line along trackage blasted out of the rocky escarpment. Locomotives still burn birchwood from piles stored at convenient places.

Igarka, on the edge of the taiga beyond the Arctic Circle, has become a flourishing lumber camp, and there are other thriving settlements whose growth has been phenomenal. Stock raising and even a limited manufacturing have been introduced. Lenin, the Apostle of Bolshevism, was exiled to the province of Yeniseisk from 1897–1900, and his successors have been tireless in their efforts to revitalize Siberia.

Sometimes the Yenisei's crumbling banks reveal trophies of the past, when far different forms of life roamed its swamps and forests. The first specimen of the woolly rhinoceros was thus unearthed from its frozen bed in 1771, while hairy mammoths have also been exhumed, one specimen so well preserved that its stomach contents was analyzed and the carcass eaten by native dogs.

From ages of profound slumber the great river is at last awakening to the urge of modern civilization and faces a future of brighter promise than its unproductive past.

II

The Pacific Group

THE AMUR—ASIA'S "GREAT BLACK DRAGON"

Length—2,900 miles. Drainage area—766,000 square miles

FROM a remote and almost inaccessible region of Central Asia two rivers flow in a northeasterly direction toward the far away Pacific. Both rise within a few miles of each other on the flanks of the Ketei Shan whose peaks reach a height of 7,241 feet. The upper stream, known as the Shilka, winds its way through that jumbled terrain south and east of Baikal, the abysmal lake which holds more fresh water than Superior. The lower, or Kerulen, traverses outer Mongolia to that other lonely lake, Kulun-nor, whence it emerges as the Argun to join the Shilka on the northwestern corner of Manchuria.

Their union forms that vast stream vaguely known to us as the Amur, a contraction of the Tartar Kar-Amur-An, or "Great River of the Black Dragon." This name is well chosen, for like a dragon emerging from the hidden recesses of high Asia it coils about Manchuria, that battleground of greedy world powers which seems destined to a role of ominous import upon the stage of international affairs.

For some eight hundred miles the Amur flows toward the southeast to separate Manchuria from Russian territory. Had it continued to the Sea of Japan, it would have changed the history of the Orient. But it turns abruptly northeastward and cuts its way through the Khingan Mountains in a series of gorges 140 miles long to pursue its course for another eight hundred miles. Here it is an imposing stream two or three miles wide and often two hundred feet deep. Many islands dot its surface, while in floodtime its valley broadens to an elongated lake. Through a single mouth ten miles broad it pours its waters into the Gulf of Tartary over against the big island of Sakhalin to mingle in the icy currents of the Okhotsk Sea.

In its course of nearly three thousand miles the Amur traverses a varied terrain. The Kerulen skirts the Gobi Desert, a region of dreary emptiness. The upper Amur, however, flows through rugged country with rich bottom lands and slopes timbered with white and black birch, pine, larch, and linden. Through its middle course the river is fringed with forests of elm, maple, ash, birch, and oak broken by extensive grasslands. The lower Amur divides the rolling country toward the north from the extensive forests on the south. Much of the valley is quite as fertile as central Europe.

The Khingan gorges with their cliffs and pinnacles present vistas perhaps unsurpassed on any other river. One precipice is crowned by ruined temples and monuments inscribed in Sanskrit with the mystic formula of Hindustan: "*Om mani Padme Hum.*" [Who set them there no one knows.]

Along the upper reaches of the Amur, Major Perry Collins observed natives paddling birch-bark canoes like North American Indians. Manchu junks have long sailed the mid-section together with huge rafts bearing beef cattle for market. Although the river's mouth is impeded by shoals and sand bars, steamers of shallow draft proceed for two thousand miles from the sea to the upper Shilka, where river traffic connects with the Trans-Siberian railway. October frosts convert the river into a sheet of ice for more than half the year. Equally unfortunate is the outlet upon an ice-encumbered sea. Hence, instead of a great highway to the heart of the continent, it has remained a neglected backwater.

Although the Amur, according to E. G. Ravenstein, drains an area of 766,000 square miles, it is essentially the great river of Manchuria. The main channel forms the northern boundary; a tributary stream, the Ussuri, defines the eastern limits; another, the Argun, the northwestern border, while through the heart of that rich province flows the largest of the Amur's many branches, the Sungari, called the Mississippi of Manchuria.

The wild tribes of the Amur basin are mentioned in Chinese annals as early as 1100 B.C. Principally nomadic Tungus, they hoveled in subterranean dwellings, smeared their bodies with pig fat, and wore garments of hide or fishskins. Even now the Chinese claim that the reindeer Tungus of northern Manchuria have little in common with men but rather "resemble dogs or horses."

Manchuria's four hundred thousand square miles was alien territory, but Chinese culture had a profound influence upon the people who dwelt beyond the Great Wall. Many times their natural yearning for the luxuries and refinements of the south threatened the peace of empire. In 1606 the strong Manchu ruler, Nurhachu, assuming the control of various discordant tribes, welded them into a cohesive whole and dared defy the great Ming dynasty. When, in 1644, that empire was rent by civil war, the Manchus were invited within the Great Wall and captured Peking. With the aid of a famous Chinese general, Wu San-kuei, who has ever since been regarded as the Benedict Arnold of China, they overran the distracted country, and six years later Shun Chi, a descendant of Nurhachu, usurped the Dragon Throne as the first emperor of the Manchu dynasty. The Manchus governed China until its virtual collapse in the present century and added noteworthy names to its long list of enlightened sovereigns. Jehol, beyond the Great Wall, remained a favorite site and has been aptly called by Sven Hedin "the City of Emperors."

While the Manchus were turning southward from their ancestral home in the valleys of the Amur to the conquest of China, dark clouds were gathering along the northern horizon. In 1638 daring Cossacks who had swept from southern Russia clear across Asia to the Okhotsk Sea apparently heard of the great river to the south. In that same year other Cossacks on the Lena also learned of the Amur from nomadic Tartars. Five years later, in 1643, they reached its shores near the site of the present Russian city of Blagoveschensk. In 1648 still another Cossack band crossing the Yablonovy Mountains gained the banks of the Shilka.

The advent of these ruthless invaders spread consternation among native settlements. Fire and sword marked the progress of the white man down the Great River, while one leader during a famine-stricken winter resorted to cannibalism. In 1649 the Cossack Khabarov entered the valley via the Shilka and two years later made his winter headquarters at the junction of the Amur with its southern tributary, the Ussuri, a site marked by the city of Khabarovsk.

Clashes with Manchu outposts were inevitable, but for a long time Chinese influence remained paramount. The armies of the emperor restored order and the Treaty of Nerchinsk was signed in 1689 at the courts of both Russia and China.

This pact, which had the novelty of remaining in force for 169 years, defined the boundaries between the two empires, the valley of the Amur remaining under Chinese dominion.

But Russian expansion coupled with the weakness of China made Manchuria an inevitable battleground. The Russians, exerting pressure, wrung a concession to build a railway across that province to ice-free Port Arthur on the Yellow Sea. This aggression, followed by further encroachments on the moribund Korean kingdom, led to war with Japan and the temporary defeat of Russia. By the resultant Treaty of 1905, Russia withdrew from Korea and southern Manchuria, while retaining a sphere of influence over the northern area.

When the czarist power collapsed in the First World War, Japan took advantage of the weakness of the Soviet Government to overrun Manchuria. Here a new empire arose called Manchukuo, with Pu Yi, the last of the royal Manchu family, a puppet ruler under the Mikado.

Meanwhile the unchecked banditry in northern China induced a mass migration of peasants into Manchuria which surpassed all similar transfers of population. Lured by wide-open spaces, fertile soil, and the prospect of better homes, more than thirty million persons poured into the country of their traditional conquerors. The native Manchus were submerged until they formed scarcely 6 per cent of the total population. The soybean with its almost limitless adaptations to food and industry was the chief magnate, but other farm products were only secondary. Moreover, in the western sector over a million Mongolians continued to pasture their flocks and herds, forest products were made available, and the country proved to be one of the world's great storehouses of mineral wealth. Seams of coal four hundred feet thick were unearthed, together with rich deposits of copper, lead, zinc, gold, and molybdenum.

New railways were built until Manchuria boasted more miles of trackage than all China. For the energetic Japanese, whatever their faults of international policy, developed the country until Mukden, ancient city of Nurhachu, became a growing metropolis of more than a million people.

The Sungari, the central river of Manchuria, bears in flood-time more water than the Amur itself. Rising in the Changpaishan, or "Ever-white Mountains," it flooded Harbin in 1932, driving a hundred thousand people from their homes. A dam 266 feet high, impounding fourteen billion cubic feet, lessened the flood hazard, created a vast artificial lake, and generated enormous electric power. What might have resulted from the introduction of such modern projects in the valley of the Amur will never be known, for the last World War spread ruin and demoralization everywhere. The prostration of Japan, which barred the banner of the Rising Sun from continental possessions, while theoretically freeing Manchuria from a despotic yoke, really condemned that rich country to virtual chaos.

True, the Russians, having looted all movable machinery, have withdrawn their armed forces, but the baleful influence of Red Communism remains. Upon the verge of this seething whirlpool of unrest, the United States has so far stood hesitant and undecided. But the tragic aftermath of conflict is all too apparent. The valleys of the Amur which seemed to be emerging from centuries of neglect to a belated prosperity have once more relapsed into turmoil and confusion. Nor does even this gloomy view complete the picture. For, like the Balkans, the region remains a focal point of international suspicion—a potential threat of war.

When the Great Black Dragon awakens once more, let us hope its dark current will not be lighted with the glare of burning cities or reddened with human blood.

THE HWANG HO—"CHINA'S SORROW"

Length—2,700 miles. Drainage area—400,000 square miles

For twenty-seven hundred miles across northern China, like a tawny serpent, writhes the Hwang Ho. "Yellow River" is the literal translation, and so yellow are its waters with the wind-blown dust of Central Asia that the very ocean into which it flows is known as the Yellow Sea.

But the Hwang Ho has other names. Fifty million people in its drainage basin of four hundred thousand square miles call it also China's Sorrow and by humble offerings strive to placate the demons of the flood that lurk beneath its treacherous surface. For of all rivers it is the most dangerous and destructive. In 1887 it burst its levees to convert fifty thousand square miles of fertile acreage into a shallow lake. Famine and pestilence stalked the subsiding waters in the shadow of wrecked homes and ruined farm lands until more than a million hapless Chinese had perished. Yet this catastrophe was but a minor incident. In 1851 the entire river vaulted from its bed and, gouging out a new channel through the populous countryside, poured its maddened torrents into the sea more than two hundred and fifty miles from its former mouth. Should the Mississippi swerve suddenly aside below Memphis and rage unchecked across Mississippi, Alabama, and northern Florida, the devastation, though appalling, would present no adequate parallel. For in its lower reaches the Hwang Ho traverses a vast alluvial plain, one of the most densely peopled areas on earth, where few elevations offer even temporary refuge. Yet nine times in the past twenty-five centuries of recorded history has this ungovernable river thus changed its bed.

Far away in the remote borderland of Tibet the Hwang Ho has its source in a number of unusual lakes filled with the melted snows of the gigantic Kunlun Mountains. The largest of these lakes, Tsaring-Nor and Oring-Nor, lie at an elevation of nearly fourteen thousand feet. Flowing eastward, the river forces its way through breath-taking gorges to coil about the famous Amne

Machin range. Few white men have ever seen these Mountains of
Mystery, yet vague rumors invest them with an altitude surpass-
ing that of Everest. In 1930 Joseph F. Rock, returning from an
expedition of the National Geographic Society into this almost
unknown region, related how upon beholding them from a height
of sixteen thousand feet he "shouted for joy as I surveyed the
majestic peaks of one of the grandest mountain ranges in all
Asia." He thought the vast dome of Drandel Shukh the highest,
but the pyramidal Shenrezig the more imposing, and did not wonder that "Tibetans worship these snowy peaks as emblems of
purity."

Through cavernous defiles Rock also saw foaming waters
emerge to sweep in a whirlpool around a craggy point, and wrote,
"No other white man since time began ever stood here and beheld these deep gorges of the Yellow River."

Life here was quite as unusual as the surroundings. Sheep bore
spiral horns which projected so far toward the ground that old
rams sometimes starved because they could not reach the grass.

A perverted Buddhism was the prevalent belief. Along mountain trails dried shoulder blades of sheep were suspended by yak-
hair cords bearing prayers to be released when passing travelers
brushed against them. A monk was patiently imprinting Buddhas
on the surface of the Yellow River by immersing brass molds
fastened to a board, then strewing barley on the water as a votive
offering. Caves in the hillside, too low in which to stand upright,
sheltered Buddhist anchorites who passed their lives in medita-
tion, subsisting on barley flour in winter, on stewed nettles in
summer. Drinking tea with a hospitable lama was no treat for a
squeamish stomach, as the servant scoured the dirty cups with
powdered goat dung. Here, beyond the pale of Chinese influence, dwelt lawless tribes—Nguras, Ngoloks, and others. One
man showed scars upon his abdomen formed by holding burning
rags against it to cure indigestion! Farther along the river valley
fierce conflicts raged between Ngura nomads and the Moslems
of the great province of Kansu. When wild tribesmen rode down
the Moslems, impaling them on thirty-foot spears, the latter re-
taliated by hanging up their captives by the thumbs, disembow-
eling them alive, and stuffing the gory cavity with hot stones.

From savage regions such as these the Yellow River emerges as a mountain stream to enter upon its less troubled but eccentric middle course. At Lanchow on the ancient Silk Route to Turkestan the torrent is spanned by a steel bridge built under American supervision in 1909. It is the only one for twelve hundred miles. Turning northward, the river makes a gigantic loop through the Ordos Desert, into the barren Gobi, then, diverted by mountain ranges, turns south for five hundred miles to form the boundary between the populous provinces of Shansi and Shensi. At the Hu-kou Falls it makes a sheer drop of sixty-five feet, with a further descent of forty-five in the next mile of foaming rapids.

Down the western side of this vast loop winds the Great Wall of China. Twice it crosses the river or rather pauses on one bank to resume on the opposite shore. For two thousand miles it twists and turns over mountains and down valleys, the stone-faced battlements of the eastern section yielding to mere embankments of tamped earth toward the west. The material in this gigantic structure would form a wall eight feet high and three feet wide entirely around the earth at the equator. Now long neglected and fallen into ruin, it is being undermined in places by the rapacious river.

On this loop the Hwang Ho traverses the famous loess region where yellow dust, borne by the great winds of Asia, has buried the landscape to a maximum depth of nearly a thousand feet. This earthy deluge has submerged not only farms but entire cities. Caves carved in the claylike substance provide homes for millions of people, while its eroded surface has given the Yellow River its color and its name.

At the lower extremity of this great loop the river turns abruptly eastward. Here it is joined by the most important tributary, the Wei, at the famous Kwang Tung Pass, long known as the Gate of Asia, for through it led the principal trade route to the west. The Hwang Ho now crosses the province of Honan down a gentle gradient to the sea. This vast alluvial plain is really a delta region built up from the accumulated wastage of the uplands.

Marco Polo knew the Hwang Ho as the Kara-Moran (his rendition of Chinese syllables was seldom felicitous) and described it as "of such magnitude both in respect to width and depth that no solid bridge can be erected upon it. The country bordering upon it produces ginger and silk."

The river, Marco said, "is a mile wide and upon its water great ships freely sail. Large fish in considerable quantities are caught." This was the lower river, for, he added, "about a mile distant from the sea is a station for fifteen thousand vessels," which were kept in readiness by the Emperor to suppress rebellions or for expeditions to remote regions.

Small junks and high-sided cotton boats still sail the Hwang Ho, but much of its course is too shallow or impeded by sand bars. Chinese ingenuity, however, has solved the navigation problem for a seven-hundred-mile stretch along Mongolia and through Kansu by the use of curious rafts. W. Robert Moore describes these as frameworks resting upon inflated sheep or ox hides. Five hundred sheepskins may be required for the larger rafts, which represent an investment of six hundred dollars in gold. The skins, treated with salt and oil, remain serviceable for three years when they are sold for leather. At the journey's end they are deflated and laboriously packed overland to the starting point, as the current is too swift for a return voyage. Native thrift finds the larger oxhides convenient receptacles for wool, which thus avoids the exactions of the tax collector.

The Hwang Ho is more important as a source of irrigation than as an artery of commerce. Huge water wheels sometimes seventy feet in diameter raise the water endlessly to thirsty fields where the annual precipitation may be less than six inches.

Maynard Williams, motoring across Asia, found the Hwang Ho in the great loop section "far from a dirty stream," and admired the "pleasing contrast with ruddy cliffs and golden sand reflected in the blue water." But he also noticed violent dust storms and distant dunes hundreds of feet high. The upper current, frozen from late November until early March, provides a convenient highway.

The Yellow River is woven like a golden thread across an embroidered screen upon the very background of Chinese history. Though it has sometimes been "the scourge of the Sons of Han," within its sheltered valleys flowered the art and poetry and philosophy of Old China.

During the closing years of the past century archaeologists examined thousands of fragments, mostly tortoise shell, in the market places of Honan. Some of these fragments, dating from the twelfth century B.C., were covered with an archaic script, the most ancient known specimens of Chinese writing. From such evidence the fabulous Yin dynasty now looms vaguely through the mists of fable.

Later centuries found vassal states in the valley of the Yellow River or its western tributary, the Wei, developing settled governments and exerting some control over less enlightened regions. The oldest of these so-called dukedoms, known as Chou, is believed to have had its origin about 1122 B.C. and to have survived for eight hundred years. As it declined, more vigorous states arose: Ch'i, Chin, and Ch'in, the latter of special interest since it gave us the name word—China.

During this period of slow emergence from chaos those systems of philosophy were formulated which determined the national character. Confucius, the grand old man of China, was born in the province of Shantung, that mountainous promontory projecting into the Yellow Sea. Once an island, it has become incorporated in the mainland by the silt deposits of the Yellow River, which ever since has swerved now to the north, now to the south of the massive obstruction through alternate mouths two hundred and fifty miles apart.

The fourth monarch of the Ch'in dynasty was one of those virile characters who mold history. Having established his sway over neighboring states all the way to the Yangtze Valley and enlarged his capital upon the river Wei, he assumed, in 221 B.C., the imperial title under the name Shih Huang Ti and gave China its first conception of national unity. His masterpiece was the Great Wall of China, in which he incorporated existing defenses to shut out Tartar raiders of the far frontiers. He might have been revered as the founder of the Chinese Empire had it not been for one despotic act which alienated his people. Irked by traditions of the past, he determined to destroy most of the ancient classics and upon a clean slate sketch his bold conceptions of the future.

Innumerable manuscripts were burned by his edicts, and many scholars suffered death, but the Chinese, conservative above all other races, preserved their ancient learning, either concealed or memorized, and the baffled dictator only gained for himself the epithet of "the book burner," which has smeared his memory for more than two thousand years.

Under the enlightened Tang dynasty the culture of the Yellow River reached its peak. Ming Huang, "the Brilliant Emperor," who ruled China from 713–756, made his capital Chang An on the river Wei the most splendid city in Christendom. His reign was like the Augustan Age of Rome. Then among lesser contemporaries, Li Po, the Chinese Shakespeare, was enriching literature with his luminous imagery. But it was also an age of unparalleled disaster under the evil star of Yang Kwei-fei, the Emperor's favorite concubine, whose influence was far more tragic than that of Cleopatra. For her the infatuated monarch neglected the affairs of state, and at her behest placed in control unprincipled incompetents. Then came the storm as the Tartars overran the empire, destroyed Chang An, and slaughtered its inhabitants, while in the resultant chaos it has been estimated that thirty-six million people perished. No wonder Li Po, exiled and penniless, wrote of vanished splendors, "Do you not know that the waters of the Hwang Ho flow toward the sea and never come back again?" Then, turning for solace to his wine cup, he added, "I want to forget that life is sad and Paradise an illusion."

Although the shallow current of the Hwang Ho bears to the sea only an estimated 116,000 cubic feet a second, scarcely one third the outflow of the Indus, its silt burden is amazing. Prior to the year 1000 the Chinese regarded this silt as a welcome enrichment of the soil not unlike the fertilizing inundations of the Nile. But great areas in the interior were so denuded that the wretched peasants in time of famine ate ground corn cobs, the bark of trees, and as a last relief from gnawing hunger the very silt itself. In the loess region this silt sometimes comprises 40 per cent of the weight of the water, while in tributary streams Walter Lowdermilk found that percentage rise to 54, or more than half. The Expedition of 1792, under Lord Macartney, estimated that every year the river bore to the sea seventeen billion cubic feet of silt. Though this total has been challenged, the river bed across the great alluvial plain builds up three feet a century, so that in places it is twenty-five feet higher than the surrounding country, and every year the seacoast at the outlet advances a hundred feet or more.

How to tame what remains an untamable river has baffled the skill of China for three thousand years. Far back in the shadowy Chou regime it was the duty of the Minister of Public Works to "maintain the dikes, keep the canals dredged, and dig new canals as a precaution against flood." Ages before the advent of our own New Deal the Chinese practiced bench farming to avoid erosion. They built levees reinforced with mats of kaoliang, a reed resembling sugar cane, while along canal banks they planted protective willows. But this modern labor of Hercules is not for coolies, but rather for those mechanical titans, steam shovels, bulldozers, and dredging machines. Even the technical skill and unlimited equipment which has placed a strait jacket upon the Mississippi would encounter more formidable problems in the valley of the Hwang Ho. For in its last three hundred miles the latter has no tributaries, nor is the construction of reservoirs or lateral sluiceways practicable.

During the late war the Hwang Ho was enlisted against its country's enemies, as cut levees and inundated fields arrested the advance of Japanese armies, but it remains a perpetual menace.

Here, indeed, is a challenge to the engineering genius of the future. For while the great river has been the cradle of Chinese culture, to countless peasants it has given only an untimely grave. Today along its banks two-wheeled carts creak along dusty roads as they did in the days of Marco Polo. Today gardeners with painstaking care cultivate their tiny plots of cucumbers and onions, of radishes and sweet potatoes, and girls braid straw for wide-brimmed peasant hats. Tomorrow may bring bursting levees, a demoniac rush of muddy waters, and swift oblivion. But it would require the genius of Li Po to pen the vanished riches and enduring wretchedness, the mingled song and pathos of the Hwang Ho.

THE YANGTZE KIANG—CHINA'S LIFE LINE

Length—3,400 miles. Drainage area—750,000 square miles

Li Po, the Shakespeare of the Orient, who once resided in the Upper Valley of the Yangtze Kiang, wrote of it: "All things pass with the waters of the east-flowing river." There, indeed, ruined fanes, roofless palaces, and crumbling pagodas are mute reminders of former glories, while the tireless current still flows on—a great artery to the throbbing heart of China.

The Yangtze Kiang has other names. In native language it means Great River. Nashi tribesmen in the interior, washing glittering flakes from its sands, call it the Gold River; and coolies in the Ichang gorges, straining every nerve as they drag some great ship upstream against its current, think of it as a writhing white dragon, savage and untamable.

If, as archeologists believe, the valleys of the Hwang Ho to the north were the cradle of the Chinese race, those of the Yangtze Kiang have become their home. For there they swarm to the estimated number of two hundred million.

Unlike the Hindus, who venerate the Ganges, the Chinese have invested their favorite river with no such atmosphere of sanctity. They are a worldly wise and practical people, more concerned with the present than with an indefinite hereafter. Theirs is the tolerant skepticism of Omar Khayyám in his advice to "take the cash and let the credit go." But they do appreciate their Great River and have long exploited its possibilities.

The Yangtze, flowing eastward from the chaotic mountain mass of Tibet, cuts China literally in two. The division is a natural one, more determinant of national character than any Mason and Dixon's line blazed by the surveyor. In northern China dwells a race, taller than their southern relatives, subsisting upon wheat and millet rather than rice, speaking another language, grown more rugged from battling the fierce winds and fiercer nomads beyond the Great Wall. The dwellers in the south, blest with a softer climate, are of slighter build, given to farming the seas which open out upon the fabulous East Indies, addicted to the Circean spell of the poppy. Since commerce intrigues them, and the lure of far countries, they have been more accessible to the outside world and have comprised the bulk of Chinese immigration.

Nowhere else is there more convincing proof of the profound influence of great rivers. Had the Yangtze, like the Mississippi, flowed from north to south, it would have linked the two divergent sectors in a community of trade and custom and culture. Instead, by natural cleavage, the river has separated China into two halves quite unlike, which have seldom coalesced into one body politic save under some powerful emperor, usually the founder of a new dynasty, or a conqueror of alien birth. Hence has arisen that fatal tendency to split asunder rather than unite, with a resultant weakness of the central government which has frequently proved powerless to prevent aggressions from outside peoples relatively few in number and of inferior intelligence.

The Yangtze is roughly thirty-four hundred miles long. Rising as it does in one of the most inaccessible regions in the world, the exact figure is conjectural, as is the drainage area, computed at 750,000 square miles. Sometimes referred to as the Chinese Mississippi, it yields to the latter both in length and area; but its volume is greater, for it pours into the Yellow Sea an average of 770,000 cubic feet a second. No other comparable area so vitally affects so many people, hence the Yangtze has been called the most important river in the world.

Geographically it is separated into three zones, clearly marked by a topography of abrupt and startling change. Its headquarters lead into some of the wildest scenery on earth. Several tributaries from the interior of Tibet, flowing at an elevation approaching seventeen thousand feet, wind about colossal ranges collecting melting snows and glaciers. The main channel sometimes parallels its course as it twists about some mountain mass. For long distances the Yangtze, the Mekong, and the Salween flow side by side through a strip of territory scarcely fifty miles broad, each separated from the others by impassable ridges. Yule likens this convergence of three great rivers through a compressed terrain four hundred miles long to a "thunderbolt fascis in the clutch of Jove." According to Kingdon Ward, the Salween, somewhat lower than the Mekong and the Yangtze, may ultimately "behead" those great systems. If so, it will mark only another incident in a prevalent river piracy. Dr. Gunter Kohler believes that the upper Hwang Ho once flowed into the Yangtze Kiang but was diverted by some vast upheaval. Confucius wrote, "The course of the Kiang begins on the Minshan." This tributary may once have been the main river and then joined the Mekong, a legend that still persists among Moso tribes. The Kinsha-Kiang, another tributary, according to C. Y. Lee, represents the beheaded waters of the Yuan or Red River, which flows southeasterly through Tonking in the French possessions. The upsurging of mountain ranges in this portion of Asia has repeatedly rejuvenated worn-down river valleys and caused a bewildering rearrangement of their channels.

Here life is largely determined by its environment. In bamboo thickets high up on mountain slopes dwells that mammalian curiosity, the giant panda, with other unique species found nowhere else. And here the pattern of human life is quite as strange. Beyond the pale of Chinese rule a lawless independence reigns. Most aboriginal tribes are of Tibetan descent, but there is also a remnant of white origin, a racial eddy in a Mongolian tide. The prevalent belief is Buddhism darkened by demonology, the corruption of a noble faith in a savage environment of appalling gorges and unscalable peaks scourged by icy winds. The snow-crowned monarch of the scene is Minya Konka (or Gongkar), towering 24,900 feet, a white-crested wave in an ocean of crag and chasm. Joseph Rock, on an expedition for the National Geographic Society through the native kingdom of Muli, wrote, "The scenery hereabout is overwhelmingly grand. Probably its like cannot be found elsewhere in the world." The Yalung, a tributary of the Yangtze, winds through a canyon that he felt certain "was unsurpassed in grandeur," while a smaller tributary, the Buchu, approached the very base of Minya Konka. In 1943, Richard L. Burdsall and Terris Moore climbed this "snowy promontory" to enjoy one of the most magnificent views in the world. A lonely monastery at the base of a glacier preserved the ageless calm of a gigantic seated Buddha 196 feet high, carved in the face of a sheer cliff twelve hundred years ago.

The gorges of the upper Yangtze, where it forces its way through the Li-kiang Mountains, rival those through which the Brahmaputra cascades from the sky line of Tibet to the plains of India. Even when the river has descended to an elevation of little over a mile it foams between Mount Dyinaldo, rearing over nineteen thousand feet on one side and almost equally lofty heights on the other, a frightful gulf thirteen thousand feet deep! In places the tortured current, scarcely twenty yards wide but immensely deep, rushes like a millrace between sheer precipices rimmed with jagged crags. More sloping mountain flanks, however, are clothed in spruce, fir, and giant rhododendron.

Navigation, always dangerous, is often impossible. On one occasion Joseph Rock crossed the Yalung by lashing two canoes together for greater stability. He braved the boiling current of the Yangtze seated upon two inflated goatskins, the motive power provided by five naked swimmers each with a similar skin lashed to his stomach. Although three swimmers pulled while two pushed, the racing current carried them more than a mile downstream before they could effect a landing.

Throughout much of its course the Yangtze conforms to the underlying rock structure, eroding ever deeper the depressions between mountain ranges or traversing the beds of ancient lakes which follow the tectonic lines of flanking mountains. In the mid-section, however, the river cuts across uptilted rock strata, the "grain structure" of the earth, in a series of canyons which terminate in the renowned Ichang Gorges.

In its mid-course, which stretches from Pingshan to Ichang, the river traverses the province of Szechwan, as large as France, with a population exceeding sixty million. The climate is temperate, agriculture flourishes, primeval forests still clothe the mountain slopes, and vast mineral deposits lie but half revealed. Salt wells drilled by succeeding generations penetrate depths of three thousand feet; some of the world's richest coal fields are scarcely touched; while natural gas piped through bamboo tubes was utilized here long before western nations awoke to its possibilities. Here stands Chungking, city of a million people, the recent capital of a China despoiled by the Japanese but still unconquered. Although connected with the outer world by the Burma Road and maintaining a precarious intercourse by airplane "over the Hump," the only natural outlet for this rich hinterland is the Yangtze.

Junks pass to and fro along this stretch of river, even ascending a few miles above Pingshan, where they yield to rude canoes and coracles of hide. Crooked side streams are navigated by some of the most curious boats in the world. These are convex on one side, slightly concave on the other, to permit their pivoting around rocky projections in a narrow channel. Where necessary, they reverse and go stern foremost. Nor should we smile at the eyes painted upon Chinese junks to enable them to see their way about, for the figureheads on Roman galleys, viking dragon craft, and our own clipper ships had much the same function.

River navigation, less hazardous than in the upper river, is sufficiently beset by perils in the mid-section, particularly at the exit through the Ichang Gorges, 350 miles below Chungking. Here, at the gateway to interior China, the third or last section of the Yangtze may be said to begin.

These gorges, some thirteen miles in length, have received photographic names, such as "the Yellow Cat," "the Lamp Light Gorge," and "the Tiger's Teeth." Sheer cliffs that rear three thousand feet frown down upon a ribbon of foam that sometimes speeds along at thirteen miles an hour. This "crooked water" is caused not so much by rocky obstructions upon the bottom as from sheer lack of room to accommodate the volume. In flood the demented current rises a hundred feet above normal levels, while in canyons farther upstream a rise of two hundred feet has been reported! The mighty river, in its battle with the mountains, conforms to a rocky strait jacket but rages in protest.

Nowhere else is river traffic so perilous or so picturesque. In places the channel narrows to 150 feet, attaining a mean depth of 420. Whirlpool or "boil water," and even the less tumultuous "sand water" which seethes with silt, make nighttime navigation quite out of the question. Narrow roadbeds have been excavated along the face of sheer cliffs, roads that the Chinese say with grim humor are "good for ten years and bad for ten thousand." Along these dizzy trails sometimes as many as four hundred coolies, tailing onto a bamboo cable twelve hundred feet long, toil upward, bent double and gasping for breath as they fight inch by inch to drag some heavy ship upstream against the current. Occasionally the cable catches on a jutting rock when some nimble climber must release it before the sharp rock gnaws it in two. A broken cable sends a junk spinning downstream like a teetotum, her crew of eighty, perhaps a hundred, men yelling like demons and pulling for their lives at the sweeps to get her "head on" into the current. Shipwrecks are not uncommon, but loss of life is held to a minimum by red-painted lifeboats manned by competent officers and crews which are maintained by the government for just such emergencies.

On the return journey the current is all-sufficient. The native pilot, standing by the bow, signals the helmsman continuously by waggling forefingers, while beside him crew members jab colored poles into the water every five seconds to test the depth.

In many places ascending craft must wait the signal for "clear water," for downcoming ships have the right of way where there is no room for passage in the narrow, crooked channel. Junks that carry a hundred tons of freight are common amid innumerable smaller ones. Steamers thread the gorges, fighting the current, belching black smoke, their boilers racked and straining, but even they must sometimes be eased through narrow passageways by steel cables wound upon the capstan.

Here beggars swarm, and opium smugglers, and, according to local superstition, malignant demons as well. In quieter stretches junks sail athwart the bows of oncoming steamers to sidetrack pursuing devils. Sometimes the crews of capsized craft are left to drown, as rescue would only antagonize the evil spirits of the waters. For on the Yangtze hundreds of thousands of people have no other home the year round but floating junks.

In the first sixteen hundred miles of its course the Great River descends some sixteen thousand feet; through the final sixteen hundred miles that descent is scarcely eight hundred. Pingshan is 1,630 miles from the sea, Ichang roughly a thousand. And that last thousand miles is across an almost level plain; from

Hankow to the sea the gradient is but an inch a mile; from Nanking onward through the delta the river reaches sea level.

From its remote sources in Tibet the Yangtze presents in graphic panorama the life of a great river: its upper course the impetuous youth of a mountain stream; its mid-course, through Sczechwan, the maturity of lusty strength eager to grapple mountains; its lower course the serenity of age drifting slowly onward to lose itself in the oblivion of the sea.

Many tributaries both from north and south here swell the current. The most arresting feature, however, is the lakes which cling to the main channel like leaches, now swollen with surplus floodwaters, now disgorging their contents through ensuing drought. These lakes, natural excrescences upon the parent stream, which function as reservoirs and sluiceways, have been skillfully supplemented with artificial canals. Among them are such considerable bodies of water as Poyang, Chow Hu, and Tung Ting, beloved of emperors. Li Po wrote luminous verses while drifting in a boat over the latter's enchanting surface, which sometimes overspreads an area of two thousand square miles when the flooded river rises forty feet or more.

The lower Yangtze basin was outlined in Mesozoic times. Much of it is a vast alluvial plain borne down through the ages by the washings of the uplands. The annual silt burden of the river is estimated at four hundred million tons, with an additional two hundred million tons held in solution or rolled along the bottom as a submerged traction load borne onward to the sea. This enormous freightage of material represents about a ton and a half for every living Chinese. Before its irresistible impetus the delta advances along a broad front at the rate of about a mile in sixty years.

Extensive irrigation ditches tap the river current. Entire families toil endlessly on treadmill water wheels which raise the water to thirsty fields. Approaching the sea, the current is confined between dikes. More than two thousand years ago one Li Ping attempted to control the floods on branches of the Yangtze Kiang. His admonition, carved on stone, still rings true: "Dig the channel deep; keep the spillway low." To avoid soil erosion, pebble mulching has been employed for centuries. River gravel, spread over the land to the depth of two or three inches, absorbs the rainfall which sinks into the soil. By such incredible labor does the small farmer insure his meager holdings for two generations. The third generation must renew the protective covering. Among favorite crops are cotton and melons.

Across the so-called delta region the Yangtze broadens to ten miles or more and finally merges with the "gray salt sea" through an estuary fifty miles wide, nearly bisected by the big island of Tsungming. But its silt-laden waters may be distinguished far offshore, as the shallow China Sea becomes increasingly yellower and more shallow.

In this valley a canal 140 miles long has converted some eight thousand square miles into one of the richest rice-growing areas in China. Much reclaimed land, like that of Holland, lies below the level of the sea.

Chinese commerce has always flowed along watery channels, and the carrying capacity of the various rivers has been largely augmented by canals. Even now, since railways are infrequent and poorly equipped, the very life of the nation depends upon its waterways, both natural and artificial, which comprise a total of a hundred thousand miles.

Long ago the Chinese attempted to provide a waterway from north to south which would also connect their two great rivers, the Yangtze and the Hwang Ho. This project, one of the great engineering achievements of antiquity, is the famous Grand Canal, some twelve hundred miles long. Considerable sections were excavated as far back as 485 B.C. Marco Polo described it as "a wide and deep canal which the Great Khan has caused to be dug in order that vessels can pass from one great river to the other." He referred to Kublai Khan, descendant of Genghis, but this Mongol emperor seems merely to have extended the canal northward from the Hwang Ho to Tientsin, the port of Peking on the sea. The canal has also been extended southward from the Yangtze to Hangchow on the Tsien-tang River.

The Grand Canal was crossed by innumerable bridges, many embodying that graceful arch which seems to have eluded Grecian architects with all their mastery of form and outline. In its heyday it was a pulsing artery of commerce crowded with shipping, a veritable life line of empire. Now much of its channel has silted up, the retaining walls collapsed, the beautiful bridges crumbled or destroyed, while the regions it once made prosperous are desolated by the recent war or present internal dissension.

Marco Polo, with his usual enthusiasm, wrote of the Yangtze, "it is the largest river in the world, its width being in some places ten, in others eight, and in others six miles. Its length to the place where it discharges itself into the sea is upward of one hundred days' journey. It is endebted for its great size to the vast number of other navigable rivers that empty their waters into it which have their source in distant countries." On one occasion, at the city of Singui, he observed "no less than fifteen thousand vessels."

In the spacious river valley, fertile and populous, great cities blossomed as naturally as lotus blooms. Chungking, the recent capital, far up the river beyond the Ichang Gorges, has already been noted. Ocean liners steam grandly upstream for six hundred miles to Hankow, industrial city sometimes called the Pittsburgh of China. On the Whangpoo, a tributary of the delta region, stands Shanghai, the greatest city of Asia, with a population of three and a half million. Farther upstream, at the head of the so-called delta, is Nanking, the ancient capital of South China, a city of memories and ruins. Here once stood the most splendid of the pagodas that the Chinese erected along their canals and rivers. Octagonal in form and three hundred feet high, it was built in the years 1413–32. Its glittering covering of glazed tiles —red, white, blue, green, and yellow—made it conspicuous for a great distance over the nearly level plain. Unfortunately it was destroyed in the Boxer Rebellion, one of those convulsions of insane rage in which China, maddened by poverty and hardship, sometimes indulges to its cost.

Another famous monument, the Pagoda of the Six Harmonies, crowns Moon Girdle Hill at Hangchow at the southern terminus of the Grand Canal. Its thirteen stories rise 334 feet above the base, which is reinforced by masonry against tidal bores which rage up the river in crested billows fifteen feet high.

Although the Yangtze has never been so wantonly destructive as the Hwang Ho, flood control remains a perennial problem. The waters which rise to incredible heights in the remote upstream gorges sometimes record a "high" of fifty feet even at Hankow. But when the mighty river does break through its restraining levees to inundate wide areas of fertile farm lands, it numbers its human victims by the tens of thousands. In the disastrous flood of 1931 at least a hundred and fifty thousand hapless Chinese perished.

The history of the Yangtze River has never been written, since, like the stream itself, it trails away into an inaccessible hinterland of legend and fable. Great forests once clothed much of its valley, however, together with a fauna now extinct. According to Roy G. Forest, elephants were common there down to about the year 500 B.C., while they seem to have survived in Kwangsi as late as 700 A.D. Most of the forests have now disappeared to make room for crowded millions, a factor which adds greatly to the flood peril. The dead hand of antiquity also rests heavily upon a land overpopulated, with limited farm acreage, in the many cemeteries. These silent cities of the dead encroach upon the cities of the living by appropriating land that might support an additional population of thirty million.

Meanwhile creaking junks, their painted eyes bleared with grime and weather, their drooping sails "one fourth matting, one fourth holes and one half nondescript material," move slowly up and down this most picturesque of rivers as they have been doing for thousands of years. The patience of the East survives in China those vicissitudes that wrecked Egypt and Persia, Greece and Rome, as well as many a younger state; an unconquerable persistence like that of its greatest river. The western world might well agree with Bertrand Russell, who wrote of this land of the Yangtze, "I came to teach and stayed to learn."

III

The Malayan Group

THE IRRAWADDY—"ON THE ROAD TO MANDALAY"

Length—1,250 miles. Drainage area—158,000 square miles

THE VAST ranges of the Himalayas and the Tibetan table-land beyond extend roughly east and west to barricade all India against the bitter winds and arid wastes of Central Asia. As these lofty highlands approach the Chinese borders, however, they are contorted into parallel ridges that trend southward to form the core of the Burma-Indo-China region terminating in the elongated Malay Peninsula. Through valleys between these compressed ridges flow three of the world's great rivers: the Mekong, the Salween, and the smaller but commercially more important Irrawaddy.

This is the glamorous river immortalized by Kipling as "the road to Mandalay," beloved of the British Tommy who, marooned in London, hears "the East a-callin'" and longs for his Burmese sweetheart amid "the sunshine an' the palm-trees an' the tinkly temple-bells." Movie travelogues have also familiarized the western world with its sampans and rice boats, its lush jungles and fabulous ruins.

The Irrawaddy is the great river of Burma. Its headwaters tap the borderlands of China and Tibet, where they approach within a few miles of the Salween and the Luhit branch of the Brahmaputra. For nearly thirteen hundred miles the river flows almost due south through a drainage area of 158,000 square miles. The upper plateau, according to J. K. Stanford, is "an enormous sea of some of the densest and least-known jungle in the world." Through such forests drenched by tropic rains, in an atmosphere

of steaming humidity, the river attains a width of more than
two miles and in floodtime pours into the Bay of Bengal, through
a broad delta, half a billion tons of water.

The headwaters of the Irrawaddy penetrate that little-known
hill country which British residents near the seacoast call "the
back of beyond." There racial strains of Hindu, Malayan, and
Chinese have mingled with aboriginal jungle dwellers in a medley
of strange tribes. Such are the Kaws, the Shans, the Khuns, and
the Padaungs whose women stretch their necks with a collar of
brass rings one above the other, perhaps the acme of physical
discomfort.

At Poshaw two great rocks called the Gates of the Irrawaddy
constrict the channel to a width of scarcely fifty yards, producing
savage whirlpools. But steamers ascend nearly a thousand miles
from the sea to Bhamo, the Gate of China, while smaller launches
proceed a hundred and thirty miles farther upstream to Myitkyina
and its ruby mines.

The Irrawaddy has several branches, the most important the
Chindwin, which joins the main stream some four hundred miles
from the sea. This river, which rises in the wild hill country of
the Naga tribesmen, is also navigated for considerable distances
by flat-bottomed stern-wheelers of shallow draught. Torrential
downpours are a peril in the side streams, where the current
may rise twenty feet in a single day to dwindle to a mere trickle
a few hours later.

The Irrawaddy empties into the sea, through a swampy delta,
by nine principal mouths. Only two, however, are much used
for navigation: the Bassein Channel and the so-called Rangoon
River upon which the great city of Rangoon is situated.

The Irrawaddy is an important artery of commerce. To the
tourist a flotilla of rice boats with triangular sails drifting down
the river is an unforgettable sight. So, too, are the water taxis
or sampans, unstable craft resembling foreshortened gondolas,
in which the boatman stands up and pushes on the oars. He
must see where he is going in a muddy millrace which sometimes speeds at seven miles an hour. That current is a malevolent
thing as it swirls past the mooring buoys to which steamers tie
up, for even capable swimmers pitched overboard from a cap-

sized sampan may be dragged to the bottom and drowned. Still more primitive are the craft resembling Arab dhows, the canoes, and the great rafts of teakwood from upcountry. A novel feature is the floating market, a barge loaded with fruits, vegetables, and other commodities, towed up and down the river and stopping at various villages along the route. "The Irrawaddy," says Sir Harcourt Butler, "is a beautiful river"—and he particularly extols the sunsets which flame above the jungle and dye the current a gorgeous crimson.

Burma is noted for its tropic forests. Among numerous species the mottled trunk of the bo tree, sacred to Buddha, is conspicuous. A much rarer tree, the object of an extended search some years ago, is the chaulmoogra, which grows wild in the isolated hill country. It supplies an oil long considered a remedy for leprosy. Most famous of all, however, is the teak tree, useful for a variety of purposes, but best of woods for shipbuilding as it seems "mothproof" against the destructive teredo, or ship borer, which riddles oak planking. Sailing vessels of teak are still seaworthy after a round century of service.

The teak tree grows singly amidst lesser species, a forest monarch whose straight trunk is buttressed with ridges. Cutting is regulated by the government. Only trees exceeding a certain diameter are chosen. These are first deeply ringed and the date blazed three years before they may be felled. Meanwhile the tree dies, otherwise it would not float down feeder streams. Burmese timber "cruisers," armed with heavy jungle knives or dahs, slash paths through dense undergrowth. In such pioneering operations "My Lord the Elephant" is an invaluable partner. He is cheaper than a machine, never stalls or runs out of gasoline, requires no irreplaceable spare parts and, even more important, can think for himself. Kipling's Tommy marveled at "elephints a-pilin' teak" as countless other observers have done.

Elephants are not only captured from the savage wilds and broken to service but are also bred in captivity. While too young for heavy work, they are used as "travelers," to bear passengers and important messages. No Army jeep can batter its way through difficult terrain so readily. When about eighteen years of age, elephants are put to light timber work and attain their full strength at twenty-five. They possess an uncanny skill in breaking a log jam. "Travelers" are often turned loose equipped with trailing leg chains to discourage long jaunts and wooden bells to advertise their whereabouts. Unfortunately the intelligent creatures are subject to disease, particularly the dreaded anthrax.

Someday the Irrawaddy may become invaluable as a source of irrigation, so far but little needed in its moist valleys. Rice not only satisfies the needs of the inhabitants, but harvests overflow to India and Java. When Japanese occupation shut off this supply, a million hapless natives of Bengal perished of starvation.

Fishing is an important industry, and curious weirs or fish traps festoon the shores like spider webs along a dewy path. Still more fascinating are the mineral deposits in this rich valley which is one of the great gem-producing areas of the world. Zircons, garnets, aquamarines, and other semiprecious stones are eclipsed by sapphires and by rubies from the famous Mogok mines in the Upper Valley. For miles along the river wells are dug and bamboo sweeps installed. These clumsy mechanisms, weighted with stones, raise baskets filled with earth to be washed in much the same manner as Alaskan sourdoughs once panned gold dust. Finest of all are pigeon's-blood rubies, more costly than diamonds of equal weight. The largest specimen unearthed in recent years was the Peace Ruby of forty-two carats, purchased by an Indian rajah for $130,000.

Most Chinese jade, so-called, comes from a region in Upper Burma about forty miles long by five or six broad, where this lustrous mineral has been mined for centuries. Of various colors, the most valuable is mottled green, that Imperial jade admired by Chinese mandarins. Specimens of this hard stone ranging in size from "an apple to a cookstove" are here unearthed at the cost of much labor and no little danger, for the region seems cursed by a virulent type of malaria. In a Chinese temple are recorded the names of more than five thousand Chinese merchants and traders who during the nineteenth century succumbed to deadly maladies while seeking jade.

The civilizations that have developed in the valley of the Irrawaddy are quite as glittering as its gems, as transient as its forest products. The native Burmese, semi-Mongolian in feature, are neat, attractive, industrious, and artistically talented. True, murderous dacoits lurk on the outskirts, but every frontier has known its outlaws.

Pagan is perhaps the finest example of native cities that have enjoyed an exotic heyday only to plunge into a prolonged decline. Once the capital of a prosperous state, its ruins stretch for eight miles along the riverbanks and extend two miles inland. William H. Roberts writes that no other city can boast so bewildering a multitude of temples. These number five thousand or more. Most imposing is that miracle of white marble topped with gilded spires called the Ananda, "rising like a structure of foam."

Pagan had its brief hour in the sun shortly after the year 1000, when its enlightened ruler, Anawrata, introduced Buddhism, the prevalent religion of Burma. Kublai Khan, the Mongol emperor of China, having overrun Yünnan, the wildest and most southerly of his provinces, sent his destroying armies into Burma. In the ensuing battle, described by Marco Polo, the native troops were routed and Pagan fell, never to rise again.

Among the Portuguese adventurers who followed Vasco da Gama to India were soldiers of fortune who enlisted under the banners of Burmese kings. The exploits of these ruthless wanderers read like pure romance and almost surpass belief. Burma, however, like other Asiatic states, suffered in comparison with the mechanized European. The British, having absorbed India, gained a foothold in Burma also and finally incorporated the country as a part of their world empire. The Burmese, however, though conquered, were unsubmissive. When I visited the country shortly before the recent World War, riots broke out in the city of Rangoon and many Burmese welcomed rather than repelled Japanese invasion. Independence, recently announced, is perhaps the inevitable result.

Among the cities which still adorn the Irrawaddy, Mandalay, some hundreds of miles from the sea, is known by its musical name and Kipling's tinkling verse. But the metropolis is Rangoon, with more than half a million people, some twenty-two miles from the mouth of the Rangoon River. Visiting steamers anchor off the shoaling delta to await a pilot. The voyage upstream is a continuous panorama of grotesque fish traps and lush rice fields, with gilded dagobas rising above the more distant vegetation. Rangoon itself is proud of the Shwe Dagon, perhaps the most famous temple in Asia. This magnificent structure, surrounded by no fewer than fifteen hundred lesser shrines, crowns a low hill. A splendid monument to Buddha, its huge dome, 1,355 feet in circumference, shelters innumerable silver bells. Unlike most domes, however, its sides undulate upward to a needlelike spire which pierces the heavens at a height of 370 feet. It is covered with plates of burnished gold and flaunts a metal banner encrusted with precious stones. Resplendent in the noontide sun, it is scarcely less impressive in the darkness when illuminated by tier upon tier of electric arc lights. Day and night it dominates not only Rangoon but a wide arc of fertile delta, a visible expression of the riches of the Irrawaddy Valley and of the glittering but bizarre cultures that have flourished there.

THE SALWEEN AND THE BURMA ROAD

Length—1,770 miles. Drainage area—62,700 square miles

Perhaps least known of the world's great rivers is the Salween, which flows southward between Burma and the bizarre Kingdom of Siam. Yet it is longer than the Ganges or the Danube and traverses some of the most picturesque scenery to be found anywhere.

True, it attained a vague familiarity through Kipling's jingling verses:

> By the old Moulmein Pagoda, lookin' eastward to the sea,
> There's a Burma girl a-settin', and I know she thinks
> o' me . . .

The poet took all kinds of poetic license with local geography, but Moulmein *is* an oriental city situated on one of the Salween's two mouths where it empties into the Gulf of Martaban on the great Bay of Bengal, not far from the delta of the Irrawaddy. In fact, the Salween parallels the latter river through much of its course, but it is longer (1,770 miles) and rises in a remoter hinterland, Tibet, beyond the Himalayas. Here it approaches branches of the Brahmaputra. Its source, however, has not been definitely determined, hence statistics on its drainage area are sketchy and incomplete.

John Hanbury Tracy followed the Salween into some of the most rugged territory in the world. He called it the Black River of Tibet, though in flood its color was a "deep milk chocolate." Nor does its channel grow less troubled through Yünnan, wildest and least traveled of the provinces of ancient China, with its hopeless medley of discordant races. In summer the river is a chain of foaming cascades; in winter a winding highway of ice. Here, where men gather in monasteries and indulge in devil dances, wild life, under Buddhist protection, becomes remarkably tame. Peaks worthy of the Himalayas mark this mountainous borderland. The range which separates the Salween from the Irrawaddy, only a few miles distant, culminates in Kenyichunpo, nearly twenty thousand feet high, but beyond, toward the Mekong, looms Myetzimu, nearly twenty-four thousand. In places marble gorges are bordered by cliffs hundreds of feet high that fairly overhang the current foaming far below.

The Salween was introduced to the western world during the construction of the famous Burma Road, a wartime project designed as a life line to Chinese resistance against Japanese aggression. This road, one of the great engineering feats of all time, linked two great rivers with their extensive waterways and spanned two others through almost impassable terrain. Rangoon, on the lower Irrawaddy, was the southern terminus; Chungking, on the Yangtze Kiang, the other. Twenty-one hundred miles lay over familiar river routes; the formidable barrier was the mountainous highland from Lashio in upper Burma to Siakwan in China. Here the road spanned the valleys of the Salween and its even larger neighbor the Mekong, farther to the east. In one stretch of 307 miles across these turbulent streams over two hundred thousand engineers and coolies were concentrated, one man to less than three yards of roadbed. The canyons of the Salween presented the grandest scenery. The Hweitung suspension bridge now spans the river at an elevation of some twenty-five hundred feet above sea level. The roadbed on both sides was blasted out of the solid rock. Heavy landslides in the season of drenching monsoons added to the hazards of travel and for a time made the roadway all but impassable.

In former days coolies toiling over the Kao Li Kung range from the Irrawaddy and descending to the Salween called it the Fever Valley and claimed that it was deadly to strangers. Perspiring from their exertions and plunging into the river to refresh themselves, they were taken with cramps and drowned in the rapid current. Horses and mules sometimes suffered the same fate. But the Salween proved indeed a fever valley as Army doctors found when they were called upon to combat some particularly malignant types of malaria, with an occasional visitation of bubonic plague.

Between the Salween and the Mekong lies the plain and city of Paoshan. This is the ancient Vochan where, according to Marco Polo, twelve thousand Mongol soldiers of Kublai Khan, Emperor of China, defeated sixty thousand Burmese with a formidable battalion of war elephants. This disaster brought ruin to the Burmese capital, Pagan, that wonder city of the five thousand shrines, on the Irrawaddy.

The Salween, with a current that ranges from half a mile to ten miles an hour, is a river of moods and caprices. In intervals of drought white sand bars appear, broken by rocks and shingle beaches. In flood the current, rising ninety feet or more, becomes a raging torrent. Launches voyage from Moulmein to lower Burma, but frequent cataracts and shoals set definite limits to navigation. Nor are irrigation projects of much importance in a region which is sparsely settled. Hence the Salween, of all the world's great rivers, save those which flow into the Arctic, is of the least economic importance.

And yet there is something appealing about its unknown source in the bleak Tibetan highlands, its marble gorges, the fever-ridden valleys of the Burma Road, and that glamorous picture of "elephints a-pilin' teak" by old Moulmein. Perhaps this is due to the mystery of the Orient; perhaps to that poignant undertone which Wordsworth felt when he wrote of "old, unhappy, far-off things, and battles long ago."

THE MYSTERIOUS MEKONG

Length—2,600 miles. Drainage area—350,000 square miles

The longest river of southern Asia is the Mekong. Rising in the tableland of Tibet, it flows a bit east of south for twenty-six hundred miles to empty through an extensive delta into the China Sea.

The sources of the Mekong are imperfectly charted and have never been surveyed. They lie high up the flanks of snowy Dza-Nag-Lung-Mung at an altitude of 16,700 feet, hidden behind the tangled mountain ranges that veer southward from the Forbidden Kingdom into the great Chinese province of Yünnan. Here the precipitous slopes are well wooded, particularly with giant rhododendron. Above the snow line, so Tibetans claim, is the abode of the fabulous mountain men who are occasionally observed, white, naked, carrying clubs and running swiftly over the glistening surface. In that rarefied atmosphere, amid dazzling drifts, such figments of superstitious fancy are easy to explain.

Here the frightful gorges of the Mekong are crossed by swaying rope bridges of the crudest construction. A single rope of bamboo is stretched across the current, the nearer end much higher than that upon the opposite shore. Over this cable slides a hollowed log about a foot long from which the passenger is suspended in a swing. Seated upon this pendent perch, he may clasp the log above but must avoid the searing friction of the rope. When released, he goes shooting down and out across the current, a mere ribbon of foam far below, to be catapulted to a safe elevation on the farther side. Two rope bridges are required at each crossing as a similar one is needed for the return journey. Horses and mules are transported in the same dizzy manner, much to their alarm, as the terrified animals sometimes lie down and refuse to move. The rope is greased with yak butter and must be renewed every three or four months. Where traffic is heavy, several hundred crossings daily, it will wear out in a few days. A break in transit is too unpleasant for contemplation.

The Tibetans of the upper Mekong are a friendly folk, though incredibly ignorant and filthy. That grotesque creature the yak thrives at such altitudes and is quite as useful there as is the camel to the desert Arab. Incidentally, the bulls only are yaks, the cows being known as dri. Though bulky, they seldom yield as much as a quart of milk daily, which instantly sours as milking utensils, never washed, are thickly crusted. The flesh of the yak is also eaten, while a favorite dish, which even foreigners relish, is tsamba, a mixture of tea and roasted barley.

The rupee of Hindustan is the prevalent currency. Thrifty Tibetans, in making change, cut the silver coin in sections. Tea and salt, however, are preferred as mediums of exchange.

Joseph F. Rock, who explored this region, says of it, "Where in all the world is to be found scenery comparable to that which awaits the explorer in northwestern Yünnan . . . and southeastern Tibet?" This lofty upland is being eroded by several great rivers. At one point three of them, the Salween, the Mekong, and the Yangtze Kiang, are confined by mountain ranges within a narrow strip of territory only forty-eight miles wide. A colossal glacier descends to the Mekong from the jagged sky line of the Kaasperu. On the ridge that shuts off the valley of the Yangtze, Mount Peimashan towers twenty thousand feet. But there are loftier summits, including Miyetzimu, nearly twenty-four thousand feet high, which Rock called, "that most glorious peak . . . like a castle of a dream, an ice palace of a fairy tale." Pious Tibetans measure their length along the ground in crossing sacred Mount Dorkela, between the Mekong and the Salween, sometimes, in fanatic zeal, hurling themselves headlong down its slopes. Terrific gusts of wind howl through the canyons and falling rockslides sometimes bury unfortunate pilgrims.

From its birthplace above the clouds the Mekong descends through a series of foaming cascades to lower levels, though still amid lofty hills. The famous Burma Road spans it on the Kungkwo Bridge. Chinese coolies toil up these steep slopes, sometimes bearing 400-pound burdens on their toil-bent shoulders. Native mountaineers are often disfigured by goiter. Frock noticed one sufferer whose lower jaw was so weighted by this abnormal growth that he could close his mouth only with difficulty.

Emerging from Chinese Yünnan, the Mekong skirts the country of the Laos, one of the turbulent native races under French dominion. Their capital, Luang Prabang, once boasted two hundred pagodas. Teakwood logs are floated down the river and many dugout canoes are engaged in catching fish. A toothsome variety is the plabûkan, which sometimes weighs 130 pounds. A sauce called nioc mam is compounded of various ingredients mixed with putrid fish! At one point on the plain, two hundred feet above the current, volcanic vents smoke ominously. Mermaidens are thought to lurk beneath the swirling waters to drag unwary swimmers to their death.

The river now widens to a mile and a half, exposing numerous sand bars. Gold dust is panned from these sands. Still more interesting minerals are found farther down the channel in a stratum of gem-bearing gravel. According to H. Warrington Smith, this is from five to twenty inches in thickness and is overlaid with red clay ten feet deep. The gravel, collected in baskets and washed in the current, yields sapphires and other gems. In the wooded areas tigers and elephants abound.

Rich seams of anthracite coal are found in Tonking, the northernmost province of French Indo-China. The Laos region produces tin; Annam, phosphates; while Cambodia, extending to the sea, is famous for its gems. The chief wealth, however, is agricultural. Rice is the staple food of Tonking and Annam, most densely peopled of the French possessions. Great rafts 120 feet long and 30 broad drift down the Mekong freighted with rice. Indian corn, however, is the food of the upper Mekong. Was it indigenous or imported from the New World, and if so, how was the transfer made? But this is one of many enigmas in a region still largely unexplored.

To introduce modern dynamos along this river of oriental settings seems incongruous, yet the Mekong offers what is probably the richest single source of hydroelectric power in all Asia. That is where the river, eight miles broad, goes foaming down the series of cascades and waterfalls known as the Khon. Although the total descent is only seventy feet, the water volume exceeds four hundred thousand cubic feet per second, or roughly double that of Niagara.

The Mekong is too much impeded by shoals to be a commercial highway, but its value for irrigation is incalculable. It has been termed a second Nile, though it bears equal fertility to a larger area. The lower valley is a checkerboard of ditches, distributing water and fertilizing silt over a vast alluvial plain.

The delta region is green with bamboo thickets and lush rice fields. The channels seem like lagoons, their verdant shores mingling with the gray waters. Many natives spend their lives in sampans roofed with thatch. Ducks have strings tied to their legs, while babies have pieces of bamboo attached to their waists to keep them afloat should they fall overboard.

Such a river valley, blessed with abundant water supply, a soil of unexcelled fertility, and a tropic climate, would seem to offer just the environment for the development of a great civilization. Nor should we be surprised to find here perhaps the most impressive ruins in the world, the imposing capital of the lost Khmers, forgotten for centuries and now moldering in the jungle. It was situated on the shores of Tonle Sap, the big lake of Cambodia, whose periodic pulsations are among the most interesting of lake phenomena. This lake is a natural enlargement of a tributary of the Mekong, flowing southeasterly from the borders of Siam. In time of flood it sometimes rivals Ontario, but as its shallow waters subside rice is sown upon the exposed bed.

The Khmers are something of a mystery. Probably of Hindu origin, they brought their religion with them, so that the visage of Siva, the Destroyer, now stares stonily at the beholder through the jungle from crumbling temple walls. They built a great city called Angkor Thom, and a temple, Angkor Vat, to overshadow many lesser ones. Its central towers still rise majestically above a vast structure, approached by a broad avenue guarded by seven-headed cobras carved in stone.

According to fragmentary records, the city which became the metropolis of Indo-China was founded in A.D. 889 by Yacovarman, the "King of Glory." A more sinister epithet was also his, the "Leper King," for legend had him afflicted with this dread disease.

The Chinese traveler Tcheou-ta-Quan, who visited the proud capital in the days of its greatness, entered through what he termed "the gate of the five Buddhas." Among other wonders that impressed him were carved lions of gold and the great moat, seven hundred feet broad and three miles in circuit, that surrounded the chief temple.

What occurred to change the greatest city of southern Asia into a tenantless ruin is a question which remains unanswered. Several explanations have been offered: conquest by the rival powers of Annam or Siam; a bloody uprising of the enslaved population; some nameless pestilence which drove the population in panic from their homes. Only the Mekong knows. But to its tireless current, wearing down the mountains of Tibet to build its ever-broadening delta, the rise and fall of empires are unimpressive incidents.

IV

The Rivers of India

THE BRAHMAPUTRA—FROM BEYOND THE SKY LINE

Length—1,680 miles. Drainage area—361,000 square miles

NO OTHER RIVER bears so exalted a name as the Brahmaputra, "Son of Brahma" the Creator. Yet to most of us it is a vague entity eclipsed by the more familiar Ganges, the Holy River of India.

Geographically, the two are linked and someday will be twin branches of one greater river, if indeed they should not already be regarded as a unit. In this partnership, far from being the lesser member, the Brahmaputra is the longer and has the greater volume.

It rises beyond the vast rampart of the Himalayas amid chaotic mountain peaks and glaciers. The Swami Pranavananda, who spent some time in this region, traces its source to the Kubi glaciers. There the Tibetans, who regard the birthplace of a river as holy ground, have erected commemorative cairns and Mani stones. Sven Hedin has also investigated this fascinating region where, within an area of fifty miles, the headwaters of the Indus gush forth to flow westward, a branch of the Ganges trends to the south, while the Brahmaputra, bursting its mountain shackles at an elevation of 15,500 feet, pursues an easterly course for seven hundred miles across the tableland of Tibet.

This tableland, some fifteen hundred miles long by eight hundred broad, suggests wide-open spaces, chill and wind-swept, oppressed with a brooding atmosphere of mystery. Its people, isolated, ignorant, and suspicious, call the Brahmaputra by many names, but the most significant is Tsang-Po, the Purifier. The towering monasteries of Lhasa, the Forbidden City, look down upon one of its tributaries, the Kyi Chu, while Shigatse, the second city of Tibet, is located upon the main stream. Here, shut out from the outer world by vast deserts and almost impassable mountains, a noble faith has become a stagnant eddy. The Dalai Lama, or living Buddha, bears little likeness to that saintly character Ghautama, while the latter's eightfold path to righteousness has been choked by a jungle of ritualism darkened by a frightening demonology.

So peacefully does the great river flow through this strange landscape behind its mountain walls that Tibetan boats, often mere coracles of hides, navigate it without difficulty and flat-bottomed ferries cross to and fro. For four hundred miles the river is the chief highway of transportation and commerce in that drafty attic of the world.

But the transition is as imposing as it is abrupt when, awakening from his Buddhist calm, the Son of Brahma bursts through tremendous gorges to irrupt upon the plains of India. Swinging in a gigantic loop from east to south, the river goes foaming between Mancha Barwa, 25,445 feet high, on the one hand, and Gyali Peri, 23,740, on the other, a portal fit for the triumphal advent of a Hindu god. Here the river changes name as well as character, to become the Dihong, a series of cataracts through frightful chasms.

In his illuminating account entitled *The Riddle of the Tsang-Po Gorges*, F. Kingdon Ward writes, "The falls of the Brahmaputra have been for fifty years the great romance of Geography. The Tsang-Po near Lhasa flows at an altitude of 12,000 feet . . . The Dihong issues from the Abor Hills at an elevation of 1,000 feet or less . . . It has bored its way through the mightiest mountain range in the world and in doing so has descended the enormous height of 11,000 feet. What more natural than to suppose that somewhere in the depths of that unknown gorge was hidden a great waterfall."

Through the canyons of the Brahmaputra the monsoon winds sweep upward from the humid plains until stopped by the mountains. In these uplands, so different from the barren wastes of Tibet, Ward enumerated delightful regions like "the land of the

Blue Poppy" and "a rhododendron fairyland." He found the slopes of the riverbank clothed with forest dominated by tsuga trees two hundred feet high, from which natives sawed great planks eight feet wide. Step by step the river tumbled in a series of cataracts and minor falls. A beautiful specimen was the Rainbow Falls, about thirty feet high, but Tibetans claimed there were no fewer than seventy-five others. At one point the river descended 384 feet within a distance of four miles; at another a hundred feet in a quarter of a mile. By no abrupt plunge, but down a stairway fashioned by the titans, does the Son of Brahma descend from the clouds.

Through Assam the Brahmaputra, now assuming its common name, becomes a second Congo, six miles wide, enclosing many islands. One of these, Majuli, has an area of 485 square miles. This is the region of the world's heaviest rainfall, where the circling monsoons, buffeting the ramparts of the Himalayas, gyrate endlessly. At Cherrapunji all records have been broken with an annual downpour of 905 inches. A single period of twenty-four hours deluged the landscape with forty-one inches of water or nearly three and a half feet! No wonder the river sometimes rises forty feet and converts its broad valley into an elongated lake.

Flanking the Garo Hills with heights of 4,650 feet, it crosses the densely peopled province of Bengal for a hundred and fifty miles to join the main stream of the Ganges at Goalundo. As the sea is nearly two hundred miles distant, these two rivers become really one, known as the Padma. This plows majestically through a maze of lesser channels and low-lying islands to empty into the sea through a broad estuary nearly fifty miles wide.

True, the picture is complicated by the world's largest delta, a fan-shaped maze of twenty thousand square miles spreading westward for more than two hundred miles. Its far-western outlet is the Hooghly, that much-traveled thoroughfare to Calcutta, but the Padma is unquestionably the main channel.

The Brahmaputra is 1,680 miles in length, its drainage basin 361,000 square miles, while its volume probably exceeds 500,000 cubic feet a second, or the normal outflow of the Mississippi. In flood, however, the combined Ganges and Brahmaputra pour through the muddy channels of the delta a volume of nearly 1,800,000 cubic feet a second.

Although the source of the Brahmaputra has but recently been revealed and is still a matter of dispute, the lower course has been navigated for more than two thousand years. Ocean steamers ascend freely for eight hundred miles, a matchless approach to a rich hinterland, peopled by backward tribes and so far but imperfectly developed. As the India of the future emerges from the clash of Moslem and Hindu factions, this great river may well play an important part in world affairs.

THE GANGES—HOLY RIVER OF HINDUSTAN

Length—1,540 miles. Drainage area—432,480 square miles

The Ganges is *the* river of India. It presents a sweeping panorama of Indian history and culture and character. No other river holds so deep a meaning for so many people. In its hot valley they swarm by tens of millions; more human beings than may be found in any similar region, save that of the Yangtze Kiang. Across the upper peninsula of Hindustan the Ganges forms a broad highway along which the tides of conquest have repeatedly ebbed and flowed. Upon its banks splendid cities have sprung up, enjoyed their glittering heyday, and fallen into ruin. Into its waters, from time immemorial, have waded Brahmins and outcasts, beggars and kings, to wash away their sins. For although the swirling current is foul with silt and ashes, it springs from the high places of the gods among the icy peaks of the Himalayas.

If mountain heights deserve the reverence of primitive peoples, then the Ganges is thrice holy, for it is fed from the melting snows of the loftiest peaks on earth. Its northern branch issues from a vast snow field 10,300 feet above the sea, but several tributaries penetrate the Himalayas to commune with such earth titans as only Asia can display. The headwaters of the Gogra wind between Nanda Devi, 25,645 feet high, and Gurla Mandhata, 25,353; the Gandak branch skirts Dhaulagiri, 26,825 high; the Kosi prongs from that Tibetan outpost Gosai Than,

26,305, while its affluents approach the flanks of Kinchinjunga, 28,177, and that pinnacle of all mountains, Everest, 29,145, better called by its Tibetan name Chomo Lungma, "Goddess Mother of the World." Along this matchless range, the backbone of Asia, over a hundred peaks rear higher than the loftiest mountains on any other continent.

As Swami Pranavananda reminds us, however, "Some writers define the source of the river as the point of its course that is most remote from its mouth, then the source of the Ganges would not lie in the Himalayas but at the head of the Chambal in central India." True enough, the southern branch of the Ganges, the less voluminous Jumna, is the longer as its Chambal headwaters rise in the Vindhya Mountains, a boundary of great historic importance between northern and southern India. Between the Himalayas on the north and the Vindhya ranges on the south, stretching roughly from west to east, is the main valley of the Ganges, the heart of the empire, site of its most illustrious cities and region of the densest population. This plain, together with the valleys of the mountain tributaries, comprise a drainage area of 432,480 square miles.

Across this plain the Ganges flows eastward for hundreds of miles at a gentle gradient of less than one foot per mile; from the sacred city of Benares that gradient diminishes to four or five inches; from Calcutta to the sea it is scarcely two. Into the Bay of Bengal the river pours through the most extensive delta in the world. Some 220 miles from its numerous mouths that delta radiates in a vast fanlike formation more than two hundred miles wide that continually advances. The upper fertile portions degenerate into reedy swamps, the haunt of Bengal tigers, then farther out slimy mud flats appear while the pilot boat awaits incoming steamers some thirty miles off the shoaling coast line.

Most easterly of the numerous mouths is the main channel, called the Padma, where the Ganges is joined by the Brahmaputra, swollen by the torrential downpours of Assam, the heaviest rainfall on earth. The influx of waters is tremendous, for the volume of the Brahmaputra usually exceeds that of the Ganges in the ratio of two to one. The latter's average is 270,000 cubic feet per second, but in floodtime the combined rivers pour out a volume approaching 1,800,000, or more than the maximum of the Mississippi.

Better known, however, and commercially more important, is the most westerly outlet of the Ganges, called the Hooghly. On this river, some ninety miles from its mouth, stands Calcutta, metropolis and commercial center of India, with a population of one and a half million. Ocean steamers breast a current that sometimes exceeds seven miles per hour, careful to avoid shoals which shift continuously, for the ship that runs aground is soon broken to pieces by the current.

The Ganges is a restless river. As the Britannica remarks, "Many decayed or ruined cities attest the changes in the river bed in ancient times; and within our own times the main channel which formerly passed Rajmahal has turned away from it and left the town high and dry, seven miles from the bank."

Alexander the Great wished to invade the valley of the Ganges, but his wearied soldiers rebelled. From the court of Seleukos, however, who inherited the bulk of the Macedonian's dominions, Megasthenes was sent as ambassador to India, where he remained for eighteen years. Of the Ganges he wrote, "When its breadth is medium it widens to 100 stadia [somewhat over 11 miles] and its least depth is 20 fathoms." Perhaps Strabo had this voluble Greek in mind when he remarked, "Generally speaking, the men who hitherto have written on the affairs of India are a set of liars." Strabo himself wrote how "the Ganges, which is the largest of the rivers of India, flows down from the mountainous country," while the river appears on the maps of Eratosthenes and Ptolemy. The latter, however, had it running roughly from north to south across a grotesquely distorted peninsula.

The Ganges is the river of glamorous cities: Calcutta, Benares, Allahabad, Cawnpore, Lucknow of the grim Sepoy rebellion, and others. Quite as rich in historic association is the Jumna, site of various Mohammedan conquests and seat of their capitals. Most extensive of these is Delhi, with its miles of ruins superimposed city upon city like pages of a blood-smeared volume. Most ruthless of its rulers were Mohammedan sultans. Mahmud of Ghazni, a favorite hero of the Moslem world whom Omar Khayyám hails as "Allah breathing lord," led no fewer than seventeen destructive raids into northern India between the years 999 and 1030. Another leader, Mohammed Ghori, completed the conquest of the Ganges Valley. His successors, from their capital at Delhi, slaughtered their helpless subjects by the tens of thousands and imposed a rule whose barbaric strength was scant excuse for its savagery. In northern India the armies of Genghis Khan met the one enemy they could not vanquish, the burning heat. But a successor of the Mongols, Baber, there laid the foundations of that empire which controlled most of India until the British came.

The Great Moguls, though favoring Delhi, sometimes transferred the seat of government to Agra, also on the Jumna. Grim Agra Fort, with its triple wall, its mosques and palaces, the Tomb of Akbar the Great not many miles distant, and that ghost city, Fatepur Sikri, are overshadowed by the Taj Mahal, a miracle in marble, the most exquisite structure in the world. The fortune lavished by the Shah Jehan upon this fabulous tomb has enriched all architecture.

The former British capital in India was Calcutta, but this was changed later to Delhi, where an imposing group of government buildings was erected. The future of this city is now beclouded by civil strife, but no possible vicissitudes can surpass the bloody orgies which it has already survived.

The two world religions which arose in the valley of the Ganges, Hinduism and Buddhism, may be observed to advantage in the sacred city of Benares. Here the northern riverbank for some four miles presents perhaps the most fantastic sky line in the world, a frieze of fanes and temples. Some are defaced by obscene carvings, some bedizened with plates of gold. A discordant note is the Mosque of Aurung Zeb, last of the Great Moguls, whose Moslem fanaticism led him to destroy many a Hindu shrine.

Of particular interest to tourists are the Temple of Durga, frightful consort of Siva the Destroyer, and that of Hanuman, the Monkey God, although Mark Twain was intrigued by the shrine dedicated to Smallpox. Here the Hindu cult, with its enlightened conception of a Trinity comprising Brahma the Creator, Vishnu the Sustainer, and Siva the Destroyer, the faith of Gandhi and intelligent Brahmins, has been corrupted by rituals and disfigured by a fungous growth of lesser deities, many of them repulsive or grotesque.

The famous ghats, or flights of stone steps descending into the river, present an unforgettable picture. Tens of thousands of worshipers throng these stairways, pilgrims from all parts of India. Some have measured their length along the riverbank from its source in the Himalayas. Joyously they descend into the muddy waters, wash their clothes, bathe their bodies, and drink from this "purifying" stream. Here and there funeral pyres burst into flame, lighted by priests from sacred altars, while the smoke of roasting human flesh rises as an almost continuous incense. The ashes are strewn upon the waters with offerings of marigold flowers, beloved of the gods. One may also observe huge slabs of rock in readiness to be attached to the bodies of sacred cows when they die and are cast into the river. Their bloated carcasses rise to the surface to drift by Calcutta, supporting great vultures which tear the decayed flesh. One would expect Benares to be a focal point of epidemics, but English engineers assert that the river purifies itself within a few miles. In its silt-laden waters swim almost sightless porpoises, which have developed a distinct species.

A few miles from Benares, at Sarnath, is the traditional site where Buddha, the great Saint of Hindustan, is alleged to have preached his first sermon. The spot is marked by a commemorative fane to which monks journey all the way from Tibet to perform services. Near by is the gigantic stupa, or circular monument, nearly a hundred feet high, erected by Asoka more than two thousand years ago. This great emperor, who gave India its finest example of self-government and is listed by H. G. Wells as one of the leading half dozen rulers of all time, sent missionaries as far as Syria and Greece to acquaint the world with the gentle religion of Ghautama, its eightfold path and its Ten Commandments. But Buddhism, although it has elsewhere become the predominant faith of the Orient, has almost died out in the land of its origin.

The Ganges, quite apart from its religious significance in the life of the Hindus, is of great commercial and agricultural importance. In its valley, irrigation has been carried on more extensively than anywhere else in the world. Great canals, which are connected with innumerable ditches, divert the floodwaters. Wells literally by the million pit the valley, where water is raised laboriously in huge leathern buckets by plodding bullocks. Silt from the Sacred River imparts to the soil all the fertility of the Nile. For a rainfall that averages seventy-five inches annually in the lower valley is often inadequate in other areas where the population, in spite of its endless labor, hovers upon the verge of famine.

Four hundred miles from the sea the Ganges still presents an average depth of thirty-five feet, while steamers proceed for a thousand miles or more. Native boats are of many patterns. A common type, high of stern and low in the bow, propelled by one clumsy sail assisted by sweeps, seems archaic in a land of railways and steel bridges. The jute plant which is indigenous to the delta region supplies a score of mills along the banks of the Hooghly, while cotton and sugar cane are crops of growing importance. Grains are a staple food, and the curries of India are famous.

Meanwhile millions of peasants in mud-walled villages cultivate their tiny farms as they have done for ages, their careworn lives forever shadowed by famine, pestilence, and the tax collector, giving thanks to Mother Ganga, the source of moisture and fertility, content if they may only die upon its banks and have their ashes strewn upon its waters.

THE INDUS OF A FABULOUS ANTIQUITY

Length—1,700 miles. Drainage area—372,000 square miles

The Indus is the great river of southwestern Asia. No other name has been so widely repeated in global geography. In Sanskrit, the ancient language of the region, the word for river was *"sindhu,"* whence the Indus. This the Persians corrupted to Hindu, and the Greeks to India. The name of both river and country stemmed from a common source and by poetic expansion embraced one of the three major oceans—the Indian. Beyond that ocean lay the fabulous Indies, which Columbus was seeking when he discovered that other tropic archipelago, the West Indies.

Mistakenly, he called its natives Indians, a name incorporated in the state of Indiana, its chief city Indianapolis, and echoed in the names of numerous American mountains, lakes, and streams. And so the currents of that far-off river of Hindustan, coursing through the obscure channels of nomenclature, have girdled the globe.

Although the Indus lay upon the border of their known world, few rivers were better known to the ancients. Eratosthenes wrote, "India is bounded on the west by the Indus River." Ptolemy sketched it with fair accuracy upon his universal map. Strabo remarked, "It is said that the Indus is joined by fifteen noteworthy rivers." Alexander the Great crossed several of these branches, fought sanguinary battles, and upon the shores of one of them, the modern Beas, reached his farthest east. There his weary troops refused to advance, and the boy conqueror, eager to invade the valley of the Ganges with its glittering fanes and cities, sulked like Achilles in his tent for three days before consenting to retreat.

Curious to follow the Indus to the sea, Alexander collected on the Hydaspes, the modern Jhelum, a notable flotilla said to number eight hundred galleys with twelve hundred tenders and smaller craft. His admiral, Nearchus, recounts how, "I offered myself for the command and promised the King that under the protection of God I would conduct the fleet safe into the Gulf of Persia, if the sea were navigable and the undertaking within the power of man to perform."

The date of sailing has been fixed at October 23, 327 B.C. Arrian gives the minimum width of the river as fifteen stadia, somewhat over a mile, its maximum at forty stadia, or near three miles. At one point where the current narrowed with increased velocity two galleys were wrecked and Alexander himself was forced to seek a protective point.

In the delta city of Patala he remained for some time, conducting forays into the surrounding country and contemplating the tombs of forgotten kings. The holy men seated by the highways wondered why anyone should wish to conquer the world when six feet of ground sufficed. Here the dissatisfied West met the impassive East on a question which has never been answered.

Near the Indus's several mouths the Greeks were terrified at the tidal bores which wrecked a number of galleys and stranded others. Alexander sailed out into the unknown sea, sacrificed to Poseidon, and as a final offering cast overboard the golden vessels of the ceremony. Then he forsook the fleet to accompany the bulk of his army by forced marches across the grim deserts of southern Persia.

The word delta, first restricted to the Nile, was now applied to the Indus and has since been an accepted term for similar river formations. Nearchus concluded, correctly, that this region was "the offspring of the river." His pilot, Onesicritus, observed, "the sea shore is covered with shoal water particularly at the mouths of the rivers on account of the silt, the flood tides, and the prevalence of winds from the high seas." Strabo wrote, "The Indus empties by two mouths into the southern sea," but Ptolemy enumerated seven.

The shifting nature of this delta and the changing river channel were even then in evidence. Aristobolus reported more than a thousand cities together with villages that "had been deserted because the Indus had abandoned its proper bed." Formerly it emptied by at least one channel into the dismal Rann of Cutch, that marshy indentation from the sea now largely silted up by alluvial deposits and wind-blown desert dust.

The sources of the Indus, though vaguely guessed at, long remained concealed beyond the loftiest mountain range on earth. Not only was the terrain incredibly difficult, but the Forbidden Kingdom of Tibet interposed an "iron curtain." Only within the past few decades have the headwaters been traced to the vast glaciers of the Kailas peaks, not far from the source of that other great river of Hindustan—the Brahmaputra.

For some distance the Indus flows at an elevation exceeding fifteen thousand feet, or nearly three miles. Its course leads northwestward between the towering Ladahk range and the main ridge of the Himalayas, through scenery that the Britannica maintains, "for the majesty of sheer altitude, is unmatched by any in the world." Swollen by melted snows and mountain streams, it traverses the Vale of Kashmir, surrounded by stupendous peaks and long regarded as one of the sights of the world. The great Mogul Jehangir, the "earth shaker," father of Akbar the Great, doubted if Mohammed's Paradise could be more beautiful and hoped that he might die while gazing out upon it. The Indus passes within sixty miles of K 2, major peak of the Karakorum range and second loftiest mountain in the world, with an altitude of 28,250 feet, while still nearer looms Nanga Parbat, 26,629 feet high, whose icy pinnacles remain unscaled and perhaps unscalable. Turning westward, the river breaks through gorges in the mountains, descending rather abruptly to a more moderate elevation of four thousand feet whence it hurries across the plains of Sind. Here it is joined by the longer Panjnad, twice as wide as the parent stream but of lesser volume, bearing the surplus waters of the Jhelum, the Ravi, the Sutlej, the Chenab, and an intricate pattern of minor streams that radiate from the mountains and resemble the tangled rootlets of an overturned tree.

The length of the Indus is usually given as seventeen hundred miles, but if its windings were accurately recorded it would doubtless approach two thousand. Its drainage area, 372,000 square miles, comprises some of the most varied scenery in the world, a profusion of snow peaks, a swift descent by foaming cataracts, an impetuous course across the Punjab, the dreary Thar or Indian Desert, the great alluvial plain built up from the wastage of the uplands and the delta encroaching upon a shallow sea.

The Indus has always been a turbulent stream. Onesicritus reported that it rose forty feet in floodtime, a conservative estimate. In 1850 it rose eighty at Attock, which forced the Kabul River to reverse its current and flow backward into Afghanistan at a speed of ten miles per hour. Within the past two centuries the Indus has cut its way through the limestone ridges at Sukkur, some three hundred miles from the sea, and gouged out its present channel.

The silt which Nearchus noted has been investigated by the Indus River Commission established by the government in January 1901. The floodwaters during a three-month period bear an annual burden of six billion cubic feet. In places the river bed is seventy feet above the level of the western plains some miles distant and offers a perennial threat of floods. Embankments and vast irrigation projects, however, divert much of the surplus waters. Like the Nile, fed by the snows of the far interior, the

Indus traverses a region of scanty rainfall. Hence four fifths of all cultivated land in the Sind area is maintained by irrigation.

In its mountain fastness the Indus and tributary streams are crossed by precarious bridges of fiber or bamboo. On quieter stretches pontoon bridges offer better means of transportation. It was probably such a bridge of boats that Perdiccas and Hephaestion assembled for Alexander and his army in 326 B.C. Farther down the river is spanned by steel bridges by the Indian Railways.

Long before the days of Nearchus the river was an artery of commerce. High-sterned flatboats still use its channel, but most commerce is now diverted to the speedier and more dependable railways.

In spite of its precipitous gorges, the upper valley of the Indus has furnished one of the great highways into Central Asia. One tributary, the Shyok, rises within six miles of the loftiest of all trade routes, the Karakorum Pass, nineteen thousand feet above the sea. The pious Chinese pilgrim, Fa-Hsien, in the early centuries of the Christian Era, found here "a difficult, precipitous and dangerous road, the side of the mountain being like a stone wall 10,000 feet high. On nearing the edge the eye becomes confused and wishing to advance the foot finds no resting place. Below there is a river called the Indus."

Across the upper branches of the Indus from immemorial times have streamed those invasions of alien peoples from Central Asia or the west. A thousand years B.C. saw the advent of the conquering Aryans in their war chariots, wielding bows and arrows, spears and battle-axes, and chanting their hymns of praise to Indra, the God of Storms, the oriental Thor of flaming thunderbolts. No mere marauders, they sought homes as well as plunder, but according to the custom of the times, they gladly appropriated the lands and goods of others. Their very word for war expressed merely a desire for "more cows." Gradually they overran all northern India and, presumably to maintain a racial purity from contamination by darker-skinned aborigines, inaugurated that caste system which has become riveted like an iron framework upon Indian society. Other invasions followed: the Persians, who incorporated some of the Indus Valley in their unwieldly empire; Alexander the Great, with his brilliant but transient

Grecian influence; ferocious Moslem raiders from Afghanistan; the savage Mongols and the armies of the Great Moguls. But if the valleys of the Indus have been one of the major battlegrounds of history, they were also the cradle of one of the earliest of civilization.

The world has long been acquainted with the cultures of the Nile and the Euphrates, but has become aware only recently of a similar culture perhaps as ancient and influential in the valley of the Indus. At Mohenjo-daro Sir John Marshall and his native aides have unearthed one of the oldest of city-states. Here and at Harappa, some hundreds of miles farther north, the spades of the archaeologists have laboriously unearthed five cities super-imposed one upon the other. Oddly enough, the lowest stratum reveals the finest culture, as though the slow flowering of unnumbered centuries of progress were succeeded by eras of comparative decline. In this ancient metropolis, according to Sir John, buildings several stories in height were equipped with "wells, bathrooms, an elaborate drainage system, all bespeaking social conditions equal to that of the Sumerians and superior to that of contemporary Babylon and Egypt." Jewelry and other articles of rare beauty have been recovered, including some of our earliest coins with the copper model of a two-wheeled cart, the oldest vehicle in existence.

To fix exact dates is impossible, but five thousand years ago the streets of Mohenjo-daro pulsed with life, while its origins may, as Sir John believes, lie even farther in the past than those of Ur of the Chaldees, now recognized as the most venerable of cities.

Some intercourse between the peoples of the Indus and the Euphrates is traceable in a similarity of craftsmanship. Long before the voyage of Nearchus ships may have navigated the Arabian Sea or overland trade routes mingled the products of Accad on the Euphrates and Mohenjo-daro on the Indus. Which borrowed from the other, however, or whether both sprung from a common and unknown source are questions which remain unanswered.

V

The Rivers of Western Asia

THE EUPHRATES—RIVER OF HISTORY

Length—1,700 miles. Drainage area—430,000 square miles

THE ANCIENT Hebrews called it "The Great River, the River Euphrates." It watered their fabled Eden, and the lush greenery of its valley was in vivid contrast with the arid regions round about. The rich alluvial soil, crisscrossed by innumerable irrigation ditches, ripened three crops annually, so that Herodotus wrote, "This territory is, of all that we know, the best by far for ripening grain." Even now the lower valley is the finest date-growing region in the world. But the canals are clogged with sand and the once peerless valley has become largely a waste of marsh and desert, a panorama of dead cities and vanished greatness.

Year by year the river cuts deeper canyons through the gorges of the Taurus Mountains; year by year its silted outlet advances into the shallow Persian Gulf. But to follow it from the sea to its remote headwaters in the wild Armenian tableland is to trace civilization as well to its oldest-known sources amid Sumerian ruins.

We commonly think of the Euphrates as moving in a south-easterly direction across a wide plain, and that is true, but its upper course is a mountain stream foaming downward through breath-taking chasms that rival, in depth at least, the grand canyon of the Colorado.

Two branches skirting the Taurus Range unite to form the main river. The upper, known to the Turks as Kara Su, and usually called the Euphrates, has its source in a circular pool at an

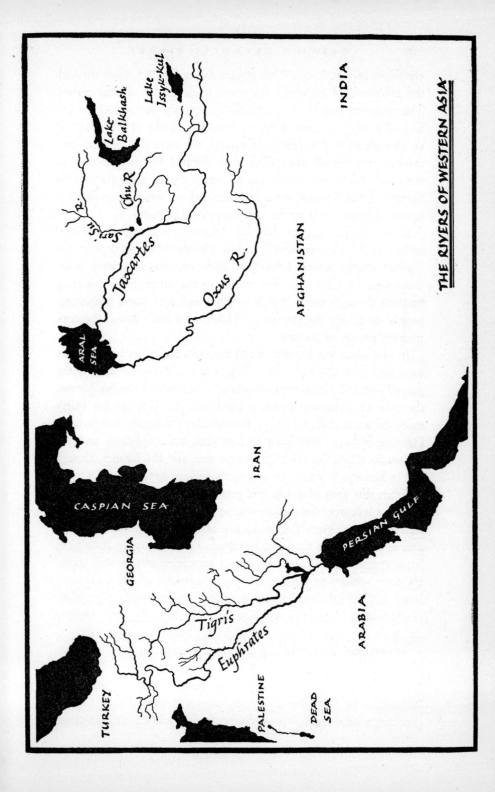

THE RIVERS OF WESTERN ASIA

elevation of 8,625 feet. This stream flows for 275 miles through the tableland of Erzerum, the great trade center of that region. The southern branch or Murad Su is, however, longer, 415 miles, and of greater volume. It issues from the flanks of Ala Dagh at an altitude of 11,500 feet, with Ararat, the mount of biblical lore, towering in the distance. The river formed by the junction of these two branches then forces a passage through the formidable barrier of the Taurus, a natural bulwark of western civilization against aggression from the vast hinterland of Asia.

Ellsworth Huntington has left graphic reminiscences of this savage and little frequented region. He mentions a gorge in the Harput Range where 1,500-foot cliffs on one side were overshadowed by 2,500-foot precipices on the other. Here the river had cut through mounds rich in stone relics of some prehistoric people, and here the fortress of Haldis had once defied the conquering armies of Assyria.

In one place the current raced through a canyon twelve miles long and four thousand feet deep, while silhouetted against the jagged sky line Huntington observed a number of the big-horned ibex. In this chaotic region a transverse canyon cut for thirty miles between cliffs which he estimated were nearly a mile high. Hanging villages suggested to him that the Euphrates and the Colorado might be about the same age, for the former, though old in history, is young as geologists reckon time.

From this area of gorge and precipice the channel emerges to pursue a less troubled middle course to the town of Hit, 720 miles nearer the sea. Here the banks are often two hundred feet high and in places more than five hundred. The country on both sides has a sparse rainfall, so that verdure appearing after spring showers soon withers in the summer heat. Formerly it was well populated, but the inhabitants now are nomadic Arabs who pitch their black tents wherever fancy dictates and not infrequently live in caves.

Settled communities along the river irrigate fields of rice, cotton, melons, and licorice root by the crudest of engineering methods. Piers of rock are thrust into the stream, raising the surface sufficiently to turn clumsy water wheels called naouras. These creaking mechanisms, with paddles of palm leaves, are sometimes forty feet in diameter. The valley, several miles in width, might support a much larger population, but much of it has reverted to a tamarisk jungle, the covert of wild pigs. Many ruins would engross the attention of archaeologists were they not eclipsed by the lower valley which is a veritable graveyard of dead cities. Two features, however, are of special interest. One is the great bend to the westward which provides a river port for the city of Aleppo, halfway to the Mediterranean Sea. Readers of *Macbeth* will recall the witch's mention of a sailor's wife whose "husband's to Aleppo gone, master o' the Tiger," for this city has commanded a commercial highway older than history.

Another spot marks the ruins of Carchemish, that stronghold of the Hittites, mentioned in the Old Testament. This mysterious people warred with Assyria and Egypt but had vanished without a trace until recent excavations unearthed some scattered relics.

This mid-section of the river also marked the northern boundary of the Kingdom of Israel under David, who became involved in battle with the Syrian ruler Hadadezer when "he went to recover his border at the river Euphrates," as related in II Samuel, 8:3. Much the same boundary separated the later Roman and the Parthian empires.

A few side streams join the river in this region, some heavily alkaline, some charged with bitumen. Although the Syrian Desert encroaches on the southwest, the country was prosperous in ancient times and under later Moslem caliphs. But appalling ruin engulfed it with the Mongol invasion from Central Asia.

The lower section of the Euphrates may be said to begin at Hit. Here the river is 750 feet wide, from 30 to 35 feet deep, and flows with a 4-mile current. Farther down it slackens to little more than a mile across a broad alluvial plain, the "fill in" of the Euphrates and the Tigris rivers for five hundred and fifty miles to the sea. Much volume is dissipated through a maze of half-ruined canals, overflow marshes, and stagnant pools. Not a hundredth part of these canals, some of them thousands of years old, remain in workable condition, while the region, once fertile as the valley of the Nile, is given over to camel's-thorn, wormwood, and other semidesert shrubbery.

Some seventy miles from the sea the Euphrates is joined by its great tributary, the Tigris, 1,150 miles in length. This river rises at an altitude of 5,050 feet amid the tangled peaks which rim Armenia's great lake, Van, of the bitter waters. Along the cliffs that mark its course are carven bas-reliefs and cuneiform inscriptions. Like the Euphrates, which it approaches within three miles, its channel is broken by numberless cascades and deeply eroded through lofty mountain ranges.

The Tigris is probably the Hiddekel of Scripture. Strabo explains how "the Median word for arrow is Tigris," descriptive of its rapid upper current. Entering the plain, it first approaches the Euphrates, then veers away to unite with the larger stream hundreds of miles to the south and east. Formerly both had separate outlets. Even in the days of Alexander the Great their respective mouths were distant "a day's journey." Possibly their junction was hastened by artificial means, for Pliny writes, "Between the mouths of the two rivers, the Tigris and the Euphrates, the distance was formerly 25 miles . . . but the Orcheni and others . . . have long since dammed up the waters of the Euphrates for the purpose of irrigation and it can only discharge itself into the sea by the aid of the Tigris." In any case, the two were destined to unite, as the delta region formed by their combined silt burden from the remote highlands thrusts ever farther into the shallow Persian Gulf, nowhere more than seventy-five feet in depth. Pliny recognized this when he wrote, "In no part of the world have alluvial deposits been formed more rapidly by the rivers." At present the seacoast at the head of the gulf advances seventy-two feet a year. How great has been the building-up process even within historic time is disclosed by the ruins of the ancient Sumerian city of Eridu, once a seaport, now 125 miles inland!

Alexander the Great crossed the Euphrates on pontoon bridges at Thapsacus, but his armies were able to ford the Tigris. Nearchus, on his return voyage from India, mentions the pearl fisheries in the gulf, which still flourish there. The region is of romantic interest. Chinese junks voyaged thither, leaving their curious currency. Some of the earliest beacons guided shipping through these treacherous waters. Early Arab geographers mention "marks of wood erected for the sailors . . . upon which fires are burnt at night to caution vessels." Here that hero of our childhood, Sindbad the Sailor, set forth on his fabulous adventures.

The fertile region between the Tigris and Euphrates is the Mesopotamia of the Greeks. Here flourished our oldest known civilization, for the crumbling mound known as Ur of the Chaldees has been endowed by archaeologists with a hoary antiquity of sixty-five hundred years. It was from Ur that Abraham, traditional founder of the Hebrew race, journeyed to Palestine. Once it was a metropolis of the Sumerians, a mysterious people whose origin is still in dispute. Whether they were Aryan or Semitic or from an earlier stock that antedated either is unknown. A neighboring city, Eridu, was sacred to the God of the Great Deep of Waters that governed the shallow and tumultuous Persian Gulf. That city then faced this gulf and was also situated upon a branch of the Euphrates. But the great river shifted its course, the ocean receded, and Eridu was ultimately abandoned.

The metropolis of the region, however, was Babylon, "that great city" of the Hebrew Prophets, model and prototype of all subsequent big cities. It was immeasurably ancient when Hammurabi, about 2297 B.C., gave to the world his famous code of laws. Will Durant has said that modern man would have felt more at home in Babylon five thousand years ago than in medieval Europe, so far had culture then climbed above the brutishness of the Stone Age. Here magicians, soothsayers, and the other wise men of Babylon developed the basis of modern astronomy, divided the great circle into 360 degrees, gave the day its twenty-four hours, the week its seven days, and inaugurated other innovations that mathematicians wish might have been retained. Our numerical system, based upon tens, is inferior to the Babylonian twelves, such was the homage man has paid to his fingers in making quick calculations. Babylon reached its zenith under Nebuchadnezzar. Of his city Strabo wrote, "The circuit of the wall is 385 stadia [or nearly 44 miles]. The thickness of its wall is 32 feet, the height thereof between the towers is 50 cubits, that of the towers 60 cubits." Herodotus embellishes these figures and adds that the city gates were "bronze."

Still more unusual were the Hanging Gardens which the mighty monarch erected to please his Median queen, pining for her native hills in the dead flatness of Babylonia. From Strabo we glean descriptive touches of the structure as "quadrangular in shape and each side is four plethra in length. [The plethrum was about 101 feet.] It consists of arched vaults . . . the ascent to the uttermost terraced roofs . . . screws through which the water was continually conducted from the Euphrates." The enormous city walls and this singular edifice clothed with trees and flowers were numbered among the Seven Wonders of the World.

Babylon seems to have been located upon a channel of the Euphrates, artificially diverted, though at times it accommodated the main current. It fell before the Assyrians, the Persians, and the Macedonians, yet Alexander the Great selected it as the capital of his unwieldy empire. And there he met a premature death, while not yet thirty-three, of a fever enduced by unbridled debauchery.

Aristobolus says that Alexander "sailing up the river inspected the canals," an intricate network where irrigation projects had been carried to a pitch perhaps unequaled since that time. On the outskirts of the Tigris and Euphrates valleys canals paralleled those rivers to the sea. One of these, known as Shapur's trench, for the Persian king of a later date, was much older, in fact was improved by order of Nebuchadnezzar. Another canal joined both rivers near the modern Bagdad, while innumerable lesser ones bore water to the thirsty fields. These were the rivers of Babylon, where, according to The Book of Psalms, homesick Hebrew exiles "sat down and wept" and "hanged their harps on the willows."

Almost equally illustrious were the cities that grew up along the Tigris. Here was located ancient Assur, which gave its name to Assyria, that despotism of blood and iron which long tyrannized over the Near East. Even Babylon was for a time eclipsed by its splendid capital, Nineveh, "that great city" mentioned in the Book of Jonah, with its temples and palaces guarded by colossal stone bulls and lions. A ring of barbaric grandeur still lingers in the very names of such monarchs as Sargon and Sennacherib. But the city was so utterly destroyed that when Xenophon and his ten thousand Greeks hurried by on their historic flight from the heart of the Persian Empire, they wondered at the shapeless mounds which marked its site.

Upon the Tigris, Seleucus, the Macedonian general who inherited the bulk of Alexander's dominions, built his capital and named it for himself, Seleucia.

Across the river from Seleucia the kings of Parthia, who alone defied the power of Rome, built their capital at Ctesiphon. The lower Tigris and Euphrates marked the eastern boundaries of the Roman Empire in the days of its widest expansion under Trajan. But even he did not attempt to follow the steps of Alexander the Great to India. Gibbon says that he "descended the River Tigris in triumph from the mountains of Armenia to the Persian Gulf," but "lamented, with a sigh, that his advanced age scarcely left him any hope of equalling the renown of the son of Philip."

Ctesiphon was also the winter capital of the Persian kings of the later Sassanid dynasty, and the ruins of their famous white palace are a melancholy reminder of their reign. A vast archway rears above the desert, a forlorn remnant of the great banqueting hall whose vaulted roof was studded with stars of gold. When the city fell to Saad, the victorious Mohammedan general, in 637, among the booty was "the royal banqueting carpet seventy cubits long by sixty wide upon which were wrought fantastic landscapes in silver, gold, and precious stones."

Some twenty-five miles farther up the river the great Caliph Mansur erected a citadel which was completed in 766 after three years' work. Around this citadel grew up the city of Bagdad, which became for a time the metropolis of the known world. Even Charlemagne sent ambassadors to the court of the caliph, whose dominions extended for six thousand miles from India to the Atlantic. Under Haroun-al-Raschid Bagdad became invested with an atmosphere of fabulous adventure which survives in tales of the Arabian Nights. For nearly five hundred years this city of the Orient presented something of that glamour commemorated by Tennyson in the lines:

> Adown the Tigris I was borne, by Bagdad's
> shrines of fretted gold.

Then, like a destroying hurricane from Central Asia, burst the Mongol invasions. Hulagu, the ruthless grandson of Genghis

Khan, stormed Bagdad in 1258, and its glory was eclipsed forever. Later the city was ravaged by Tamerlane, the morose cripple, who, as a warning against future rebellion, erected outside the city his grisly pyramid of seventy thousand human skulls. Even the brutal Assyrian despots never equaled these incredible butchers from the region of the Gobi.

But their crowning act of wanton savagery was the destruction of the irrigation canals which transformed a vast garden into a wilderness.

Navigation on the Euphrates has always intrigued visiting travelers. Herodotus wrote, "The boats which come down the river to Babylon are circular and made of skins. The frames which are of willow are cut in the country of the Armenians, above Assyria, and on these which serve as hulls a covering of skins is stretched outside and thus the boats are made without either stem or stern quite round like a shield. The chief freight is wine . . . They are managed by two men who stand upright in them each plying an oar, the one pulling, the other pushing." Such rude floats, known as kufas, calked with asphalt, still swirl past Bagdad down the current of the Tigris. Similar boats are pictured in the bas-reliefs of Sennacherib.

Rudest of all craft are the bellems, made in part of hollowed logs. On the upper river, rafts called keleks are borne upon inflated goatskins. Huntington found that six skins supported two fishermen. Passengers voyage down the Tigris in narrow meshufs either towed from the bank by ropes or poled across the shallows. High-sided sailing vessels known as turradas even venture out upon the gulf. Steamers now navigate long stretches of both rivers until stopped thirty miles above Mosul by two ancient dams. From its junction with the Tigris to the sea, some seventy miles away, the channel of the Euphrates is a thousand yards wide and varies in depth from eighteen to thirty feet.

Herodotus reminds us that this valley was the favorite trade route from Europe to the East. Kaiser Wilhelm of Germany attempted to restore this trade route along his Berlin-to-Bagdad railway. His ambitious project was halted by World War I and abandoned with the ultimate ruin of Germany.

The mineral wealth of the Euphrates basin has never been fully exploited. The ancient lead mines of Keban Maden lie in its upper valley. The Tigris shows deposits of copper, iron, and sulphur, and there are marble quarries. But the most sought for of modern minerals, petroleum, has always been in evidence.

According to the biblical narrative, Noah, preparing the Ark against the threatened deluge, "pitched it within and without with pitch," the same type of bitumen with which river boatmen still plaster their clumsy kufas. Posidonius wrote of the "springs of Naptha in Babylonia," also of "Black Naptha [liquid asphalt] which is burned in lamps instead of oil." Mosul upon the Tigris is the center of the Mesopotamian oil wells, while bordering the lower Persian Gulf are some of the richest petroleum fields known anywhere.

Enormous water power still runs to waste in the upper gorges of the Tigris and Euphrates. But the irrigation projects which once made their valley the granary of the world could be restored with less effort than the building of dams and the installation of dynamos. For this area, as large as England, could well support ten times the present population.

Six thousand years ago the Sumerians had developed a written language, were building cities and engaging in various commercial activities, while innumerable canals watered their cultivated fields. Yet this rich heritage from antiquity has been largely dissipated and what was once a densely peopled region has lapsed into a melancholy waste. The prolonged neglect of what was perhaps the first of all river valleys to provide settled habitations for mankind is a stark arraignment of modern enterprise.

THE LONELY JAXARTES

Length—1,700 miles. *Drainage area*—320,000 square miles

In the heart of western Asia, shut off from access to the outer world by inland seas, lofty mountains, and endless steppes, lies that little-known territory of perhaps a million and a quarter square miles called Turkestan. Eastward from the Caspian it stretches for fifteen hundred miles or more, its southern boundary

Persia, Afghanistan, and Tibet; its northern blending into the limitless horizons of the Siberian plains. As its name suggests, it is the traditional home of various Turkish tribes, with a pronounced infiltration of Tartar and Mongolian blood. But long ago it was the cradle of the conquering Aryans, who swept southward into Persia and India, while from a border province the Parthians issued forth to dispute with Rome the mastery of the western world.

About the beginning of the Christian Era, Chinese influence had spanned the continent to embrace much of Turkestan, where the local mandarin was called "Protector General of the Western Countries." Here the Roman dominions approached those of China and an embassy from Marcus Aurelius was received at the capital of the Han dynasty in A.D. 165.

Later, throughout this region, Islam spread the culture of the Koran, thriving universities sprung up at Bokhara and other cities, while poetry, philosophy, and science flourished in the atmosphere of exotic rose gardens. Here arose the Empire of Karesm only to be demolished by the savage raiders of Genghis Khan. Upon its ruins Tamerlane erected his far-flung tyranny, while from the environs of his capital at Samarkand that brilliant adventurer, Baber, set forth to conquer northern India and establish the throne of the Great Moguls. The detailed story of Turkestan has never been written, but it might prove as absorbing and perhaps as decisive in world affairs as that of medieval Europe.

This extensive region is now split up into various divisions of the Soviet Union, the so-called republics of Turkoman, Kirghiz, Usbek, Kazak, and others whose names reveal the dominant racial stock, amid a jumble of minority races including the growing immigration from Russia proper. But much of the lush fertility of former times is withered by the hot winds which sear the landscape into forlorn browns and yellows. The desolate Ust-urt Plateau east of the Caspian is prolonged in the dreary sands of the Kyzyl-kum, the Kara-kum, and the Muyun-kum, while certain areas have won appropriate names, such as the Famine Steppes and the Red Sand Desert. The region is one of drought and emptiness, of ruined cities and forgotten empires.

The beds of innumerable dried-up lakes tell their own depressing story, and once-great rivers now lose themselves in the engulfing sands. Much of Turkestan has a scant and erratic rainfall of less than ten inches annually. But across its parched surface, out of the snowcapped ranges which bar it from the south, two interesting rivers flow into the Aral—the blue sea of western Asia—rivers dimly known to Ptolemy as the Jaxartes and the Oxus.

The ancients regarded the Jaxartes as part of that boundary which separated the known regions of western Asia from the unexplored beyond. Nor has the lapse of more than two thousand years seen it emerge from the twilight zone of fact and fancy, for the modern name Syr Daria conveys rather less meaning to the average reader than the more venerable Jaxartes.

The Persians extended their empire to this river and appropriated some territory beyond. Upon its banks they built their outpost city, Cyreschate, and called the region Sogdiana. Alexander the Great, who crossed the river in 328 B.C. to impress the nomads of the steppes with the potency of Grecian arms, also built a city which, with his usual modesty, he named for himself, Alexander Eschata.

But neither Persians nor Macedonians knew anything of the source of the Jaxartes among the mountains, or of its outlet into the Aral Sea. In fact, they confused the latter with the Caspian. Strabo wrote, "The Jaxartes is distinct from the Oxus from its commencement to its termination and empties itself into the same sea," which was true enough, but he thought that sea was the Caspian and it so appears upon the maps of both Eratosthenes and Ptolemy.

The Jaxartes rises as the Naryn River in the icy Tien Shan, which early Chinese travelers called the Mountains of Heaven. Cascading downward from an elevation of twelve thousand feet, and swollen by many tributaries, it cuts its way through a savage gorge where within a short distance it descends four thousand feet only to continue its course by a series of yawning chasms through parallel ranges and across the beds of fossil lakes to emerge at length upon the vast lowlands beyond. The channel through the upper areas is girdled with loess deposits thirty to fifty miles in width which suggest the upper valley of the Hwang

Ho. These benchlands when irrigated are fertile, but eroded silt makes the river current very muddy.

In the beautiful Ferghana district apricots grow wild among apple orchards and groves of pistachio trees, while cotton flourishes in the rich soil of the river valley.

Traversing a considerable territory where the elevation is perhaps a thousand feet, the Jaxartes enters the plains which mark the bed of the Sarmatian Sea, whose surviving remnants number the Caspian, the Aral, and a host of lesser salt lakes. Across these plains the river flows in a northwesterly direction for 850 miles.

Here it falls under the baleful influence of the desert. Former tributaries no longer swell its current but debouch into swampy lakes or are absorbed by the sands. The Chu River, six hundred miles long, which rises south of that isolated big lake known as Issyk-kul, now empties into dwindling Lake Saumal-kul some sixty miles from the Jaxartes. Feeders of the Chu come foaming down from the mountains only to lose themselves in the desolate Muyun-kum.

Another onetime tributary, the Sari-su, skirts the Famine Steppes for 570 miles, then empties its depleted waters into that maze of shallow lakes called Uzun-kul. Former feeder streams have been dried up by the parching winds of the steppes.

Agriculture depends wholly upon irrigation. The climate is one of fantastic extremes. Summer temperatures often soar above 100 degrees, while the glare of the sun upon parched wastes is blinding. Hot winds, like the breath of a blast furnace, add to the discomfort. Winter temperatures drop to zero, and the lower river remains frozen for an average of 123 days. The lakes and mantling vegetation which once moistened the atmosphere have largely disappeared.

The river splits into two or more channels to unite later on, but more curious phenomena are the channels which wander off into the plain, seeking an outlet. Most considerable of these is the Yani-daria, which finally reaches the Aral Sea, more than a hundred miles from the main delta. The Kirghiz claim that this queer stream was once an irrigation canal, widened and deepened by floodwaters.

The Jaxartes empties into the northeastern sector of the Sea of Aral through a delta which continually advances. Much of the coastal plain is of similar formation. In time of flood the current overflows to a width of twenty miles and, subsiding, leaves reedy swamps, the breeding places of countless mosquitoes. But these swamps bar the advance of sand dunes which flank the river on both sides for long distances.

The normal outflow of the Jaxartes has been estimated all the way from much inferior figures up to 312,000 cubic feet a second. The channel varies in depth from eighteen to thirty feet, while the current flows at a speed varying from three to five miles per hour. Without this influx of waters and that contributed by the Oxus, according to the English scientist Major Herbert Wood, the Aral Sea, though one of the largest bodies of inland water in the world, would dry up within fifty years.

Steamers now ply the lower river, although commerce on the shallow Aral, harassed by fierce gales, has never been extensive. The metropolis of the region is that ancient trade center, Tashkent. The Russians, having assumed authority over the clashing races that have milled about for centuries, are striving to develop the drainage area of the Jaxartes, which comprises some 320,000 square miles. Throughout its varied course of seventeen hundred miles the river is a challenge to modern enterprise. But the struggle to implant the seeds of industrialism in the valley of what has always been an oriental river is a discouraging one. Wasted by evaporation and irrigation ditches and with depleted tributaries, the modern Syr Daria seems content to remain the Jaxartes of antiquity.

THE WANDERING OXUS

Length—1,500 miles. Drainage area—115,000 square miles

De Quincey thought the very names Ganges and Euphrates suggested Asia and were invested with an oriental atmosphere. He might also have included the Jaxartes and the Oxus, those rivers isolated beyond the mountains of Persia and Afghanistan that flow into the landlocked Aral Sea.

Ancient names do not always survive. The Ister of Herodotus is now the Danube, and his Borysthenes is the Russian Dnieper. In Turkestan periodic streams, or wadies, are known as sais, permanent rivers as darias. But it is doubtful if the modern Amu Daria is so familiar as the more sonorous Oxus.

This great river rises in the upsurging mass of The Pamirs, called the loftiest tableland in the world. It is a chaotic jumble of elevated valleys and still higher mountain ranges and probably contains the most extensive glaciers in the world, outside those continental refrigerators Greenland and Antarctica. Natives call the region Bam i Dunya, "The Roof of the World." Marco Polo crossed it on his famous journey from Venice to the court of Kublai Khan and made two shrewd observations, both accurate, both ridiculed by his contemporaries. "So great is the height of the mountains," he wrote, "that fires do not give the same heat nor produce the same effect in cooking food," his recognition of the scientific fact that the boiling point of water decreases with the altitude. Among native wild life, Marco also noted, "Sheep of a large size having horns . . . six palms in length. Of these . . . they construct fences for enclosing their cattle." Here we recognize the *Ovis poli*, named for Marco, monarch of the sheep family and perhaps the rarest of big-game trophies.

Three impetuous streams traverse the Pamir in roughly parallel valleys for a hundred miles or more to unite as the Oxus. One branch was traced by Lieutenant Wood in 1838 to what he considered its source in Lake Victoria, 14,230 feet above the sea. Later explorations show that this lake, which is rapidly silting up, is but a receiving station for melted waters pouring down from tremendous glaciers in the Nicholas Range beyond. Another branch rises about forty miles from the imposing peak known as Tagharma, 25,800 feet high, with ice-encrusted Muztagh Ata looming in the distance. The southern slopes of the Pamir Mountains swell the headwaters of the Indus.

At first the Oxus goes foaming through cavernous gorges whose cliffs sometimes overhang. At lower altitudes the slopes are clothed with forests, the valleys fertile and well cultivated. Here pomegranate, mulberry, and pistachio trees mingle with wild maple, ash, and juniper. Licorice root is cultivated for export.

For 680 miles the Oxus forms the boundary between Afghan-istan and the Russian dominions. Where it turns northward across the plains of western Asia its elevation is scarcely five hundred feet. Snowy mountains and sheltered valleys now give place to deserts in that extensive drying-up process which em-braces so much of Turkestan. Temperature fluctuations are also disastrous. In summer the fiery blasts from the Kyzyl Kum sands are almost unbearable; in winter entire caravans have frozen to death in terrific blizzards called shamshirs that come raging down from Siberia.

Throughout the final 550 miles of its course the gradient of the Oxus is only a few inches per mile. Rolling sand dunes en-croach upon the channel, recalling Matthew Arnold's lines in *Sohrab and Rustum:*

> To hem his watery march and dam his streams
> And split his currents, that for many a league
> The shorn and parcelled Oxus strains along
> Through beds of sand and matted rushy isles.

Eventually the river empties through an extensive delta into the southern sector of the Aral Sea. Older maps showed a gulf extending southward for eighty miles but now silted up into marshes and millet fields. Wild boars and tigers infest the reedy thickets which obscure the channel.

One of the unsolved mysteries of the Oxus is its possible for-mer outlet into the Caspian Sea. A ridge of sand dunes known as daryalik seems to mark this course for some distance. Ac-cording to the English traveler Anthony Jenkinson, who jour-neyed from Russia to Turkestan in 1559, he sailed across the Caspian, then up the Oxus, which he described as "greate and very swifte." He also mentions a branch of this river which turned northward to empty into a lake in China. Geography in those times was mainly hearsay and speculation, and older maps often confused the Aral and the Caspian.

Geologists still argue about the capricious wanderings of the Oxus in the Middle Ages, and Russian scientists have even advocated diverting it to the Caspian in an attempt to arrest the alarming subsidence of that extensive sea.

Across the lowlands the Oxus is an imposing river swollen in floodtime to a width of two or three miles, a depth of sixty feet. Then its current, which may exceed three miles an hour, erodes the banks and sometimes devours entire farms. On both sides stretches the desert, but irrigation ditches are filled by water wheels known as chigirs, motored by blindfolded donkeys circling endlessly. Along this narrow ribbon of verdure wheat, barley, and other crops flourish.

The river is well stocked with fish, and rude nets and seines are numerous. The most valuable catch is the huge sturgeon of the Aral.

Although the upper stream presents a few passable fords, crude rafts of inflated skins provide the usual means of crossing. Curious ferries are employed on the lower river, flat-bottomed boats propelled by two swimming horses, their bellybands attached to and partially supported by outriggers. There are legends of former bridges long dismantled, and the Russians have spanned the Oxus for their railroad through Turkestan.

The river valley provides one of the three great routes from the outer world to Central Asia. Strabo wrote of it, "The Oxus which divides Bactriana from Sogdiana is said to be of such easy navigation that the wares of India are brought up it into the sea of Hyrcania [the Caspian]." At that time the Oxus may have had an exit to the Caspian, but the Aral is more probable. This route led across the passes of the Hindu Kush into India. The Oxus also opened a doorway toward Mesopotamia and the Euphrates across the narrow lowlands along the southern shore of the Caspian. Of the other two great trade routes, one led westward, north of the Caspian, to Russia; the other eastward across the Gobi to China.

Queer craft navigate the Oxus. Broad of beam, the single mast is an untrimmed tree trunk, sometimes two, one spliced above the other. The Russians have also introduced side-wheel steamers of shallow draught that maintain a regular schedule.

The ancient Persian Empire embraced both banks of the Oxus, as did that of Alexander the Great. The maps of Eratosthenes and Ptolemy delineate the river's course with fair accuracy but show it emptying into the Caspian. The Arabian geographer Abu Biruensis, however, about the year 1030, had it flowing into the Aral Sea.

Many cities once flourished in the region that stretches from the Oxus to the Jaxartes. They no longer enjoy their former opulence and some are only memories. Great religions, with their attendant cultures, have also risen and declined. Zoroaster, founder of the current Persian belief, a sublime faith later corrupted by Magian black art, is said to have held forth at Balkh across the Afghan border. This former metropolis of the East, known as the Mother of Cities, is now marked by miles of ruins. Marco Polo visited Balach, as he wrote it (spelling was never Marco's forte), and described it as having "sustained much injury from the Tartars. It contained many palaces constructed of marble and spacious squares still visible though in a ruinous state. It was in this city, according to the report of the inhabitants, that Alexander took to wife the daughter of Darius." The ruins of Termez, another important city of antiquity, may be observed some distance down the river on the opposite shore.

Buddhism followed Zoroastrianism as the altars of the Magi, with their never-dying fires, were replaced by giant statues of Ghautama with his features of unruffled calm. The Chinese traveler Hsuen Tsang, who passed that way about A.D. 630, observed many statues and Buddhist monasteries in Balkh and Termez.

Christianity also invaded the region about the fourth century and Episcopal sees were established at Merv and Samarkand. But all other religions were borne away in the tide of Mohammedanism which swept in a single century from India to Morocco on the faraway Atlantic. And it was in Turkestan that Saracenic architecture flourished more luxuriantly than anywhere else, except perhaps in Spain.

A peculiar glamour centers about Samarkand, that city of exotic memories situated upon the Zerafshan, once a tributary of the Oxus, now swallowed up in isolated lakes and marshes. A favorite seat of Mohammedan sultans, it was stormed by Genghis Khan, whose Chinese chronicler, Ye Liu Chutsai, thus describes it: "Around the city to an extent of several miles are everywhere orchards, groves, flower gardens, aqueducts, running springs, square basins and round pools," adding rather wistfully, "Indeed, Samarkand is a delicious place."

Tamerlane made this city of mosques and palaces his capital and is buried there under a splendid dome of now mutilated tiling.

Bokhara, also upon the river Zerafshan, later became the metropolis of the region and a renowned center of Mohammedan culture. It is still an important trade center.

In its course across the desert the Oxus, like the Nile, not only acquires no tributary but suffers much loss of volume from evaporation and irrigation. Like the Nile also, its basin is relatively narrow, comprising only about 115,000 square miles. Its volume of waters is variable but is reported as "three times that of the Colorado."

Under the Soviets, irrigation has been fostered and commerce expanded. Steamers now cross the shallow and tempestuous Aral from the southern port, Kant Usyak, to the northern, Aralskoe More.

What mineral wealth may lie concealed in the Oxus basin is still conjectural, although natives wash gold from the sands of the upper streams and Strabo wrote, long ago, "It is said that in digging near the river a spring of oil was discovered," suggestive of petroleum fields.

But the river pursues its course past the ruins of once great cities, through crumbling faiths and cultures, much as it did in the days of Zoroaster. Though called the Amu Daria, it is still the Oxus of the Orient.

PART FIVE

The Great Rivers of Africa

~~~~~~

ALTHOUGH Africa, next to Asia, is the largest of the continents, it has few great rivers. Of its more than eleven million square miles, nearly three and a half million form interior drainage basins from which no drop of water ever reaches the ocean.

The coast line is singularly free from great indentations. Mountains appear rather in isolated masses than in chains like the Rockies or the Andes. The Atlas Range in the northwest peers over the horizon with peaks exceeding thirteen thousand feet in height; the Drakensberg, at the other extremity of the continent, shows elevations of more than eleven thousand. The loftiest peaks, however, are in the east-central section, the Ruwenzori, or Mountains of the Moon, the Kenya mass, and isolated volcanoes culminating in snowy Kilimanjaro, over nineteen thousand feet high.

No peaks equal those of North or South America, and they fall far short of the icy giants of Central Asia. In fact, Africa might be called the Continent of Uniformity and Moderate Extremes.

In only one respect does Africa excel—its Sahara is the greatest of deserts. Evidently it was once more limited, for many human habitations and, in fact, entire cities have been engulfed. Moreover, its barren sands and rocky valleys are marked by ancient stream beds. It is a region of high barometric pressure whose winds radiate outward, bearing dust and heat, like the sirocco of

Sicily and southern Italy. Nor is this waste which covers more than three million square miles the only desert. The southwestern coast is quite as arrid, while vast regions below the equator, notably the Kalahari, suggest the sterile steppes of Turkestan.

Although the mean height of the continent is less than that of Asia, much of Africa is a plateau elevated two thousand feet or more. Across this plateau sweeps the equatorial rain belt with the second largest tropical forest in the world. The eastern terrain is gashed by the great African Rift, some thousands of miles in length. Huge lakes that yield in size only to those of North America cluster about this fracture of the earth crust, while mountain peaks, snowcapped even under the equator, comb moisture from the clouds and treasure it in snow fields.

Yet African rivers, if few in number, are of unusual interest. Three of them turn toward the Sahara. Two, the Congo and the Niger, recoil from that parching waste, but the Nile presses steadfastly onward, its volume sapped by merciless evaporation. From its source beyond the huge inland sea of Victoria Nyanza it sweeps over a greater arc of the earth's circumference than any other river, while its marshy exit into the Mediterranean has given a name to all other river deltas.

The Congo, bending in a gigantic arc across the central rain belt, is the second in size among the rivers of the world. A broad highway through savage Africa, it offers unlimited possibilities in forest and mineral wealth and undeveloped water power. The Niger, rising near the Atlantic, penetrates the Sahara in a loop of twenty-six hundred miles before forcing an outlet through the second largest of river deltas, a maze of jungle islets covering fourteen thousand square miles. The Zambezi, streaming eastward to drain huge Lake Nyasa and empty into the Indian Ocean, first tumbles into that abysmal chasm known as Victoria Falls. In the far south the Orange River, tapping the rain belt of the Drakensberg, winds across the empty veldt, its tributaries opening routes to the world's greatest gold and diamond fields.

The rivers of Africa! No wonder they have lured adventurers through all ages and still present a fascinating study in global geography.

THE GREAT RIVERS OF AFRICA

THE CONGO—HEART OF THE DARK CONTINENT

Length—2,900 miles. Drainage area—1,425,000 square miles

In 1482, just ten years before Columbus's voyage to the New World, the Portuguese explorer, Diogo Cão, sailing down the African coast, observed a current of reddish-brown water swirling about his caravel. Lowering a draw bucket, he found the water fresh and turned aside to investigate a seven-mile gap in the red sandstone cliffs. As this proved to be the mouth of a vast river, upon its southern shore, now known as Shark Point, he set up one of the padroes, or stone pillars, brought with him to mark important discoveries.

This pillar gave the river its first name, Rio de Padrao, later changed to Zaire, a native word that yielded in turn to the sonorous Congo, more suggestive of the power and magnitude of the second largest river in the world.

Across the forested rain belt of equatorial Africa it sprawls for nearly three thousand miles like an inverted question mark. Its course may be traced upon the map through a whole series of barbaric names. From the tableland six thousand feet high which separates Nyasa from Tanganyika, its remotest affluent, the Chambezi winds southward to lose itself in the swamps of Bangweulu. Thence it emerges as the Luapula, spills over Mambirina Falls, whose thunders reverberate for miles through the jungle, and empties into Lake Mweru. From this lake it issues as the Luvua, flowing northward, and unites with the Kamolondo to form the Lualaba, or Upper Congo. Just beyond the equator it goes foaming down seven cascades known as Stanley Falls, where in a distance of sixteen miles it descends some two hundred feet. From this point it sweeps westward in a vast arc across the continental plateau for 980 miles, where the declivity is only 478 feet or less than six inches per mile. Here the mighty river broadens out in places to a width of eight or nine miles to embrace four thousand islands, the largest, Nsumba, fifty miles long by five wide. For some distance it cuts a gorge between sandstone precipices hundreds of feet high. Stanley Pool marks the limit of mid-river navigation. This curious swelling of the main channel, twenty miles long by fourteen wide, is flanked on the north by cliffs of silver sand which suggested to Stanley the chalk cliffs of Dover. A few miles farther on the channel turns westward toward the sea, catapulting down a whole series of cascades and waterfalls. The first eighty-seven miles is marked by no fewer than eighteen, with a descent of five hundred feet, followed by another fifty-six-mile stretch where ten more cataracts register a further drop of three hundred feet. At length, through a rocky gorge scarcely half a mile wide, called Hell's Kitchen, the tortured river, foaming at a speed of ten to eleven knots, enters upon its more leisurely last lap to the sea eighty-five miles away.

Much of the vast drainage basin of 1,425,000 square miles is covered by a tropical forest second only to that of the Amazon, which absorbs an annual rainfall that averages from forty to sixty inches and in some places exceeds a hundred. This is greater than the precipitation over the entire United States. Sir John Murray estimated that it totaled over twelve hundred cubic miles, or more than enough to fill the bed of Lake Michigan, and thought the outflow through the mouth of the Congo was 420 cubic miles, or approximately two million cubic feet a second. In any case, this forms a resistless torrent perceptible thirty miles offshore, while the brown waters may be traced against the gray green of the sea for a hundred miles.

The great river long guarded its unknown source with a grim secretiveness that took vengeful toll upon investigators. True, Diogo Cão fought his way up to the first cataract, where upon a rock in characters still legible he inscribed the words "Here arrived the ships of Dom Joam of Portugal." Returning, he received from that grateful monarch an annuity of ten thousand reals, but died on his second voyage, 1485–86, in an unsuccessful attempt to reach the Cape of Good Hope.

In 1816 the British Admiralty commissioned Captain Tuckey to lead an expedition up the river from the sea. Tuckey managed to advance beyond the first cataract, but succumbed with sixteen of his companions and was buried on Price Island in the lower river.

Efforts to approach from the opposite side of the continent

were equally hazardous. Penetrating inland from the Indian Ocean in 1798, the Portuguese Dr. Lacerda discovered the Chambezi, the headwaters of the Congo, only to fall victim to its deadly fevers. In 1873 Dr. Livingstone followed the same tangled waterways, which he believed to be the sources of the Nile, into the swamps of Bengweulu, only to perish of dysentery. It remained for Henry M. Stanley to complete the first rude survey in his voyage of 1876–77 down what he called a "liquid wilderness," an epic of modern exploration.

Stanley had the boat in which he had sailed those inland seas, Victoria Nyanza and Tanganyika, borne in sections through an all but impenetrable forest. In his journal he jotted down descriptive touches: ". . . the gloom . . . the slopping moisture . . . eternal interlacing branches . . . tall aspiring stems rising from a tangle through which we had to burrow like wild animals on hands and feet." The natives had four names for wooded areas: scattered trees, a denser growth, a matted jungle, and a timbered chaos quite untranslatable, which the Arab bearers termed the "devil's forest." Tippu Tib, their leader, remonstrated, "This country was not made for travel—it was made for . . . monkeys and wild beasts. I will go no further." But the devoted blacks who had accompanied the expedition all the way from Zanzibar remained faithful, and the boat was eventually launched, together with a small fleet of dugout canoes, on a rapid river which Stanley named for his old friend—the Livingstone. At the junction of the Lualaba and the Luama he wrote, "A secret rapture filled my soul as I gazed upon the majestic stream. The great mystery that for all these centuries nature had kept hidden away from the world of science was waiting to be solved—my task was to follow it through to the ocean." This he accomplished, braving innumerable dangers from hostile natives and unknown rapids. Although he was invariably just in his dealings and fought only in self-defense, his progress was a series of battles. Native canoes were of impressive size: one was eighty-five feet long, while a still larger craft had forty paddlers on each side. The foaming rapids necessitated frequent portages. In one of these dangerous passages nine of his men were drowned; in another, the Massassa Cascade, his only white companion, Frank Pocock, and two natives perished. Some of his followers, despairing of success in the conquest of so formidable a river, deserted, but the remnant fought doggedly onward to the final cascades, where runners were dispatched to the coast for help. This was presently forthcoming, and the remote headwaters of Drs. Lacerda and Livingstone were at last linked with the vast river of Diogo Cão and Captain Tuckey. Abandoning his beloved boat, Stanley now plodded on foot to the nearest white settlement. There a number of his exhausted followers lay down to die, saying, "We have brought our white master to the Great Sea, and he has seen his white brothers." Stanley, however, did as he had agreed and carried the survivors all the way back to Zanzibar via the Cape of Good Hope. As he embarked upon the ocean he turned for "a farewell glance at the mighty river on whose brown bosom we had endured so greatly."

An enumeration of the tributaries of the Congo would present only a jumble of unintelligible names. Some of these rivers are inky black from decayed vegetation, others brick red from dissolved sandstone. Two at least deserve mention: the Ubangi, curving downward from the north to join the main channel there eight miles wide, and the Kasai, swinging upward from the south, bearing watery tribute from numerous affluents that penetrate the tropical grasslands beyond the forests.

According to E. H. L. Schwartz, the present plan of the Congo "is the most puzzling of all rivers." Until recent geological times it seems to have pursued its course northward to water the southern sector of the now barren Sahara. Here tributary streams found little choice between veering toward Lake Chad or uniting with the Congo. The present outlet below Stanley Pool, with its roaring rapids, is a recent break-through to the coast. The channel extends in a submerged canyon four thousand feet deep for a hundred miles out to sea until the continental shelf dips downward to the oceanic abyss. Several side streams have advanced like blind alleys toward the sea, as though feeling for weak spots in the coastal cliffs, seeking to provide additional exits for the pent-up floods of the interior plateau. The tides are an unimportant factor, as the maximum rise at the river's mouth is only six feet.

Several of the world's great lakes are woven into the river pattern. In addition to Bangweulu and Mweru, gigantic Tanganyika, one of the three or four most capacious of the world's fresh-water reservoirs, slops over intermittently into the Congo through the sluggish Lukunga River. Farther down its course the Congo empties some of its floodwaters into Lake Ntomba, twenty-three miles long by twelve broad, to receive them back again in time of lesser rainfall. There are two flood seasons, one in May, the other in November, but river levels are subject to no such fluctuations as in the Amazon or the Orinoco.

The flora of the Congo is amazingly prolific. Stanley called it the "tropic river of fancy," with its densely wooded banks, its graceful palms and brilliant flowers. Mahogany, ebony, and other hardwoods abound. The sap of certain trees drips into the river to coagulate in lumps useful in making varnish and exported under the name copal. Several varieties of trees produce rubber. The fiber of the raffia palm is woven into coarse cloth. Palm-nut oil is a valued ingredient in soapmaking and steel manufacture. Plantains two feet long are an important food item.

Along the lower river grow isolated baobabs with their bulbous trunks, their rootlike branches, and fruit resembling swollen boxing gloves. On the bark of one of these trees, some sixty feet in diameter, near the town of Boma, Stanley carved his name. Fringing the broad estuary, mangrove trees rise above the mud, their roots encrusted with oysters. Among innumerable flowers are terrestrial orchids six feet high. H. H. Johnston wrote of these, "Scarcely any flower in this world can equal," their gorgeous blossoms "red and mauve with a gold center."

Several hundred species of fish infest the Congo's thousands of miles of waterways. Most curious are the mudfish that flop about on exposed shallows. Sluggish manatees invade the lower river, together with sharks, sting rays, and other ocean migrants. Land crabs honeycomb the banks with their burrows. Farther inland crocodiles and ponderous hippos abound. Almost all the big-game animals of Africa swarm in the Congo's spacious uplands. Leopards are particularly abundant. In the forested gloom lurk garishly colored mandrils, primitive lemurs, and the most intelligent of the big apes, chimpanzees. Gorillas make their home in certain mountainous regions, while the denser forests shelter that retiring species of the animal kingdom, the striped okapi, sole living relative of the more familiar giraffe. As sunset reddens, tens of thousands of huge bats, called flying foxes, darken the sky in their passage across the river. Stanley mentions water snakes, "leaden colored and seven feet long"; venomous mambas, black and green, are related to the cobras of India. Pythons, hugest of snakes, are not infrequent, their flesh relished by the natives.

Insects thrive prodigiously. Most spectacular are the driver ants, advancing in black columns six inches wide, marshaled by larger brown ants that stand aside as though for inspection. Before their onslaughts all other creatures fly for their lives. Incredible tales are told of their voracity, how within the space of a few hours they will pick clean the bones of a wounded elephant. Wild bees are numerous and their honey eagerly sought. Mosquitoes rise in clouds above lagoons that seem to seethe with life. Huge beetles, six inches long, lumber about, while the gloom is brightened by swarms of iridescent dragonflies and butterflies.

Quite in keeping with the wild life are the native tribes. Among them are several distinct types of pygmies, with their poison arrows. In fact, the vast river presents a veritable mosaic of races of diverse origins, customs, and languages. Although early explorers thought dwellers along the riverbanks numbered not over 125,000, the population of the entire drainage area probably exceeds 30,000,000.

Here, indeed, is the heart of the Dark Continent, pulsing with weird cultures and barbaric superstitions. Much latent talent is evident. Native smiths were adept iron smelters long before the coming of the white man. Basket weaving and pottery display an innate appreciation of beauty. The blacks are intensely musical, and the wild rhythm of their chanting is sustained by throbbing drums. The largest of these instruments, which can be heard for a distance of sixteen miles, carry messages by a primitive Morse code. But art among such backward peoples soon degenerated to the monstrous and grotesque. Naked bodies are gashed in various patterns; bracelets of elephant hairs a sixteenth of an inch in diameter are admired, along with even more curious adornments. Weird rites are practiced in the gloom before repulsive idols.

Witch doctors, whose painted visages, according to one writer, "would frighten a bulldog," perform their incantations and administer native poisons as tests of guilt. Murder by suggestion has become a sinister art. Pulverized leopard's whiskers or the bristles of the brown hog, when mixed with food, prove quite as deadly as a diet of ground glass. In some tribes unfaithful wives are staked out for the driver ants to devour. As these insects enter every bodily orifice and gnaw their way out, few deaths can be so excruciating. Most fearsome is that dreaded society known as the "leopard-men." Its initiates, garbed in leopard skins, their fingers tipped with steel claws, leap upon unsuspecting victims in the night and maul them like enraged leopards. Major Claude Wallace wounded one of these human nightmares who had attacked a porter. Among other foul rites, cannibalism and human sacrifice still linger. Slavery was a curse of the Congo before the dawn of history and is not yet wholly stamped out. Tropic diseases are rife: dysentery, malaria, leprosy, a deadly blackwater fever, and that lingering torment, sleeping sickness.

The aborigines thought Europeans were strange beings that had come up out of the sea. Not tamely has the black submitted to the white, and even now the latter's graves are sometimes violated. Settlements have been sporadic. The Dutch, long ago, settled at the river's mouth on a point of land which they called Banana, because, so the English say, "there were no bananas there." Boma, farther up the river, has been a trade center for a century. Matadi, at the base of the first cataract, marks the entrance to an undeveloped empire. From this point a railway flanks the impassable rapids to Leopoldville on Stanley Pool, where further navigation is unimpeded for a thousand miles to Stanley Falls.

Stanley bore the first steamboat, in sections, to the Upper Congo, an arduous undertaking that consumed two years. Assembled in 1881 as the *En Evant*, she was a paddle-wheeled vessel of shallow draught forty-three feet long. Since that day many larger boats have been introduced into these alien waters, some from the Mississippi where they had outlived their usefulness. Lord Leverhulme, the British soap king, was a pioneer in such traffic.

In 1876, Leopold II of Belgium headed an international association whose purpose was to aid in exploring and civilizing Africa. In 1885 the heart of the Congo basin was incorporated as the Congo Free State, with an area of more than nine hundred thousand square miles. This anomalous state gradually won recognition from the so-called great powers, most of them covetous of African territory. Originally international in scope, the association gradually developed into a purely Belgian enterprise; supposedly humanitarian in its treatment of the natives, it was accused of merciless exploitation. After much international wrangling, the entire region, its boundaries clearly defined by treaties, was formally annexed by Belgium.

The vast area is one of fabulous riches. Forest wealth seems inexhaustible. Cultivation of the soil, though widely practiced, is wasteful and inefficient. The vast hinterland opens out upon one of nature's great treasure vaults of mineral wealth. Diamonds, though more abundant in South Africa, are found here. The Kilo-Moto mines are rich in gold, and the Katanga copper mines, as a side product, produce half the world's cobalt. Half of the global output of radium also comes from the Congo.

The curious geology of the region confines the navigable river mainly to the continental plateau, barred as it is by rapids from access to the sea. But this apparent drawback, from a navigation viewpoint, presents other possibilities of far-reaching import. An era is forecast when this titan among the rivers will be harnessed to electric generators. For in the Congo and its tributaries, according to recent estimates, is concentrated one sixth of the potential water power of the globe.

THE NIGER—"WHERE CANOE AND CAMEL MEET"

Length—2,600 miles. Drainage area—584,000 square miles

Some five degrees north of the equator the Atlantic coast line of Africa turns abruptly eastward for fifteen hundred miles to form that great continental indentation called the Gulf of Guinea. This 1,500 mile stretch is broken up into sections known as the

Grain Coast and the Ivory Coast, all reminiscent of those days when trade and exploration went hand in hand into perilous regions. But the area is also of interest because of Africa's third largest river, the Niger, one of the most remarkable of all rivers.

It rises near the western extremity of this coast line at a point scarcely a hundred and fifty miles from the sea. But its waters flow nearly in the opposite direction to make an enormous loop into the Sahara before they eventually reach the gulf, much farther eastward, after an adventurous journey of twenty-six hundred miles.

Unlike the vaster Congo, unsuspected until its discovery by the Portuguese Diogo Cão in 1482, the Niger was vaguely known to antiquity. Herodotus hints at such a river; Pliny wrote about the African Nigris; while Ptolemy thought that a certain Niger flowed somewhere through the hinterland of the Dark Continent. The Mediterranean world gained its scanty knowledge through the trade route from Morocco across the Sahara to Timbuktu, that city of legend where "canoe and camel" meet. The Arabian geographer Idrisi thought that both the Niger and the Nile had their sources in the fabulous Mountains of the Moon. Ibn Batutu, whose wanderings rivaled those of that other medieval globe trotter, Marco Polo, visited the Niger near Timbuktu and called it the "Nile of the Negro." An audacious Frenchman, D'Isalguier, spent eight years, from 1405 to 1413, on the shores of the Niger some four hundred miles below Timbuktu, but his records seem to have been lost, like those of other forgotten adventurers. Prince Henry the Navigator ordered his captains to search for the mouths of the Niger, masked by dense growths of mangrove trees. But the first European who traced the great river through much of its obscure course was Mungo Park. Commissioned by the English African Society, he landed at Gambia not far below Cape Verde, which shelters the present great seaport of Dakar, and penetrated inland. On July 20, 1796, he beheld the upper Niger there flowing eastward, "glittering in the morning sun as broad as the Thames at Westminster." He thought it a branch of the Congo, but to test that theory he returned on a second expedition and sailed down the Niger for nearly two thousand miles, only to be murdered by the natives at

Bussa. Nor were river hazards less formidable when approached from the sea. There the Niger Delta forms the Bight of Benin, whose evil repute found expression in the mariners' doggerel:

> Beware and take care of the Bight of Benin
> Where few come out though many go in.

In 1828 Moffat and Smith paddled up the river to Benin, which they called the City of Blood. On its outskirts they observed human skulls bleaching in the sun and vultures gorged on newly beheaded corpses. The king was a slave trader. Incidentally, his savage metropolis was not situated upon the true Niger but one of the side streams that empty into the delta. Smith presently succumbed to dysentery.

At a somewhat later date, 1831, an expedition headed by Richard and John Lander reached Bussa, where Mungo Park met his tragic end. There they found the Niger scarcely a stone's throw in width in the dry season, but after the rains a torrent from one to three miles wide that broadened toward the sea to five or six.

In 1893 Lieutenant Emil Hourst sailed down the river in an aluminum boat. Though drawing only eighteen inches of water, his canoelike craft was ninety-eight feet long by seven and one half broad and carried nine tons. Aluminum, preferred because of its lightness in making portages about the frequent rapids, proved to be too easily dented by the rocks.

The Niger is quite as extraordinary as that legendary river that flowed so long through a blurred landscape of mingled fact and fancy. It rises among the granite hills of Tembi Kundu near the border of the British protectorate of Sierra Leone, not far from the northwestern corner of Liberia, that noble experiment in colonization set apart for the African slaves of the southern states. Gushing from a mossy rock in a ravine at an elevation of 2,764 feet, the waters overflow a small lake in a rapid stream known as the Tembi which is soon joined by other streams. Lofty elevations are all about, Mount Drouple towering 9,750 feet. The river presently known as the Joliba, in its first 260 miles, goes foaming down a series of cascades for a total descent of 1,664 feet. Farther on it becomes navigable for nearly a thousand miles. Veering northwestward, it enters a swampy district with numerous lakes, the largest Faguibini, 70 miles long by 12 broad, with soundings of 160 feet. Here the river sometimes overflows to form a shallow lake as large as Erie. But this watery surplus vanishes as it approaches the Sahara. Just beyond its farthest north lies the city of Timbuktu, connected with the river, eight miles away, through its port Kabara. Here desert caravans connect with river traffic. Flowing eastward from Timbuktu, the river enters the Burrum gorge, where it is sometimes constricted between sandstone cliffs only three hundred feet apart. For fully five hundred miles it skirts the desert, often flanked on both sides by lofty sand dunes. At Ansonga, 430 miles below Timbuktu, the current is broken by huge ledges, and while there are other navigable stretches, the channel to the delta is frequently impeded by rocks.

As it approaches the sea the Niger unites with its most important tributary, the Benue, rather more than a mile wide. This river drains a vast, fertile region stretching for hundreds of miles to the eastward, almost to Lake Chad.

The Niger delta, far more extensive than that of the Nile, embraces some fourteen thousand square miles, equal to the combined area of Massachusetts and Connecticut. It begins 150 miles from the sea with a frontage of 120 miles. Of its numerous mouths, the Nun River is the largest, but the Forcados, two miles wide and eighteen feet deep, is the favored ship channel.

For a long time this lower river, flowing southward, was called the Quorra, nor was there any known connection with the distant Joliba, flowing northward, or that eastward-moving river of Timbuktu and the Burrum gorge. Oddly enough, geologists are inclined to agree with these early divisions and to believe that the Niger is really a combination of two distinct and quite unlike rivers flowing in opposite directions, to be joined later by the present looping mid-section. The French scientists Gautier and Chudeau have sketched the former geography as it may be traced in dried-up river beds and vacant lake basins of the Sahara. The Joliba, or upper Niger, at one time continued much farther north into what is now the desert to empty into a vast salt lake, the Juf, since disappeared. The Quorra, on the other hand, rose in the now desolate Ahaggar Mountains, in the remote Sahara over against Algiers, and flowed southward, eventually reaching its present outlet. But the sweeping desiccation that has blighted most of northern Africa, expanding southward, dried up the lower reaches of the Joliba and the headwaters of the Quorra until both ancient streams were united in the mid-section which the desert now overlaps. This section, the result of recent river capture, has, according to Chudeau, "no past, it scarcely has a present." By such a curious juncture of distinct and widely unlike rivers has the Niger come into being.

Meanwhile momentous changes in climate and terrain foreshadow an ominous conclusion. Tributaries from the once well-watered northland are now bone-dry wadies parching in the sun. From the west the Senegal is encroaching upon the headwaters of the Niger, while at the opposite extremity of the river basin, as though in retaliation, the Benue is penetrating ever eastward to rob fast-dying Lake Chad of its sustaining moisture. Few areas present so clearly the ceaseless warfare of a great river with a menacing climate, an unfavorable terrain, and the merciless competition of other streams. For half a thousand miles the Niger is the sole barrier against the continued encroachments of the Sahara. Let its headwaters dry up, as have so many other rivers farther to the north, and heat-parched wastes may sweep southward to the very seacoast.

The Niger is approximately twenty-six hundred miles long, its drainage basin 584,000 square miles. Through this extensive area the flora, fauna, and the native populations vary widely. Few rivers present sharper contrasts than that between the swift Joliba, losing itself in a maze of lakes and marshes, and the desert stream beyond Timbuktu. The upper valleys abound in those tiny mollusk shells called marginella, the cowries of native currency. The Sultan of Segu gave Mungo Park five thousand of these shells, which the explorer thought might have the purchasing power of a pound sterling.

Timbuktu, though no longer the great metropolis of the Middle Ages, and shorn of its romantic setting, remains a trade center of considerable importance. Prominent among its items of commerce are dried fish, grain, rice, and that much-prized luxury of the back country, salt. Desert vegetation is sparse indeed, if we except the date palms that fringe distant and widely scattered oases. From a native grass the French residents brew a tea called citronelle. Animal life is more abundant, for the river is well stocked with fish, an important food item. Insect pests are constant irritants, especially a kind of gadfly whose needlelike sting penetrates thick clothing.

The desert loop has long been within the sphere of Arab influence, although the nomadic Tuaregs remain a disturbing factor. Armed with spears and oxhide shields, they appear unannounced from the desert on their fleet camels and vanish as suddenly. The French colonial empire, sweeping southward from the Mediterranean, has overrun much of the Sahara and advanced in places to the Gulf of Guinea. Along the Niger discontented French officials in lonely stations battle heat, insects, and the unpredictable vagaries of the natives, while dreaming of a happier life in the homeland.

In its lower course the Niger traverses the British possession of Nigeria with an area larger than Texas. Native tribes and nations to the number of fifteen million people inhabit the drainage basin with its great tributary, the Benue. In color they range from tawny yellow to jet black; in religion, from a bestial Voodooism to Mohammedanism, with a sprinkling of Christianity.

The dense forests abound in ebony, mahogany, satinwood, the oil-bearing palm, and many other tropic varieties. Hippos and crocodiles infest the rivers, while most of Africa's big-game animals are found in the uplands. In the delta region sugar cane, cotton, and the indigo plant seem indigenous, while corn, yams, and plantains are staple foods. Rice flourishes in the submerged swamplands. Mangrove trees encroach upon the mud flats, while beyond lies a dense and tangled jungle.

Navigation, as on the Congo, is confined chiefly to the great mid-section and the area near the sea. Here steamers ply to and fro amid native dugout canoes often formed of two logs expertly joined.

From the neighboring port of Lagos the British have constructed a railway into the interior which crosses the Niger on a steel bridge at Jebba. Henry M. Stanley once predicted that

Africa would belong to the first nation that built a railroad through it, an opinion elaborated by that farsighted empire builder, Cecil Rhodes, in his lifetime dream—a Cape-to-Cairo Railway.

The rivers of Africa, however, will long remain the chief arteries of traffic between the inland and the sea. The explorer Henry Barth, while chained and expecting sudden death, wrote of them as "moving paths" to the heart of the Dark Continent and thought "the best way of winning the blacks from their barbarism is to create centers on the great rivers." If that opinion is correct, both France and England, though guilty of native exploitation, have performed a service to humanity in their pioneering enterprises along the remote waterways of the Niger.

THE STORIED NILE

Length—4,053 miles. Drainage area—1,293,000 square miles

Romance has invested the Nile with a fabulous antiquity. Its fertile valley nourished that civilization which carved the Sphinx and reared the Pyramids. Herodotus wrote, "It possesses more wonders than any other country and exhibits works greater than can be described," a sterling endorsement from a member of that superior Grecian race which looked down upon other cultures as barbarian. All this we owe to the river, for Strabo, quoting older authorities, spoke truly when he said, "Egypt is the gift of the Nile."

The historic background, however, is but an incident in a far lengthier drama. Dr. K. S. Sandford tells us that the lower Nile Valley was once a gulf of the Pliocene Mediterranean, a fact that Herodotus glimpsed when he observed, "Beyond the city of Memphis seems to me to have been formerly a bay of the sea." The triangular outlet was the original of all river deltas, so called because it resembled the Greek letter of that name. This delta, Herodotus decided, had been built up by the river, remarking, "A day's sail from land if you cast the lead you bring up mud . . . this shows an alluvial deposit," and he gravely speculated how, were the Nile to turn aside into the "Arabian Gulf," it might fill up that body of water in "twenty thousand years."

Though one of the first rivers known to man, the Nile remained a geographic puzzle until modern times. Its source was set in some fabulous region in the heart of Africa, where it was fed from snowcapped peaks that Aristotle called the Silver Mountains, and later geographers, the Mountains of the Moon. But all this was pure conjecture, for Herodotus complains, "With respect to the sources of the Nile no man of all the Egpytians, Libyans, or Grecians with whom I have conversed ever pretended to know anything." True, he listened to tall stories from a certain temple registrar who "seemed to be trifling with me," then, proceeding upstream to the first cataract "made my own observations as far as Elephantine and beyond that obtained information by hearsay."

Eratosthenes, the learned librarian of Alexandria, hinted at equatorial lakes as a probable river source. Strabo, like Herodotus, investigated for himself as far as the first cataract. The Emperor Nero sent an expedition much farther upstream, but it was halted by impassable swamps. Diogenes, a Greek merchant of the Indian Ocean, told a weird tale of a twenty-five-day journey inland to two great lakes which were "the source of the Nile." Arab adventurers of the Middle Ages mentioned these lakes and Ptolemy actually drew them on his map of the world. Leonardo da Vinci, who wrote about almost everything, said of the Nile, "It is known that it issues from the Mountains of the Moon by several unexplained sources." Even the priests of ancient Egypt apparently knew that the Blue Nile rose in the mountains of Abyssinia and had traced the course of the main or White Nile far into the steaming jungle. But it remained for modern research to solve the riddle which had mystified the world for centuries.

John Speke, an officer of the East India Company, was the first European to sight Victoria Nyanza, the principal source of the White Nile—the year, 1858. Albert Nyanza, the other great lake of the Nilotic system, was discovered by Sir Samuel Baker in 1864, while it was not until 1889 that Henry M. Stanley, following the Semliki branch of the Nile beyond Lake Edward, saw, looming above the jungle, the snow-crowned sky line of the Ruwenzori, the legendary Mountains of the Moon.

Like the great Siberian rivers, the Nile flows from south to north, but unlike them, its waters are drawn from the tropic rain belt. Its main current is incorporated in fresh-water seas unrivaled elsewhere save in North America. Its tributaries are comparatively few: the Semliki, skirting the gloomy forests of the Congo and the still-smoldering Mfumbiro volcanoes; the Blue Nile, cascading downward from azure Lake Tana in the Abyssinian highlands; and the still lengthier but less voluminous Atbara. From the junction of the latter stream the great river receives no single tributary for 1,610 miles as it crosses the vast Sahara to the Mediterranean.

No other river courses through so varied a terrain. This comprises snowy mountains, dark forests, huge lakes, reed-choked swamps, savage jungles, and the world's most extensive desert. At times its current turns back upon itself as though uncertain which way to proceed; at times it races across cataracts or down foaming waterfalls; in some regions it is smothered by vegetation, in others withered by the sun. Once regarded as the longest river in the world, it may still deserve that title. Its remotest headwaters are the Kagera River, which rises in Belgian territory not far from Lake Tanganyika. This river, 430 miles long, pours ten thousand cubic feet a second into Victoria Nyanza. From the mouth of the incoming Kagera across the lake to its outlet, the Victoria Nile, the distance is approximately 150 miles. From lake to sea along the river channel is another 3,473 miles. These *disjuncta membra* of a single river system total 4,053 miles. American geographers, fond of stretching the Mississippi-Missouri, give its length as forty-two hundred miles or more. But the engineers of the Mississippi River Commission report this figure as "approximately 3,986 miles." The length of the Amazon, the only other competitor, is variously given from thirty-nine to forty-two hundred miles. The upper figure is probably to be preferred, although exact statistics of that tremendous river must await more accurate surveys. If the Nile is not the longest of rivers, it is the most elongated. From its remotest headwaters to the delta mouth in a straight line is twenty-six hundred miles. Were the Mississippi thus extended, it would drain Great Slave Lake in upper Canada.

Most interesting of Nilotic features are the lakes which form an integral part of its system. The largest is Victoria, crossed by the equator, with an area of 26,200 square miles. Next in order is Albert Nyanza, 1,640 square miles, surrounded by the still-steaming vents of the great African Rift. Lesser lakes are Edward and George, Kioga, a semi-morass, and Tana in its setting of barbaric mountains. In a former geological period the Nile may have drained gigantic Tanganyika, as it almost certainly did Lake Kivu. But these lakes now turn westward to the Congo. The upper current of the Nile, though swallowed up in Victoria, is clearly discernible in the lesser lakes of the system. To be sure, it fumbles through Kioga, mantled with blue water lilies, but it sets strongly northward across Albert Nyanza, while the current of the Blue Nile is plainly perceptible across Lake Tana. All these lakes are but bulges or enlargements of main river channels.

Although the Nile follows no such troubled course as the Zambezi or the Congo, it encounters some noteworthy obstructions. The first cataract in Upper Egypt usually marked the limits of the Pharaoh's dominions. There the island of Elephantine guarded the threshold of Elephant Land, or Ethiopia, and the country of the blacks. Other cataracts lying beyond made navigation even more difficult. In 1625 Father Lobo, a Portuguese priest, followed the Abbai or true headwaters of the Blue Nile to its source in mountain springs. These, he wrote, are "two holes each about two feet in diameter a short distance from each other. One is about five feet and a half in depth—the other has no bottom." This river, the Astapos of Ptolemy, he traced across Lake Tana, flowing "with so violent a rapidity that the waters of the Nile may be distinguished through all the passage." Some fifteen miles from its outlet the Blue Nile plunged over a steep cliff in "one of the most beautiful waterfalls in the world."

The White Nile also has its waterfalls. Shortly after this river emerges from Victoria Nyanza through a cleft five hundred feet wide in a rocky escarpment two hundred feet high, it spills over Ripon Falls. Although the descent is only sixteen and one half feet, Speke, who first observed it, wrote, "It was a sight that attracted me for hours . . . the roar of the waters . . . the thousands of passenger fish leaping at the falls . . ."

Some twenty miles before reaching Albert Nyanza the river plunges through a cleft only eighteen feet wide for a sheer drop of 120 feet. Sir Samuel Baker, its discoverer, named it Murchison Falls and found the fury of the river thus funneled into space awe-inspiring.

Between Ripon and Murchison Falls, however, the great river broadens out into Lake Kioga, whose amoeboid outlines shift continuously. Here the current meanders aimlessly through dense growths of vegetation, forming floating islands upon which the natives erect thatched huts. Still more unusual is the Sudd region north of Albert Nyanza, but before the river unites with its principal tributary, the Blue Nile.

Here lie the swamps which halted Nero's expedition, although their most prolific growth seems of more recent origin. In 1862 Sir Samuel Baker found a clear channel at least one hundred yards broad which was choked up ten years later. Mrs. Patrick Ness describes the region as "that great stretch of unending swamp one third the size of the British Isles . . . where the precious water is lost by evaporation or soaked up by rank vegetation and through which the Nile winds a tortuous passage which becomes at times completely blocked. . . .

"Downstream will come floating islands, those strange breakaways from the sudd . . . papyrus, elephant grass, and Nile cabbage . . . and pithy branches of the ambatch, that shrub with a yellow blossom which interchanges on the bank with masses of purple convolvuli."

Here boats were wont to tear out a channel by dragging Nyam-Nyam anchors, so named from their resemblance to the filed teeth of a neighboring tribe of cannibals. But the British have introduced more scientific methods. Edward S. Crispin relates how "the first difficulty is to discover the true channel in what seems a meadow," for the bridging sudd is so firm in places that it will bear up an elephant. Probing with poles usually reveals this channel, which is fifteen to twenty feet deep compared with depths of two or three feet elsewhere. Next in order is burning off the papyrus, that graceful reed that gave the world its first paper. Men armed with huge saws then cut out chunks which a steamer tows away and allows to drift downstream where they disintegrate. The chief components of this tough vegetation are papyrus, creepers, sword grass that cuts like razors, elephant grass, a kind of bamboo twenty feet high, and the ambatch, a prolific soft-wooded tree that roots in the decaying vegetation. Numberless blue water lilies and the sacred lotus of Egypt impart a seductive beauty which is enhanced at night by myriads of fireflies. Mosquitoes are particularly bloodthirsty, while amid the abundance of bird life is the grotesque whale-headed stork which looks as though its beak were carved from a wooden shoe.

The sudd soaks up water from the river like a titan's strip of green blotting paper. More than eight hundred billion cubic feet of water are lost annually by plant transpiration, according to the Egyptian Ministry of Public Works. For 475 miles this loss of water more than offsets the gains from all tributary streams. No other river is subjected to so great a drain upon its volume from such a cause.

Escaping at length from its living green fetters, the great river continues its northerly course until, 1,652 miles from Victoria Nyanza, it is joined by the Blue Nile tumbling down from the Abyssinian Plateau. Though only 850 miles long, this tributary in flood has four times the volume of the White Nile, whose output, fed by giant lakes, is generally uniform. In fact, the swollen torrents of the Blue Nile cause those periodic inundations of the lower valley which so puzzled Herodotus and the priests of Osiris. Some distance nearer the sea the Nile receives its last tributary, the Atbara, longer but less voluminous than the Blue Nile, draining the outskirts of the Abyssinian highland and broken by innumerable rapids.

Across the Sahara the Nile has eroded a deep but narrow valley confined between cliffs that resemble the Palisades of the Hudson, cliffs that mark the tightly drawn lips of deserts stretching away on either hand. Here the current suffers still further diminution from evaporation under an almost cloudless sky and from numerous irrigation ditches.

Seven great branches once marked the delta mouth, but all but two have dwindled to mere canals. These two, the Rosetta and Damietta outlets, are both twenty-three feet deep, but the latter seems slowly silting up. Near the former outlet the famous Rosetta Stone, a basaltic stele, was discovered in 1799, whose inscription in three languages gave Champollion the key to undeciphered hieroglyphics.

Nile River boats were depicted on the walls of tombs six thousand years ago. Herodotus describes some methods of navigation of his day. The "Etesian" winds which blew steadily from the north enabled sailing craft to advance upstream and drift back upon the current. Other boats known as baris were towed upstream just as Chinese coolies now drag junks up the gorges of the Yangtze Kiang; downstream a hurdle of tamarisk reinforced with wattlework was suspended at the bow, while a stone dragging from the stern kept the craft in the channel. Various types have been evolved: markabs, or freight boats; feluccas, and the graceful dahabiyehs, with winglike sails, which seem to drift out of a remote past by the still-towering Pyramids.

Dugout canoes, along with crocodiles and hippos, infest the midstream of the Nile, while larger craft with lateen sails navigate Victoria Nyanza. The white man's steamers also sail across that vast expanse of waters, or approach from the sea, for the Nile is navigable for twenty-nine hundred miles.

How long this sheltered valley has been inhabited no one knows. In the British Museum, curled up in a shallow grave, reposes a member of that aboriginal race before the Egyptians came. Beside him lie the stone implements designed to aid him in the spirit world. His hair is curly, and red! Conjecture dates him somewhere between seven thousand and ten thousand years ago. Later arrivals, coming no one knows whence, developed that racial stock known as Hamitic, in distinction from those other great branches of the white race, the Semitic and the Aryan. The Hamites were a slender people, tall, industrious, developing a written language expressed in such pictographs as the Chinese still employ, and building vast tombs and temples and monuments which continue to astonish the modern world quite as much as they did Herodotus twenty-three centuries ago. Tales of their wars against the Hittites, the Assyrians, and the Babylonians fill many pages of the Old Testament, for at their peak their conquests extended nearly, if not quite, to the shores of the Black Sea. In general, however, they were content to remain in that fertile valley watered by Father Nilus, which still remains one of the garden spots of the world.

Grown prosperous and peace-loving, they were overrun by Asiatic conquerors. Cambyses added Egypt to the Persian Empire, while Alexander the Great followed in his gory footsteps. The country was appropriated by one of his generals, Ptolemy, who founded a Greek dynasty. There the great Julius Caesar dawdled for some months of his crowded life, beguiled by the charms of Cleopatra, while for her smiles Mark Antony threw away the Empire of the World, as various authors from Shakespeare to George Bernard Shaw remind us. Alexandria was the second city of the Roman Empire, and the first in learning, with its renowned library of seven hundred thousand volumes. As the cult of Isis yielded to Christianity, the city became one of the four centers of the Early Church, together with Rome, Constantinople, and Antioch in Syria. When Egypt was engulfed in the Saracen invasion, Christianity, along with earlier cults, was swept away in the flood tide of Islamism. The enlightened Arab conquest, however, was followed by some centuries of Turkish misrule. More recent British oversight of Egyptian affairs has been challenged by a seething unrest and a nationalistic urge for freedom.

Many cities have marked the course of the Nile. Memphis, the ancient capital of Egypt, is now the site of a wretched village, a colossal granite statue of Rameses the Great, with broken feet, and an alabaster sphinx rescued from Nilotic mud. But Nineveh has fared even worse.

Thebes, another proud capital, yielded long ago to Alexandria, which remains one of the great ports of the Mediterranean. Cairo, however, which has grown up almost within the shadow of the Great Pyramid, is now the capital and the most populous city in all Africa.

Far up the river, at the junction of the Blue Nile, stands Khartoum, chief city of the Anglo-Egyptian Sudan, the city of Chinese Gordon, who there fell victim to fanatical natives, those

Fuzzy-Wuzzies whose fighting prowess, immortalized by Kipling, won the respect of British Tommies.

In the highlands of Abyssinia, Coptic Christianity found a refuge under the leadership of semi-savage monarchs who assumed such titles as "the Lion of Judah" and "the King of Kings." It was Mussolini's short-lived conquest of this country which upset the precarious balance of the late League of Nations.

The White Nile penetrates far into the African hinterland with its jumble of discordant tribes ranging from ferocious cannibals to the superior barbarism of Uganda, while the more remote headwaters lie in British territory, Kenya and Tanganyika, with their healthful climate and largely undeveloped resources.

The Nile not only watered ancient Egypt but fertilized the soil with silt. Here the native fellahin still conduct farming operations as they did in the days of Rameses the Great. Water is dipped up by shadoofs—crude well-sweep affairs, such as are pictured upon ancient tombs. Sakiehs, or water wheels, turn endlessly, their motive power donkeys or oxen, or often men endowed with the tireless patience of the East. The average farm comprises about three and one half acres. Cereals, particularly rice, are staple crops, as are long-fiber cotton and sugar cane. Tobacco, a plant from the New World, thrives here amazingly. Most of Egypt's 350,000 square miles is desert; scarcely 12,000 is cultivated. In this thin ribbon of fertility along the river dwell sixteen million people.

The engineering skill which built the Pyramids attempted some control over the Nile. The locks and sluiceways which admitted surplus waters into Lake Moeris and drained them off during the dry season roused the admiration of Herodotus. Many irrigation canals were dug down the centuries, but the agricultural regeneration of Egypt really began with the construction by Great Britain of the Aswan Dam near the site of the first cataract. Against this enormous structure, 2,000 yards long and 172 feet high, the river backs up for more than a hundred miles, impounding 2,250,000,000 cubic meters of water. A hundred and eighty sluiceways permit the outlet of floodwaters, while canals equipped with locks allow the passage of shipping. At the time this was the world's most ambitious flood-control project. By conserving water it fostered intensive farming, with three or four crops annually. Several other dams or barrages now span the Lower River.

Egyptian engineers recorded the height of the Nile at its annual maximum. Shakespeare refers to this custom in *Antony and Cleopatra* where he says:

> . . . they take the flow o' the Nile
> By certain scales i' the pyramid.

These scales, or Nilometers, however, were not in the Pyramids but located at strategic points along the river's course. The most famous was at the island of Elephantine near the Aswan Dam. This was a flight of stone steps upon which the height of the waters was marked for future reference. Thanks to the Emperor Nero, who has encountered little save criticism at the hands of historians, this venerable marker was repaired and provides a summary of flood levels extending back nearly forty-five hundred years, an unequaled record of river action.

During that time the Nile has deepened its channel through the Semna Rapids by twenty-four feet, or some two millimeters, annually. Based upon the same calculations, the lower river bed silts up at the rate of four and one half inches a century. Within recent years the maximum rise at Aswan has been somewhat over thirty-two feet, at Cairo twenty-three.

The Nile has added one color to our recognized list—Nile green. The "Blue" Nile owes much to sapphire Lake Tana and cloudless skies, for its current in flood is reddened with the ash from extinct volcanoes. Speke found Victoria Nyanza covered with a white sheen which perhaps accounts for the "White" Nile.

In spite of its few tributaries, the Nile's great length gives it a drainage area of 1,293,000 square miles. The volume, which suffers much loss from cultivated fields and the desert air, is less at Cairo, twelve miles from the delta, than at Berber, thirteen hundred miles farther upstream. Still, its average outflow has been estimated at 420,000 cubic feet a second.

Impressive in sheer length and other dimensions, and even more noteworthy by reason of its varied terrain and fabulous history, the Nile is the most interesting of all the world's great rivers.

THE ORANGE RIVER—BOERS, GOLD, AND DIAMONDS

Length—1,300 miles. Drainage area—400,000 square miles

Adventurous tales of animal-like Bushmen and Hottentots, of savage Kaffirs and grim Dutch *Voortrekkers* still linger about the Orange River. For thirteen hundred miles it winds across South Africa in a westerly direction from the jagged Drakensberg, through rolling veldt and rocky spitzkops and coastal desert, to empty into the Atlantic some four hundred miles north of the Cape of Good Hope. With the Vaal and other tributaries it drains four hundred thousand square miles, an area greater than that of the Indus or the Yukon.

Its source is the Senku, a rapid stream issuing at an elevation of ten thousand feet from the flanks of Mont au Sources, the loftiest of Drakensberg peaks. Another headwater stream springs from those gloomy heights known as the Giant's Castle, only a hundred and thirty miles from the Indian Ocean, while still another, the Maletsunyane, plunges over a sheer escarpment for an unbroken fall of 630 feet.

After its descent from such uplands the Orange River flows across the African plateau at an average elevation of forty-three hundred feet. From the south come many tributaries; from the north still larger ones: the Caledon, 230 miles long, and the Vaal, 750 miles, which also rises in the Drakensberg, 170 miles inland from Delagoa Bay, that old-time rendezvous of Portuguese caravels en route from India.

Through arid Bechuanaland the Orange erodes a narrow bed between steep banks until it dashes madly down the reefs and ledges in the Aughrabies, or channel of the "hundred falls," where in a space of sixteen miles it descends four hundred feet.

Beyond its juncture with the Hartbeest and Molopo in the vicinity of these falls the Orange receives no other tributaries, although the skeletons of dried-up streams mark the dreary waste on either hand. In this sun-parched emptiness the river loses much volume by evaporation, so that when it breaks through the coastal mountains in a wide detour its diminished current empties into the ocean through a single mouth less than a mile wide and much obstructed by sand bars. Here the channel, scoured by forty-foot floods, silts up again in time of drought.

Small boats venture up the river from the sea for thirty miles or more, and there are other navigable stretches, but the river has little value as an artery of commerce. Nor is irrigation widely practiced, although the Dutch of Orange Free State have made some use of surplus waters. Several dams have been constructed across the Vaal River, where many shoals and fords are known as drifts.

The Orange and its tributaries mark important boundaries. The lower river separates Cape Colony from Orange Free State, while the more extensive Transvaal, as its name implies, lies beyond the Vaal River. These once independent republics were settled by discontented Dutch poineers who chafed under the restrictions of British rule and sought more freedom in the vast interior. The great trek occurred in 1838, when thousands of Boer farmers in their "homestead" wagons, accompanied by their flocks and herds, emigrated across the Orange and Vaal rivers and even penetrated the passes of the Drakensberg into what is now Natal. Such wide-open spaces offered ample room for conflicting ideologies, until the discovery of gold in the Transvaal attracted a swarm of foreign adventurers, when a clash between the stubborn conservatism of the Transvaal President, "Oom" Paul Kruger, and the dreams of Cecil Rhodes to expand the red of the British map over all South Africa became inevitable.

The resistance of Boer farmers against the full might of the British Empire was as heroic as it was unwise. For three years the war dragged on. The deadly Boer sharpshooters, who, so Kipling's Tommy complained, "knocked us silly at a mile," and their familiarity with the rugged terrain, made conquest a formidable task. Only by concentration camps and sternly repressive measures were the last of the Dutch raiders finally subdued.

In spite of British efforts at conciliation, not a few descendants of the Voortrekkers maintain a surly aloofness. Refusing to accept the English language, they have substituted a synthetic Afrikander, have designed a flag of their own, and many stood aside while the Empire was fighting for its life during the recent World War.

The aborigines of the Orange River region were the Bushmen. Short in stature, with bridgeless noses, yellow rather than black in color, their women grossly misshapen, they were among the most primitive of humans. Without settled homes, they subsisted upon roots, grubs, and worms when larger game failed their vicious little bows and arrows. Yet they etched figures of men and animals with artistic skill upon hard diorite, perhaps using uncut diamonds as tools. They were bullied by the larger Hottentots, also yellow rather than black, but of more settled habits, while these in turn were crowded into the coastal regions by invading Bantu tribes from the north, who were black, athletic, armed with oxhide shields and razor-sharp assegais that spitted an adversary like a pat of butter at 150 feet. A branch of these so-called Kaffirs, the warlike Zulus, gained a fearsome reputation by their superior discipline. Their terrible regiments raided far and wide, burning and destroying, until their victims numbered tens of thousands. But the power of their ferocious king, Dingaan, was curbed by Dutch marksmen at the Battle of Blood River near the Drakensberg, more than a hundred years ago. Boer riflemen, barricaded behind wagons whose wheels were covered with tautly stretched oxhides, while women and children loaded their guns, mowed down three thousand savage warriors, until the Zulu learned that the white man possessed arms superior to his deadly assegai.

The Orange and Vaal rivers enclose one of the world's great storehouses of mineral wealth. There are rich seams of coal, deposits of iron and copper, and traces of petroleum. But the glitter of gold and diamonds has thrown more prosaic mining operations into the shade.

The Kaffirs picked up shining pebbles from the gravel beds of the Vaal River, as did later Dutch settlers. But the skill of Amsterdam craftsmen was required to release from its rough exterior the sparkle of the diamond. Fabulous deposits have been discovered, the most famous at Kimberley, midway between the Orange and Vaal rivers. Here a volcanic vent of blue clay has yielded millions of pounds worth of these carbon crystals. Cecil Rhodes here laid the foundation of that fortune which enabled him to dream of empire so largely and successfully, and here other penniless prospectors became millionaires.

Still richer were the gold-bearing reefs of the Transvaal. The Wit, a branch of the Vaal, furnished water to develop the Witswaterrand with shafts more than a mile below the surface. The steaming temperature is made endurable only by cool water pumped down to those subterranean depths. Around this master lode, the city of Johannesburg has become the metropolis of South Africa, with a population exceeding the half million mark. No other city has stranger surroundings: artificial hills of crushed quartz excavated from the depths. Timber shipped halfway around the world from Puget Sound shores up the passageways where human termites burrow in darkness and stifling heat. The gold mines of Johannesburg brought President Hoover a fortune as a mining engineer.

Someday, no doubt, the glint of diamonds and the sheen of gold will yield to more prosaic farming and stock raising. The upper valleys of the Orange are healthful for white men, a sparsely settled region which fairly beckons to the famished millions of Europe. And England, which faces crisis after crisis at home while her Far Eastern empire is crumbling, may find in South Africa brighter prospects for the future.

THE ZAMBEZI AND THE "SMOKE THAT THUNDERS"

Length—2,200 miles. Drainage area—513,000 square miles

Fourth in size among African rivers is the Zambezi. There is a barbaric lilt to that name which echoes the throb of native drums. Across the southern part of the Dark Continent it loops in a series of undulations suggesting a flattened letter S. Sometimes its course is north and sometimes south, though it trends ever eastward toward that arm of the Indian Ocean called the Mozambique Channel over against the big island of Madagascar.

As its drainage area of 513,000 square miles lies mostly within the region of good rainfall, it ranks in volume among the leading rivers in the world. It is also one of the most unusual.

Its source has been traced to a boggy marsh some five thousand feet above the sea, not far from the border of Northern Rhodesia.

It is not certain, however, that the Lu-ena, issuing from Portuguese Angola, is not the longer of the headwater streams.

In its twisting course of twenty-two hundred miles, the great river traverses a terrain of singularly varied features. Its upper valleys lie in rugged territory heavily forested, yielding to broad savannahs and more open bush shaded with borassus palms. In a distance of 220 miles to Kakenga the river level falls to an elevation of 3,600 feet. Its five-hundred-mile journey across the great African Plateau is marked by a further decline of six hundred feet. Some of its numerous tributaries, reaching northward, encroach upon the territory of the mighty Congo. "At the time of heavy rains," so Cornet asserts, "the vast swamps serve as a common source to brooks flowing both to the Congo and the Zambezi." This assumption, if correct, presents one of the strangest watersheds in the world.

In its leisurely course the Zambezi suddenly disappears into an appalling chasm in places four hundred feet deep and only sixty to eighty feet in width, which zigzags in a series of sharp angles as though cleft by the thunderbolt of Jove. Livingstone, the first white man to peer into this crevice, thought it of volcanic origin, but geologists now believe it was once a great dike of softer rock that has been eaten away by water erosion.

After the first dizzy descent, the river darts first one way and then another, in a veritable frenzy to escape from the abysmal maze in which it finds itself imprisoned, a struggle almost as impressive as the falls themselves. These, named Victoria for the then reigning monarch of the British Empire, are among the three most spectacular waterfalls in the world. In floodtime their volume exceeds that of Niagara, the very earth trembles, and the roar of the maddened waters reverberates for miles. No wonder the natives warned Livingstone that the gorge was infested with demons and frightful monsters, or that they called the place Mosi-oa-Tunga, "sounding Smoke," more vividly rendered as the "Smoke That Thunders." The narrow cleft, however, is so filled with boiling spray that the eye can penetrate but a little way, while the rising column of mist, so passing airplanes have noted, rises upward for five thousand feet!

By a strange coincidence, one of the four islands along the

jagged escarpment, like that at Niagara, is called Goat Island. Arrived upon this island by canoe, Livingstone, grasping the shrubbery for support, gazed far down the cleft with feelings that may well be imagined. Cecil Rhodes diverted his most ambitious project, the Cape-to-Cairo Railway, so that it crosses the Zambezi within a half mile of the falls, remarking that to avoid this scenic wonder would be a crime.

World travelers still debate its merits with that of Niagara and Iguassú in South America. The latter presents a vast panorama of falls nearly two miles across. Niagara and Victoria are units. Victoria is the broader—5,700 feet to 5,300—and much the higher—360 to 400 feet, as against Niagara's 158 to 167. Perhaps the pith of the comparison was best stated by an Africander I once met at Niagara, gazing fixedly at its magnificent curtain of falling waters. Having resided all his life within a few miles of Victoria, he had come to America mainly to compare the two waterfalls. His verdict of Niagara was, "You can see it better." If Victoria could be envisioned in full flood, it would probably rank as the world's major waterfall. Unfortunately it is too hidden by intervening precipices and obscured by foam to be appreciated.

The extraordinary canyon below the falls is called Batoka. At first it is a series of bizarre angles as the river, in its meteoric plunge, gnaws ever deeper into the solid rock. Some miles below the falls the river, again constricted between precipices 460 feet high and scarcely 60 feet apart, goes hurtling over a sheer drop of twenty feet. Elsewhere it is a foaming torrent fretted by successive cascades. Twenty miles below the falls it issues forth into the sun from between black walls 650 feet high. Soon it is joined by tributaries, including the Kwando. A hundred miles away it cuts a path through precipitous hills towering seven hundred to eight hundred feet in another canyon called the Devil's Gorge. This is followed by a series of interruptions terminating in the Modele Rapids, twenty-six miles distant. In less than a hundred and fifty miles since leaving Victoria the river has made a further descent of eight hundred feet.

For seven hundred miles the channel is now open to navigation, broken only by rapids at extreme low water. The final obstruction is Kebrabasa Rapids, where the river descends from the African Plateau to proceed for some four hundred miles across the broad and relatively level coastal belt. Here it broadens to a width of three to five miles between shores generally low, reedy, and infested with crocodiles and hippos. Only through the Lupata Gorge is the channel once more constricted to a width of two hundred yards.

About a hundred miles from its mouth the Zambezi receives its most interesting tributary, the Shire, bearing from the north the surplus waters of cavernous Lake Nyasa and several lesser bodies of fresh water.

The Zambezi empties into the sea through a broad delta. The four widest mouths, however, are so impeded by sand bars that navigation is directed through the lesser but deeper Chinde passage. In flood the river also overflows into Quilimane outlet, sixty miles upstream, which for a time becomes an extreme outpost of the normal delta.

Although interrupted by some of the most dangerous cataracts and imposing waterfalls in the world, the Zambezi presents long stretches of channel navigable for steamers of shallow draught. With its leading tributaries, it offers more than four thousand miles of commercial waterways. A canal flanking the Kebrabasa Rapid would permit ocean traffic to proceed almost to the foot of Victoria Falls. Steamers have long sailed up the Shire River, where Nyasa opens wide a gateway to an inland empire of enormous potential resources.

David Livingstone was the first Englishman to ascend the Shire and gaze out upon the vast surface of Nyasa. But the region had been known for a long time to Arab traders and perhaps earlier Phoenician adventurers. The gold mines of the Zambezi seem to have been worked two thousand years ago. Some writers have fixed here the legendary Ophir of King Solomon. Arab geographers knew it as the shadowy empire of Monomotapa, and maps of the period show rough tracings of Lake Nyasa. Gold-bearing rocks still outcrop along the Zambezi, together with rich seams of coal and doubtless much other mineral wealth. But their development awaits a saner, happier day than the disturbed and uncertain present.

PART SIX

The Rivers of Australia

~~~~~~

AUSTRALIA has been called the Lonely Continent. It has been isolated so long from other great land masses that its plant and animal life, like its rivers, are characteristic and peculiar.

Among queer native creatures are the kangaroo, the lovable koala or animated teddy bear, and that quaint anachronism, the duck-billed platypus; while the flora is equally unusual. Beauty appears in the flame tree and the giant lily of Queensland; a sinister note in the gastrolobium or poison bush of the arid interior. Starving camels, feeding upon its leaves, perish—or, if they survive, remain useless for weeks or months. Their jaws are bound up to prevent foraging when traversing such evil wastes. In contrast is that useful tree the eucalyptus, which has been transplanted to furnish grateful shade for sun-parched regions in South America, South Africa, and elsewhere. A botanical curiosity, it sheds its bark but not its leaves. The wood of certain species has a greater tensile strength than white oak, a durability that rivals teak, and in building operations is sometimes preferred to iron girders. Another Australian emigrant is the wattle tree, now grown in South Africa. I once accompanied a shipment of wattle bark from Beira to India, where it is used for tanning leather.

Geologically, Australia is one of the oldest of the continents. Great areas in the western and central portions are Archean

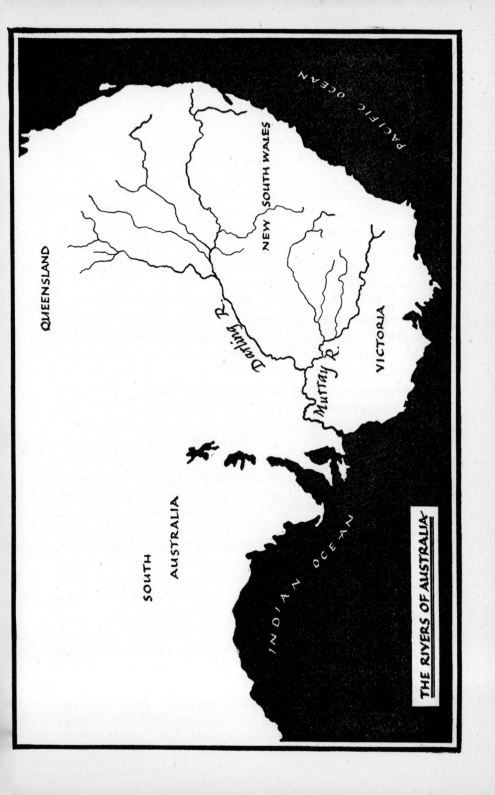

THE RIVERS OF AUSTRALIA

rock, among the most ancient of visible formations. The coastal fringe, except along the south, is relatively well watered, particularly in the north where a tropic climate prevails. Here numerous streams are found, though none of large size. The southern shore, along the great Australian Bight, presents a desert area for hundreds of miles unbroken by any waterway.

Central Australia is a semi-arid waste degenerating into desert. Half a million square miles is a steppe region of rock outcroppings and sparse vegetation, a great interior basin where scanty rainfalls never reach the sea. Some four hundred thousand square miles are alluvial plains formed by river action, a singular feature in a landscape where rivers are few in number, of capricious volume and indefinite outlet. Here the precipitation either evaporates or is absorbed by the porous ground and rock strata. Moisture-laden winds seldom penetrate this forlorn region which a blistering sun makes still more inhospitable.

Since rivers are fed only by surplus waters, we can expect to find few or none where no surplus accumulates. Hence Australia, with nearly three million square miles of area, has but one great river—the Murray-Darling.

THE MURRAY–DARLING—A STRUGGLE WITH ENVIRONMENT

Length—2,345 miles. Drainage area—414,000 square miles

The Murray-Darling is the one great river of Australia. Geographers give it a length of 2,345 miles, a drainage area of 414,000 square miles. Both figures are impressive—and misleading. For this imposing system is but a skeletal framework—a river battling courageously against a meager rainfall, a hostile climate, and a singularly unfavorable terrain.

Over its basin the annual precipitation averages only seventeen inches; in half the affected area it falls to ten inches or under. Few springs swell the river volume, and there are no such melting glaciers as sustain the Nile and the Jaxartes through similar arid regions. Summer heats cause a merciless evaporation, while a porous soil sucks up much of the depleted moisture. Even tributaries turn *away from* rather than *toward* the main channel, where the coarser silt, building up the marginal areas, effectually bars them out except in time of flood. Hence scarcely 10 per cent of the rainfall of the upper Darling ever reaches the sea, while former affluents, though making a brave showing upon the map, degenerate into starveling streams that wander off to sink into the sands or lose themselves in dismal playas, or salt pans; mere wadies often dry as those of the Sahara. The average outlet of the Murray at its mouth has been figured at thirteen thousand cubic feet a second, a mere trickle in contrast with the mighty Amazon, which pours more water into the sea in a single day than the Australian river does in a year!

The Murray has its source in the southeastern corner of the continent among precipitous rocks three thousand feet high. They are in that range of low mountains called rather hopefully the Australian Alps, in the province of Victoria. The river forms part of the boundary of New South Wales to the north and flows in a westerly direction for sixteen hundred miles to empty into Encounter Bay, an indentation of the Great Australian Bight. First, however, it mingles with shallow Alexandrina, a lake some thirty miles long by twelve broad, with an area of 220 square miles and a depth ranging from seven to twelve feet. A curious extension is the spurlike lagoon called the Coorong, which parallels the sea for nearly a hundred miles, separated only by scrubby sand dunes.

The Murray's average width in summer is about 240 feet, its depth sixteen, but in time of drought many sand bars formerly obstructed the channel until the waters became too brackish for cattle to drink. Early explorers found no true mouth to the river, for Alexandrina, frequently invaded by the salt water, merely slopped over into the sea across sand bars crested with breakers.

Some 587 miles above this outlet the Murray is joined by the Darling, which outranks the parent stream both in length and drainage area, just as the Big Muddy does the upper Mississippi. The Darling is pre-eminently the river of New South Wales, but its branches penetrate far up into Queensland. Its length to its junction with the Murray is usually given as 1,758 miles. Several once important tributaries now fail to reach it but bury themselves shamefacedly in the sands. Part of the terrain which it traverses is semi-desert, with a white population of less than one inhabitant per square mile.

Few rivers are so capricious. In 1879 it overflowed its banks to form a shallow lake sixty miles wide; again, for a period of eighteen months it ceased to flow at all, breaking up into a chain of isolated pools and sand bars.

Yet it has usually been navigable at some time during the year, for steamers of shallow draught, all the way from the sea to the town of Bourke in New South Wales, and sometimes to Walgett much farther upstream.

The final five hundred miles of the combined Murray-Darling not only receive no tributary stream but lose much volume to evaporation. In the drought of 1914 men actually stepped across the channel.

The river was called by the aborigines Millewa, which means, according to Major Mitchell, "stars magnified in clear water." These savages, in spite of their chocolate skins, are thought to be a primitive branch of the white race and were once treated like destructive animals. Now better understood, they are permitted to follow their own tribal customs in that curious environment which has been their homeland for thousands of years. Abnormally keen of sight, they have mastered the secrets of the desert as few white men could hope to do. They know the infrequent water holes and those areas where shallow digging will produce some water, and can trail a lizard across naked rocks where the more civilized observer can detect no sign. Since food and water are a perennial problem, they have become accustomed, like the camel or the wolf, to fast or gorge as occasion dictates. Spears they have, and that most eccentric of weapons, the boomerang, which seems to defy the very laws of gravity. This device they share with certain aboriginal tribes of southern India, which suggests a common origin.

Early explorers of the Murray-Darling braved such perils that they deserve the name conferred upon them—"heroes of the lonely way." The river was first sighted by Hume and Howell, November 16, 1824. In 1829 Captain Charles Sturt sailed down the channel in a whaleboat as far as Lake Alexandrina, named the river for Sir George Murray, the colonial secretary, but was obliged to return without locating its outlet. Two years later Captain Barker, in making a similar attempt, was murdered by the natives.

In spite of its limitations, the Murray-Darling has been termed the Mississippi of Australia. With its principal tributaries, it affords some thirty-three hundred miles of available waterways. A hundred paddle-wheel steamers once chugged up and down the main channel, and old rivermen still lounge in the sun spinning yarns beside hulls now rotting at their piers. An expansive program has been installed to control the water. From its juncture with the Darling to the sea the Murray is now spanned by ten great dams and weirs against which the river backs up in considerable lakes. Farther upstream are other dams. A typical example is the Hume Reservoir, where earthworks 4,238 feet long, supplemented with a masonry dam 1,042 feet in length, impound 1,250,000 acre-feet of water in an artificial lake covering 511 square miles. Such improvements linked with extensive irrigation projects would, it is estimated, enable the river valley to support an additional million persons.

Near the old exit from Lake Alexandrina several dams, the Goolwa, the Tauwitchere, and others, now stretch across marshy islands and intervening channels for nearly five miles, provided with 433 floodgates to permit surplus river waters to escape while barring ingress from the sea.

Too great optimism, however, is scarcely justified, for the Murray-Darling, draining ten times the area of the Tennessee River, has but half the latter's rainfall and one sixteenth of its outflow. Nevertheless, present improvements augur well for the future, for Australia's meager water supply would frequently suffice if efficiently conserved and distributed.

PART SEVEN

European Rivers

~~~~~~

EUROPE, as geographers recognize, is not properly speaking a continent, but rather a western projection of Asia in that great triangular land mass known as Eurasia. Its seacoast, invaded by bays and gulfs, is so irregular that it exceeds that of Africa, roughly three times its size, while the resultant peninsulas offer inadequate room for large river valleys.

Mountains appear in marginal ranges, such as the Urals and the Caucasus, which afford partial separation from Asia; or in isolated masses like the Carpathians, the Apennines, the Pyrenees, and above all the Alps, celebrated for their scenery. Desert areas are confined largely to tundra wastes beyond the Arctic Circle and those depressed regions which reveal the ancient floor of the subsiding Caspian. Extensive coniferous forests, a continuation of the Siberian taiga, overspread much of the northern sector.

As Europe lies wholly in the Temperate Zone there are no tropic rain belts to supply rivers of the first rank. Regions of heavy downpour are few and confined to mountainous or coastal areas. Throughout much of the eastern territory the annual precipitation falls below thirty inches.

This area is embraced in that great interior drainage basin which, beginning at the farther extremity of the Gobi, stretches across Asia for thousands of miles. Flowing southward across this region to the Caspian is Europe's major river, the Volga, the largest river in the world with no outlet to the ocean.

The only other European river whose size warrants recogni-

EUROPEAN RIVERS

tion is the Danube, rising in forested mountains and traversing scenery of rare charm and beauty. Several rivers, however, hover upon the threshold of greatness, such as the Dnieper, the Don, and the Dvina. Most European rivers are prominent because of considerations other than magnitude. Such is the Rhine of tragic memories, the Elbe, the Oder, the Vistula, the Rhone, the Seine, the Loire, the Tagus, and others. Smaller streams are quite as well known—the Thames for its commercial importance, the Tiber for its historic associations.

In short, European rivers, with few exceptions, are features of history or industry rather than of geography.

THE "BEAUTIFUL BLUE DANUBE"—AN INTERNATIONAL PROBLEM

Length—1,760 miles. Drainage area—347,000 square miles

The Danube was known to the Greeks as the Ister. Herodotus called it "the greatest of rivers," which was a decided exaggeration, and said that it "bisected Europe," which was a shrewd approximation of fact. Most European rivers flow northward, like the Rhine and the Vistula, or southerly, like the Volga and the Rhone, or toward the west, like the Seine and the Tagus. But the Danube, rising in the mountainous highlands of western Europe at an elevation of some twenty-two hundred feet, flows eastward to the sea. Hence geographers have said that it has the Occident at its source, the Orient at its mouth; while in the discordant nationalities that have settled along its banks mingle the languages and customs and cultures of East and West.

Along the broad highway of its valley have ebbed and flowed the conquering tides of Europe and of Asia. From the west swept the armies of Trajan, of Charlemagne, and of Napoleon; from the east the hordes of Attila and his Huns, the raiders of Genghis Khan, and the Janissaries of Solyman the Magnificent, most illustrious of Turkish sultans. Every foot of that valley, from the mountains to the sea, is historic ground.

For nearly eighteen hundred miles the Danube winds through

highland, plain, and delta. Although immortalized in music as the "Beautiful Blue Danube," its color scheme is rather black and red, for it rises in the Black Forest to empty into the Black Sea, while too often its current has been red with human blood and the flare of burning villages.

Like normal rivers, the Danube may be divided into three sections. Above the town of Bratislava it is a typical mountain stream flanked by rugged heights. Many of these are crowned by ruined castles, once the strongholds of robber barons who levied tribute upon all passers-by.

The mid-course of the river extends from Bratislava to the celebrated Iron Gates, a few miles below Orsova in Rumania. Here, for a two-mile stretch, the current swirls through a narrowing passageway between bluff highlands. The final course winds through more level lowlands to the delta, a thousand square miles, formed where the river divides into three major channels and several lesser ones amid a maze of water, swamp, and islands.

Next to the Volga the Danube is the largest river of Europe. Its drainage area of nearly 350,000 square miles embraces eight different countries. Therein lies both its strength and weakness, for its importance as an artery of commerce has long been jeopardized by national rivalries.

Herodotus tells us how Darius, King of Persia, urged on by the curiosity of the explorer and the ambition of the conqueror, led his armies into the unknown regions beyond the Danube. Entering the Black Sea, his "fleet . . . stood directly for the Ister, and having sailed up the river a two days' voyage they joined the neck of the river with a bridge at the point where the several mouths of the Ister are separated."

The great king, tying sixty knots in a cord, ordered his Grecian admirals to untie one knot daily, and if the army had not appeared by the sixtieth day to return to their respective homes. His military expedition, however, accomplished little against the elusive Scythians, who had few settled dwellings and offered scanty plunder.

Alexander the Great, whose career was strangely linked with rivers, crossed the Ister in 335 B.C. to investigate the possibilities beyond, but turned to the south and east instead. Near the outlet of the Nile he founded the great city which still commemorates his name, led his invincible phalanxes beyond the Indus, and, returning, filled with grandiose schemes of conquest, met an untimely death upon the banks of the Euphrates.

Trajan, who extended Roman conquests to their farthest limits, led his legions through the Kazan Pass where the Danube breaks through the Carpathian Mountains near the Iron Gates. Upon the face of a cliff is carved an inscription dating from A.D. 103 which commemorates the event. The Emperor constructed an imperial highway along the river. From the Iron Gates to the sea it continued to be known as the Ister, but above that point the Romans called it the Danuvius, from which the present Danube is derived. Trajan, more successful than Darius or Alexander, annexed an extensive region on the farther shore which became the Roman province of Dacia. The memory of that conquest survives in Rumania, whose inhabitants are proud of their somewhat doubtful Roman origin.

Although the Romans controlled most of the Danube Valley for half a thousand years, they abandoned such distant outposts as Britain, the Euphrates Valley, and Dacia when their empire began to crumble and hastened its decline when they permitted the Goths, fleeing from the terrible Huns, to cross the river into their eastern provinces. Ruin was assured when other Germanic invasions swept across the Rhine.

Attila led his Mongolian hordes up the Danube Valley and for a time menaced all western Europe. Although in desperation the combined Roman and Germanic armies halted his advance in the great Battle of Chalôns in modern France, his warriors settled the rich plain of Hungary which occupies some thirty thousand square miles.

In the intervening centuries white blood has almost obliterated yellow, but the Magyars remain an oriental eddy in a vortex of Aryan peoples. Also of alien race are the Gypsies, whose origin has been traced to India. Numerous along the middle and lower Danube, their colorful costumes and nomadic ways are in harmony with their tribal songs and dances.

Europe turned upon Asia, however, in 1096, when a flotilla of two thousand river craft bore forty thousand crusaders down the Danube to war upon the Saracen and redeem the Holy Sepulcher. A subsequent romantic episode saw Richard the Lion-Hearted returning from Palestine to England imprisoned in the dungeons of Durnstein by his archenemy, Duke Leopold VI of Austria.

In 1241 the Mongols, under Batu the Splendid, grandson of Genghis Khan, and the renowned Orchon Subotai the Infallible, almost annihilated the armies of Bela IV of Hungary, a hundred thousand strong, on the fatal field of Mohi near the Danube. According to Harold Lamb, "The Mongols surged steadily into the disorganized array of their foes, the terrible standard with its nine yak tails surrounded by the smoke of fires carried in pans by Shamans 'a great grey face with a long beard' one of the Europeans described it, 'giving out noisesome smoke' . . . like the Teutonic knights at Leibnitz the Templars died to a man upon the field." Bela, fleeing for his life, sought sanctuary in a distant monastery, while his huge army melted away, leaving forty thousand corpses upon the field. The fate of Europe trembled in the balance when the irresistible Mongols swept onward to the shores of the Adriatic, for no western arms could cope with their mobile cavalry and deadly arrows. But, true children of the boundless steppes and wayward as the breezes, they were recalled from their conquests by some court upheaval in the heart of Asia, and to the vast relief of Christendom they never returned.

In these appalling raids the Mongols burned both crops and dwellings, so that, according to the chronicle of the times, the remnant of "the starving people in their frenzy killed each other, and it happened that the men would bring to market human flesh for sale."

Another tide of conquest surged up the valley of the Danube when Constantinople, the last bulwark of Christian Europe against the Turk, fell in 1453. The Turkish sultan boasted that he would stable his horse in St. Peters at Rome, and for a time that ominous boast seemed destined to be realized. Twice Turkish armies, advancing far up the Danube, besieged Vienna, and for a long time they controlled the lower valley. In fact, only the past century witnessed the complete emergence of the Balkan States from Turkish dominance.

Yet another phase in the fateful history of the Danube began when at Sarajevo, on the tributary Bosna, the assassination of the Archduke of Austria exploded the international powder magazine which wracked the social and political framework of the globe.

Many cities have sprung up along the Danube. Most imposing is Vienna, capital of the Holy Roman Empire and later of that discordant group of nationalities called Austria-Hungary. Though it resisted the armies of Solyman the Magnificent, it twice fell to Napoleon, who called the Danube the "king of rivers." Second to Vienna among its cities is Budapest, capital of Hungary. Buda, amid its hills, is connected with Pesth upon the opposite lowlands by six great bridges. Third in order is Belgrade, former capital of Serbia, a storm center for centuries. Repeatedly captured by the Turks, the Serbs, the Austrians, and by Hitler, it has now fallen within the sphere of Russian influence.

Among lesser cities is Ulm in Bavaria, where Napoleon began the most brilliant of his military campaigns which culminated in the great victory at Austerlitz. Near Ratisbon, on cliffs overlooking the Danube, the Germans erected their proud Walhalla, or Hall of Fame.

Herodotus mentioned "bee armies" that made sections of the Danube Valley uninhabitable and produced vast stores of honey. This picturesque legend called attention to early industries. The upper-valley slopes are clothed with forests and vineyards, while the plains of the mid-region are a natural granary and cattle-raising country. The oil wells of Rumania mark one of the world's most important petroleum fields. Fisheries have always flourished. A favorite product is the giant sturgeon of the delta region. Here dwell Russian refugees who fled long ago from religious persecution in the days of Peter the Great. They use nets and sturgeon traps and a cruel device of bare hooks stretched across the bottom. As the great fish noses hungrily in the mud for his food, he becomes painfully entangled. The eggs of the female, sold as caviar, sometimes equal one fifth the body weight. Another unusual industry centers in the Rose Valley of central Bulgaria, where a bit of Omar Khayyám's Persia has been transported from the Orient. Here, in one vast flower garden, rose petals are picked by peasants and the oil extracted. Thirty damask roses produce one drop of the fragrant essence, while no fewer than thirty-two thousand are required for a single ounce.

The importance of the Danube as a commercial highway was recognized by the Romans. They left marks along the cliffs indicating how river craft were dragged upstream by ropes against the current. The shoals and rocks of the Iron Gate effectively barred the advance of Turkish shipping. Between the years 1890–96 many of these obstructions were blasted out and the channel deepened.

In flood the water in the delta sometimes rises thirty feet; in drought shoals may appear. Yet the copious and comparatively steady outflow was noted even in the days of Herodotus.

In severe winters the river freezes. The ice jam of 1838 caused a flood which swept away some four thousand buildings in the city of Pesth and drowned over a thousand persons. The chill wind from the Russian steppes sometimes freezes delta channels in a single night. Sulina Harbor, on the Black Sea, has yielded to Galati, some ninety miles upstream, as the ocean port.

Navigation, however, has always been hampered by artificial restrictions. As far back as 1368 an attempt was made to reconcile conflicting national interests. From 1699 to 1883 no fewer than twenty-eight treaties involved the commercial utilization of the Danube. In 1856 a Danube Commission was established, comprising representatives from all border countries. A survey was made and extensive plans adopted to maintain a 24-foot channel from the sea. Jetties were built, supplemented by dredging operations. The annual silt deposit of 108,000,000 tons a year, borne down by a current whose average discharge is 315,000 cubic feet a second, presents the usual problems of an expanding delta region. Yet the river is navigable for sixteen hundred miles. Steamers may ascend it from the sea all the way to Austria, while barges are towed as far as Ulm in Bavaria. One of the provisos of the recent peace agreement entered into by the United States, Great Britain, and Russia insured the freedom of the river.

But the shadow of the Iron Curtain now falls even upon the cathedral spires of Vienna as once again the East forces back the West in an unending struggle for the valley of the Danube.

THE DNIEPER—A RACIAL STORM CENTER

Length—1,410 miles. Drainage area—202,000 square miles

Of the Scythians who inhabited what is now southern Russia, Herodotus wrote, "Their country has nothing wonderful except the rivers which are very large and very many in number." Largest of all, he thought, was the Borysthenes, the modern Dnieper, which he described as providing "the most excellent and valuable pasture for cattle, and fish of the highest excellence and in great quantities; it is most sweet to drink . . . the sown land near it is of the best quality; and the herbage where the land is not sown is very tall; at its mouth abundance of salt is crystalized spontaneously; and it produces large whales without any spinal bones, which they call Antacaei, fit for salting"; perhaps, allowing for natural exaggeration, these may have been the giant sturgeons which still abound in the rivers that empty into the Black Sea and the Caspian. Herodotus also observed that "as far as the country of Gerrhus, a voyage of forty days, this river is known to flow from the north"; beyond was mere conjecture, but it was thought to penetrate the gloomy region of the Cimmerians who dwelt on the verge of the Polar Sea. Something of the celestial phenomena of high latitudes had been learned by forgotten Greek adventurers, for Strabo, citing Hipparchus as an authority, wrote, "On this river during the whole of summer nights there is one continuous twilight."

The mystery which then obscured the source of the Dnieper was lifted centuries ago. The river rises in the swamps at the foot of the Valdai Hills, not far from where the Volga and the Dvina gush forth to proceed on their respective ways to the Caspian and the Baltic seas. It is the great river of the Ukraine and of White Russia, while a tributary of many branches drains the extensive Pripet Marshes on the border of Poland, with their semi-aquatic landscape centering in the ancient city of Pinsk.

In shape the Dnieper somewhat resembles a distorted letter S with its main axis running north and south. In its course of 1,410 miles it makes a great bend toward the eastward, then turns abruptly southwest to empty into the Black Sea through a considerable estuary.

Professor E. V. Oppokov describes the valley of the Dnieper as a succession of floods and droughts and suggests that the current may be replenished during exceptionally dry years by drawing upon the subterranean water table.

For centuries the valley of the Dnieper has been an international battleground. About the ancient city, which Russians call Holy Kiev, developed the nucleus of Russian power. In those days Moscow, destined later to become the center of the Muscovite Dominions, was scarcely a village.

From a perennial turmoil and confusion, the conflict in the valley of the Dnieper resolved itself into a struggle between Slav and Tartar. In the time of Charlemagne, or about the year 800, much of the region was overrun by the Asiatic Khazars. A hundred years later the Slavs had pressed southward as far as the Great Bend. The year 1000 found Russia embracing most of the Dnieper region within her indefinite boundaries. Two centuries later, however, the balance swung drastically toward Asia, when the Mongol invasion burst across the river and threatened to engulf all Europe. When this torrent of flame and ruin receded, some of the Mongols and their allies, calling themselves the Golden Horde, remained in southern Russia with their favorite stronghold in the Crimea. By the year 1400 the Lithuanians, spreading southward from the Baltic, claimed the Dnieper Valley as far as the Black Sea. Poland, uniting with Lithuania, as the great power of eastern Europe, controlled the region until about the year 1750. The Polish yoke, however, rested heavily upon a half-savage and nomadic people. The seething unrest broke out in sanguinary uprisings of the Zaporogian Cossacks, accompanied by all the butcheries and barbarities portrayed by Henryk Sienkiewicz in the blood-spattered pages of his historic novel, *With Fire and Sword*. The final subjugation of the Crimean Tartars and later the Turks along the coastal regions, together with the partition of Poland, placed the main valley of the Dnieper under the Russian flag. And now that Poland has been restored, in name only, to be absorbed in the expanding circle of Communistic-dominated powers, the Dnieper may be considered once more a purely Russian river.

The fertility which Herodotus noted has made the Ukraine the granary of Russia. Ancient fisheries still thrive, while navigation on the river has notably increased as canals connect its headquarters with the mightier Volga. The government, attempting to industrialize a peasant population, has harnessed the Dnieper with a dam two hundred feet high which generates enormous hydroelectric power. This great structure, although much damaged by Hitler's bombers, has been restored.

In the vast fabric of Red Empire now being woven on the loom of time, the Dnieper is a conspicuous thread.

THE CASTLED RHINE

Length—800 miles. Drainage area—86,000 square miles

Castled heights and vine-clad slopes mellowed in an atmosphere of medieval romance are the popular conception of the Rhine. In size it has no place among the world's great rivers, for neither its length, eight hundred miles, nor its drainage area, eighty-six thousand square miles, is impressive. Yet few rivers have been so economically important or have so profoundly affected world affairs. From its Alpine source to the half-submerged delta whence it debouches into the North Sea, it flows through scenery quite as varied and picturesque as its troubled course through human history.

Every canton in Switzerland, except Geneva, swells the current of the Rhine. Its headwaters are the Hinter Rhine, which drains the melting glaciers of the Rheinwaldhorn at an elevation of 7,271 feet, and the Vorder Rhine, foaming down from Lake Toma, 7,691 feet above the sea, to wind its rapid current, broken by cascades, for some two hundred miles among superb mountains.

Emerging into Germany at an elevation of about eight hundred feet, the Rhine pursues its mid-course through terrain less grand but of more historic significance, a region once bordered by the gloomy Hercynian forests, the haunt of wolves, bears, and the shaggy aurochs now extinct. Its valley is now traced in populous cities and enormous commercial activity, and adorned with such characteristic landmarks as Cologne Cathedral and the venerated halls of Heidelberg University.

In its lower reaches the river broadens into a delta formed of silt deposits not only from the Rhine but also from the Scheldt, the Meuse, and lesser streams, with one outlet pronging northward into the Zuider Zee, its boundaries defined by dikes and canals. This is a queer region of mingled plain and water, whose monotony is relieved by billowing sails, legions of squat windmills, and some of the busiest docks in the world; a region where, as the Dutch affirm, "God made the sea, we made the shore." Here flowed the "two-horned" Rhine of the poet Vergil, clasping the ancient island of Batavia, a delta described by John Lothrop Motley as "by nature a wide morass, in which oozy islands and savage forests were interspersed among lagoons and shallows; a district . . . subject to constant overflow and terrible inundations by the sea."

The Rhine is comparatively young as geologists reckon rivers, and was once far larger than it is today. When the British Isles were united with Europe its exit lay much farther to the northward, between Scotland and Norway, and what is now the Vistula may well have been a tributary.

Some four centuries B.C. the Rhine Valley was inhabited by Celts who were forced westward by the Germans. The river then became a natural boundary between the two races. Julius Caesar, having conquered Gaul (modern France) and made it one of the richest and most powerful of Roman provinces, led his legions on a campaign of reprisals into Germany. First, however, he built a bridge across the Rhine whose construction, described in detail, has given Latin students of more recent times quite as many headaches as it caused the original Roman engineers and workmen.

Augustus Caesar, emulating his uncle, wished to add Germany to the Roman dominions, but his armies were ambushed and slaughtered by the savage warriors of Arminius, and thereafter Rome was quite content to maintain the mid-river as the limit of empire in that part of Europe.

When Roman power slowly disintegrated, the Franks, most energetic of Germanic tribes, overran the Rhine Valley and much of modern France, which was named for them. Their great emperor, Karl the Great, or Charlemagne, expanded his dominions to embrace also northern Spain and Italy and much of Germany. From his capital at Aachen in Germany, not far from where that territory meets Belgium and Holland, he sought to rebuild the Roman empire on a Germanic rather than a Latin foundation. Unfortunately he divided his dominions among his three sons, one inheriting the nucleus of modern France, another a large slice of Germany, while Lothaire, granted a wide territory between, bequeathed his name to Lorraine, that vexed borderland of clashing nationalities. The Rhine, however, remained a strictly German river for eight hundred years.

When Germany was ruined and half depopulated by the Thirty Years' War, France gained a foothold upon the Rhine which she has persistently striven to extend. It was the dream of French monarchs to restore ancient Gaul and make the river what it once had been, the boundary between two peoples. Napoleon, riding roughshod over accepted standards, accomplished this purpose, annexed much German territory together with the "Low Countries," Holland and Belgium, on the cynical pretext that they were merely "the sediment of French Rivers." After Waterloo, however, the Great Powers stripped France of much of this newly won territory. Bismarck, following the French debacle of 1870, took back Alsace and Lorraine, but thereafter the tempo strikes a dizzier pace. Germany lost the provinces in 1918, Hitler regained them in 1939, while World War II was virtually decided when Allied armies crossed the river and penetrated into the heart of a Germany bomb-shattered and demoralized. What a travesty upon human nature that the story of so splendid a river should be written in tears and blood.

Medieval legend invested the Rhine with an aura of poetry and song. The Nibelungenlied told of vast treasures concealed beneath its waters, while the exploits of Siegfried and other heroic characters are glorified in the operas of Wagner. The Lorelei, that golden-haired siren of the Rhine, lured boatmen to their death beneath a towering rock 430 feet high which overlooks the channel where it attains its greatest depth, seventy-five feet. Goethe, most eminent of German poets, was born at Frankfurt on a tributary of the Rhine, while Heine and other poets have portrayed its wild loveliness. *Bingen on the Rhine* has long been a favorite recitation poem.

Beethoven, greatest of composers, was born at Bonn. The German national anthem reminded France that "fast stands and true the watch, the watch on Rhine," while by an odd coincidence the *Marseillaise*, the battle hymn of France, was composed at Strasbourg on the same turbulent river.

Freedom of religious thought flamed at the Diet of Worms, where Martin Luther defied alike the power of Rome and the great Emperor Charles V. Gutenberg, the Father of Western Printing (the Chinese developed the art at an earlier date), was born at Mainz, but the list of distinguished men native to the valley of the Rhine might be prolonged indefinitely.

Strung like jewels upon its current is a chain of great cities, for the river traverses Europe's most densely populated area. Among these cities are Strasbourg, Cologne, and Frankfurt, and those beehives of industry, Düsseldorf and Essen, of evil memory, center of the great Krupp Works where the War God once forged his shining armor. In the low-lying delta region are such great seaports as Rotterdam, Antwerp, once the chief city of Europe, and others. Here the guilds of the Middle Ages wrought and prospered to give the world its expensive fabrics, its rare china, and other masterpieces of fine craftsmanship. There, too, flourished the Dutch and Flemish School of painters: Rubens, Hals, Vermeer, and that sorrowful genius, Rembrandt, who took his very name from the river in its Dutch rendition, "von Rijn."

The Rhine is navigable from the sea for a distance of 550 miles. The Romans, who controlled the river for four centuries, built levees and dikes, as the half-wild Frisians had done before them, and levied tolls to finance such projects. In the Middle Ages various petty princelings imposed so many taxes that commerce was greatly retarded. Nonetheless the Rhine, combined with the Danube, was the great trade route across Europe from the western countries to Byzantium and the Black Sea. In modern times the Dutch have attempted to control the river exits to the sea, but after much bickering access has been granted to the shipping of the world.

The many millions of persons who inhabit the Rhine Valley have created a commerce that few other rivers can equal. Timber rafts five hundred feet long, sometimes carrying as many as four hundred workmen, drift down the channel. Ocean steamers ascend the river to Cologne, while the number of lesser craft runs far up into the thousands. A dozen or more great bridges span the current which once halted alike Roman legions and Germanic tribesmen eager for plunder. The vast coal and iron deposits in the Ruhr Valley and elsewhere developed one of the great industrial centers of the world, and the delta region with its maze of canals formed an open gateway into the heart of Germany. At least all this was the story of yesterday, to be resumed, let us hope, in a happier tomorrow.

Although the natural beauty of the Rhine has been impaired by the smoke of steel mills and its storied heights scarred by quarries, the river retains much of its original charm. True to its troubled traditions, it remains a sore spot upon the map of the world, a pressing problem in the rebuilding of western Europe and the restoration of a civilization wracked and nearly ruined in the most destructive of all wars. The smoke of conflict has cleared, only to reveal charred and blackened cities and desperate peoples, harassed by hunger-maddened mobs. For throughout this region so favored by nature, so beloved by artists, poets, and singers, Christian nations have improved but little over those Germanic tribes who, in the words of the Roman historian Tacitus, were wont to "make a desert and call it peace."

THE VOLGA—RUSSIA'S HEART OF EMPIRE

Length—2,325 miles. Drainage area—592,000 square miles

The Volga is pre-eminently the great river of Russia. It is also the largest river in Europe, outclassing its closest rival, the Danube, in length, in drainage area, and probably in volume also; while in its influence upon the development of a powerful nation it ranks as one of the most important of rivers.

With no outlet to the sea, it empties into the landlocked Caspian. Hence its extensive commerce has been largely nationalistic, mingling little with that of the outer world. For a time in the Middle Ages, before Moscow became all-powerful, traders from distant countries came to the great fairs at Nizhni Novgorod to exchange the merchandise of East and West. But in the main Russia has been largely self-sufficient; an exclusiveness nurtured in the great interior basin of the Volga, which comprises 592,000 square miles.

Mother Volga is a name beloved of humble muzhiks, commemorated alike in the songs of the Volga boatman and plaintive melodies strummed on balalaikas. Around the great river and its far-reaching tributaries clung early Slavic culture as to a sturdy tree, emerging belatedly from Tartar despotism. And now that Russia has expanded to embrace one seventh of the land surface of the globe and overshadow border territories besides, the Volga remains the spinal cord of empire with its nerve center at Moscow on the Moskva.

In the valley of the Volga, Russians have always rallied as at a last line of defense. When Hitler's armies threatened the capital, a transfer was contemplated, but only to another Volga stronghold, Kuibyshev, on the great Samara Bend; while at Stalingrad, farther down the valley, the destroying German armies were themselves destroyed. Napoleon's dream of conquest went up in the smoke of burning Moscow when little of the ancient city save the grim-walled Kremlin survived the flames. But from that Kremlin still issue those edicts which govern the Soviet Empire and exert a subtle but profound influence upon international affairs.

Geologists tell us that much of the Volga Valley was once a gulf of the Caspian, which has shrunken noticeably even within historic time. Hence the river flows for a long distance through a depression below sea level. Its total length is given as 2,325 miles, but here the historic approach has obscured geographical features. Two of its branches, the Oka and the Kama, are probably somewhat longer than the parent stream, which rises in the dreary marshes of the Valdai plateau, 665 feet above sea level. It gushes from a spring beneath a ruined chapel to traverse several small lakes and the dried-up beds of larger ones. As this marshy region is also the source of the Dvina, which empties into the Baltic Sea, a falling raindrop has almost an equal chance of reaching the Atlantic or the Caspian. A dam thrown across the upper Volga in 1843 created a lake with an area of sixty-six square miles, a volume of fourteen billion cubic feet. This reservoir, with similar ones on tributary streams, maintains a navigable channel all the way from the sea to within sixty-five miles of the source.

From the west flows the Oka, 950 miles long, with the great city of Moscow on one of its tributaries. It joins the Volga near the site of that ancient trade center, Nizhni Novgorod, where long ago tea from China, furs from Siberia, fish from the Caspian, and iron from the Urals were bartered for the products of the more civilized West. The city, a member of the Hanseatic League, that curious commercial empire of the Baltic region, became so rich and powerful that a native proverb asked, "Who can withstand God or Novgorod the Great?" That question was answered when the Muscovite Czar, Ivan the Terrible, glutted his sadistic vengeance upon the inhabitants by condemning thousands of them to inhuman torture and death. Yet the city, shorn of its ancient prestige, survives under the Bolshevist name of Gorki.

Here the Volga, only 190 feet above sea level, turns eastward for several hundred miles to unite with another great tributary, the Kama, 1,160 miles in length, draining the western slopes of the Urals, which geographers once set as the boundary between Europe and Asia. Kazan on the Volga, some distance above this junction, was long the seat of a powerful Mohammedan khanate where the competition between Cross and Crescent remained undecided for centuries.

The southerly trend of the river is interrupted at the Samara Bend, where in a course of a hundred miles it advances scarcely thirteen. Here the river, only ninety-five feet above the sea, has eroded a gorge a thousand feet deep through limestone strata, the most picturesque scenery in the entire valley. Below this loop, near the city of Syzran, the Trans-Siberian Railway crosses the Volga on a bridge nearly a mile long, of thirteen great spans, their bases buttressed to withstand the pressure of floods and ice.

Veering somewhat west of south, the river now approaches within
forty-five miles of the Don, which set out to become another
tributary but turned westward instead to empty into the Sea of
Azov and the far-off Atlantic.

Below this interrupted meeting place of two great rivers the
shores of the Volga are darkened for twenty miles by smoke belching from the great manufacturing plants at Stalingrad. At this
turning point in modern history the river also turns at an obtuse
angle southeastward across the old bed of the retreating Caspian
more than three hundred miles away. The river now splits in
two, the smaller, Arhtuba, paralleling the main current all the
way to the sea. Both mingle, however, in transverse channels and
in flood overflow the entire valley.

In a great delta of fifty-three hundred square miles, the Volga
empties into the sea through some two hundred mouths inter-
twined with almost innumerable side channels or limans. Built
up by river-borne silt that averages twenty-seven billion cubic
feet a year, the delta continually advances, while the neighboring
sea has become so shallow that steamers approaching from the
south must lighten their cargoes forty miles offshore. The enormous influx of fresh waters here makes the salty Caspian drink-
able at least to nomad Kalmuks.

The Volga and its branches provide some twenty thousand
miles of waterways, an impressive total swollen by numerous
canals. Some of these connect with Lake Ladoga and the Neva,
which empties into the Baltic, so that St. Petersburg (now Leningrad), though not within the Volga Valley, has become its seaport.

Most of these canals were excavated across the low-lying plains
before the days of railroads, but a modern one now connects
Moscow on a branch of the Oka with the Volga to supply much
of the city's drinking water. This was a dream of Peter the Great
which awaited some centuries for fulfillment. A more difficult
engineering feat is the proposed canal from Don to Volga which
would link the latter's vast commerce with the Black Sea and
the Mediterranean.

Thousands of boatbuilding yards dot the riverbanks. Beside
rafts common to other rivers, the crudest conveyances are the
beliannes. Designed for a single passage downstream, there to

be broken up for timber like the scows on the Athabaska, one of these clumsy craft sometimes transported as much as eight thousand tons of freight.

On most great rivers the main traffic is downstream, but not so on the Volga. At Astrakhan, in the delta, upriver freight is fifteen times heavier than that moving southward. For the Volga is a doorway into Russia thrown wide open to the Caspian area and Turkestan beyond. Bulkier items include grain, salt, fish, and petroleum from the oil wells at Baku that were flowing in the days of Marco Polo. This petroleum was formerly transported in leaky wooden craft which killed the fish. Now tankers, burning mazut, a product of the refineries, bear it inland to distant manufacturing centers. Meanwhile, across the Kalmuk steppes, camel caravans bear to the Volga basin the rich products of the East as they have done for centuries.

The river channel is well buoyed and lighted by numerous beacons. Charts are continually revised and printed sheets distributed to river boats, detailing water depths, the appearance of new shoals, and other vital information. All this is reminiscent of steamboat life on the Mississippi and pilots of the Mark Twain era. In fact, the Volga is often called the Russian Mississippi. At various points along its shores docks are provided where passing craft may lighten their cargoes in order to negotiate obstructing sand bars.

The erosion of the uplands presents a never-ending problem in hydraulics. The main delta channels are kept open by cutting off numerous side branches, by building jetties and levees, and by dredging. All these, with difficulty, maintain a twelve-foot depth to the Caspian.

Winter ends abruptly the seething activity on the Volga. The countryside is mantled with snow, and river ice, driven sheet above sheet, creates dams forty-five feet thick. Navigation is at a standstill on the upper river for nearly half the year, and even the lower Volga is closed for three months or more.

Two flood seasons, one in spring, the other in autumn, sometimes raise the river level fifty feet, but in the interim many shoals emerge. Much of the drainage basin suffers from increasing desiccation, so that many tributaries once navigable are now too shallow. No doubt cutting off the forests has hastened this process, but the underlying causes are more fundamental: the rising terrain of northern Russia and Siberia, the disappearance of numerous swamps and shallow lakes, and the increasing dryness of the great winds that sweep from the deserts of Turkestan. Within the past decade Russian scientists report an alarming shrinkage of the Caspian, whose surface has subsided fully ten feet, while scorching summer heats have parched once productive wheat fields. All this is further proof of that continuous drying-out process which is global in scope.

Throughout most of the Volga's drainage area the rainfall is only moderate, while the southern sector embraces a salt desert once flooded by the Caspian. Hence the river volume is greater a thousand miles upstream than at its mouth. The Kama alone in floodtime pours into the Volga 515,000 cubic feet a second, or nearly the normal output of the Mississippi. However, the Volga discharges into the Caspian a maximum of 884,000 cubic feet a second against a minimum of something over 70,000.

Fisheries have long been an important source of wealth. Following spring thaws, shoals of fish swim up the river, including herring, voracious lampreys, and huge sturgeon. Seals are slaughtered off the river mouth, their ancestors doubtless marooned there long ago upon the breaking up of the so-called Sarmatian Ocean when rising terrain barred off the Caspian.

The development of hydroelectric power is a more recent innovation, as the Volga has no natural waterfalls. But a huge dam two miles long between the limestone cliffs of the Samara loop is designed to supply the largest power plant in the world.

Unlike the Danube (Ister) and the Dnieper (Borysthenes), the Volga was almost unknown to antiquity. True, Ptolemy mentions it as the Rha, but he had no conception of its source or extent. Finnish tribes appeared in its upper valleys in the ninth century, while Slavic culture developed later, particularly along the Oka River, extending southward. Most of Russia proper was then overrun by Asiatic invaders. Various half-wild tribes settled the eastern plains and the steppes of the Caspian. But such incursions were minor incidents compared with the deluge of Mongol invasion which swept over all southern Russia and surged unchecked to the shores of the Adriatic. No western armies could withstand Subotai "the infallible" and his peerless horsemen from the Gobi, while the fearsome banner of Genghis Khan, with its nine pendant yak tails, was a precursor of wasted fields, blackened villages, and corpses left to the wolves and vultures.

When the destroying tides ebbed back beyond the Urals, a residue of the Mongols and their allies remained in southern Russia—self-styled the Golden Horde. Another ruthless conqueror appeared in Tamerlane to do battle with Toktamish, the Mongol overlord. Tamerlane stormed Astrakhan, defended, so Harold Lamb assures us, with "a wall of ice blocks upon which the inhabitants cast water until the whole froze together," then swept northward to the environs of Moscow itself. In that black hour the inhabitants knelt before an icon of the Virgin, wailing, "Mother of God, save Russia," and Tamerlane, who was raiding rather than conquering, withdrew to wreck vengeance upon the Turks and, so legend has it, emprison their Sultan Bajazet in an iron cage.

The Volga might well have formed the continental boundary in those days of Asia's triumphs. But the Slavs, rallying in the valley of their great river, were slowly evolving a national consciousness. Kazan, seat of Mohammedan power north of the Kama, withstood their expansion eastward for two centuries until its fall in 1552. Eight years later Russian armies had recaptured Astrakhan and opened the river valley all the way to the Caspian, but two more centuries elapsed before the Tartar power concentrated in southern Russia, and particularly the Crimea was absorbed in the Empire of the Czars.

Embattled Europe on the banks of the Volga was destined to triumph over more venerable Asia, the yellow tides were beaten back, and Russia, ever-expanding, advanced her bounds of empire from the Baltic to the Pacific.

From the Valdai marshes the Volga emerges to lose itself at length in the half-stagnant Caspian. But the spirit which once flamed upon its banks has now overspread two continents and remains a factor of grave and disturbing import to the whole world.

PART EIGHT

North American Rivers

~~~~~~

THE GREAT RIVERS of North America belong exclusively to the Temperate and Arctic zones. Tropical forests and belts of heavy rainfall are confined mainly to the narrowing isthmus which culminates in Panama. But as the continent holds perhaps half the lakes of the world, several of its major rivers are fed from these natural reservoirs. Here the St. Lawrence is unrivaled, although the Mackenzie and the Saskatchewan are also outlets for a number of these fresh-water seas.

North America lacks those great equatorial forests which sustain the Amazon and the Congo, but across the width of Canada stretches the second largest coniferous woodland in the world, an ocean of greenery half as extensive as the Siberian taiga. According to W. E. D. Halliday, this forest, whose predominant tree is the white spruce, covers 1,250,000 square miles, an area roughly equal to the basin of the Mississippi.

Unlike Asia and Africa, interior drainage areas are few and relatively unimportant and there are no deserts to compare with the Gobi or the Sahara. Hence almost every portion of the continent of adequate area has a river of its own. Many of secondary rank cross the eastern coastal region from the Appalachian ranges, but the major river of the Atlantic seaboard is the St. Lawrence, an imposing entrance to the wealthy and populous empire of the Great Lakes. The great river of North America, however, and one of the chief rivers of the world, is the Mississippi-Missouri, flowing southward into the Gulf of Mexico, which also receives the Rio Grande, noteworthy for its length and its position as an international boundary.

Three great rivers empty into the Pacific or its outlying waters. Southernmost is the Colorado, which has carved out the jagged ramparts of the Grand Canyon on its way to the Gulf of California. Midway up the coast line the Columbia breaks through the mountains from that strange relic of the Glacial Age, the Columbia Ice Field, while far to the north the Yukon, winding among the loftiest peaks on the continent, empties into desolate Bering Sea.

Several important rivers flow into the Arctic. Largest of these is the Mackenzie, second only to the Mississippi, an ice-choked flood suggestive of the Lena and the Yenesei. It bears the surplus waters of Great Bear Lake, Great Slave Lake, and Athabaska. Eastward the Churchill, one of the youngest of rivers, its channel still ill defined, sets its course toward Hudson Bay, while into that same lonely annex of the Arctic empties the Nelson-Saskatchewan, hurrying down from the Rockies and across the Canadian Northwest, its current swollen by tribute from many a remnant of fossil Lake Agassiz.

I

The Atlantic Group

THE MISSISSIPPI–MISSOURI—THE "FATHER OF WATERS"

Length—3,986 miles. Drainage area—1,243,000 square miles

THE MISSISSIPPI is the great river of North America. Thirty-one states and two Canadian provinces swell the muddy tides which pour through the five mouths of its swampy delta into the sea. Some of those waters from the far-off western borders of Montana have followed the devious channel for nearly four thousand miles.

Ages ago Algonquin Indians gave the upper river the name which still survives, for in their language Missi Sippi meant Great River. Other tribes in the lower valley, which becomes a moving sea in time of flood, called it the Father of Waters. Both were appropriate tributes to the sweep and majesty of that vast stream, swollen by forty tributaries spreading from the Appalachians to the Rockies, which drains the boundless plains of the mid-continent.

Although railways, auto trucks, and airplanes have robbed this great highway of commerce of much of its former prestige, it played a major part in the development of the country. The French, battling the British for the mastery of the continent, tried to contain the latter within the seaboard area, while their encircling dominions expanded from the St. Lawrence to the gulf. Failing in that attempt, their sale of the vast Louisiana Territory turned the attention of the jealous and loosely knit colonial province toward the Far West. In the suicidal War between the States, the opening of the Mississippi by Northern arms split the Confederacy in twain and dealt a deathblow to the hopes of a Davis and a Lee. As river commerce waned, agriculture, stock raising, and manufacturing enterprises pressed to the fore. The drainage area of 1,243,000 square miles embraces the great grain-growing region of the nation, while along the river and its tributaries are centered such populous cities as New Orleans, St. Louis, Kansas City, Omaha, Minneapolis, St. Paul, Memphis, Louisville, Cincinnati, and Pittsburgh.

More than most rivers, the Mississippi has suffered from a mistaken priority of names. The upper river, 1,205 miles long, became known to white men before the discovery of the Missouri, which is 2,807 miles long. Hence the true headwaters are not, as commonly represented, in Elk Lake, draining into Itasca in upper Minnesota, a distance by winding channel of 2,384 miles, but rather in the remote watershed which separates Montana from Idaho, where the Big Muddy has its source 3,986 miles from the sea.

Hernando de Soto and his Spanish gold seekers, venturing inland from the Atlantic seaboard in 1541, were the first white men to sight the lower river. There De Soto, failing in his quest, died, and, according to tradition, was buried beneath its waters. For more than a century, however, the great river remained little more than a name. Then, in 1673, those adventurous souls, Père Marquette and Joliet, approaching from the Great Lakes, sailed down the river for about three hundred miles. La Salle, in 1682, completed the voyage to the gulf, named Louisiana for his sovereign, and felt that he had laid the foundation for a vast French Empire in the New World. But his dream faded when, exploring the unknown region which lay to the westward, he was murdered by his mutinous followers.

Under instructions from La Salle, Michel Accault ascended the upper river until stopped by the Falls of St. Anthony, water power which founded those twin metropolises, Minneapolis and St. Paul, and the building of the most capacious flour mills in the world.

The Verendryes, whose knightly exploits led to early settlements about the Lake of the Woods and the building of the Canadian city of Winnipeg, seem to have been the first white men to reach the upper Missouri. In 1797 David Thompson, in the employ of the Northwest Fur Company, descended a stretch of the river. But the Big Muddy became something more than a legendary stream when Lewis and Clark ascended it on their famous journey, 1803–06, to the mouth of the Columbia. To the many perils of the enterprise were added minor irritations, for Clark, climbing a hill to shoot a big horn, wrote, "the musquetoes were in such multitudes" that he could not keep them from the barrel of his rifle long enough to take aim. John Colter, who accompanied the party on the return journey, remained behind to try his luck as a trapper in the Rockies. Ascending the Yellowstone branch of the Missouri, he returned to civilization with tales of painted canyons, majestic waterfalls, and jets of steam that issued from the earth which fairly outdid the tall stories of Marco Polo. It was long afterward before the world realized that Colter had merely attempted to describe what is really indescribable, that region of marvels now known as Yellowstone National Park.

Romantic as are the tales of early adventure along the Mississippi Valley, the story that geologists decipher from the earth crust is even more remarkable. At one time, so they assure us, the Missouri probably flowed into Hudson Bay. What are now Lakes Michigan and Superior emptied into the Mississippi, but even they were dwarfed by that glacial monstrosity, Lake Agassiz, which sprawled over Minnesota, North Dakota, and the Canadian provinces of Manitoba and Saskatchewan. Some remnants of its original 110,000 square miles survive in Lakes Winnipeg, Manitoba, Winnipegosis, the Lake of the Woods, and countless lesser lakes that dot the landscape. Even now, according to H. Dyson Carter, a mile-long canal joining Lake Traverse on the Red River of the North with the Little Minnesota at Big Stone Lake would unite the waterway from Hudson Bay to the Gulf of Mexico.

As the glacial era waned, the Mississippi lost its big lakes to the St. Lawrence and the Saskatchewan. And this loss is reflected in its erratic outflow, now swollen by floods, now curtailed by drought. The maximum outflow reported by the Mississippi River Commission was 1,557,000 cubic feet a second, recorded at Sinclair, ten miles below New Orleans, on April 28, 1927. The minimum was 49,200 on November 1, 1939. The mean annual output is given as 513,000 cubic feet a second, about one third the maximum, more than ten times the minimum.

Records on the principal tributaries are instructive. All vary between wide limits, but the average outflow of the Missouri is 89,000 cubic feet a second, as recorded at Hermann, ninety-seven miles above its juncture; that of the Ohio, 216,000 at Metropolis, Illinois, thirty-five miles from its mouth; and that of the elongated Red River of the South, 31,000.

De la Vega, who accompanied De Soto, has left the first description of a Mississippi flood—the date, 1543. He wrote: "The flood was forty days in reaching its greatest height which was the twentieth of April and it was a beautiful thing to look upon the sea where there had been fields for on each side of the river the water extended over twenty leagues of land." De la Vega, however, owned no cattle to perish in the swirling waters, or no farm buildings to be swept away. Similar floods in the upper river appeared in quite a different light to Father Marquette, for he wrote of one in 1673, "I have seen nothing more frightful. A mass of large trees . . . real floating islands. They came rushing . . . so impetuously that we could not, without great danger expose ourselves to pass across."

The appalling loss from such a flood was brought home to the world in 1937. At Cairo, Illinois, the waters rose 56.4 feet. Some twenty-eight thousand square miles of the lower valley were converted into a lake nearly as large as Superior; 750,000 persons were made homeless, and property damage soared above $350,-000,000. New Orleans, imperiled by the mad waters which threatened to surmount the 24-foot levees, was saved only by dynamiting those barricades below the city, allowing the pent-up torrents to surge across the lowlands to the sea. Heavy rains had deluged the valley with some 250 cubic miles of water! Of this at least sixty cubic miles swept onward to the sea, a volume that the weakened levees could not contain.

In floodtime these levees offer the only refuge from inundated farm lands. The inhabitants, fleeing for their lives, flock there with their domestic animals. In such reminders of the original Deluge, sanctuary is denied to no wild life except snakes. During a recent flood small rafts were even built to support the muskrats of the delta, so exhausted from continuous swimming that they would otherwise have drowned. A widely circulated photograph showed a dead cow suspended by the horns from the crotch of a tree where the receding waters had left her. That dirgelike ditty of the Negro sharecropper, "Old Man River," was born of a wholesome respect for the Father of Waters.

Of greater permanent damage than the loss of livestock or buildings is the enormous erosion of the topsoil. Hugh H. Bennett, chief of the Soil Conservation Service, estimates that in flood the Mississippi sweeps away the equivalent of a forty-acre farm every minute!

In every cubic foot of water it carries off forty-two pounds of mud. The Big Muddy, as its name suggests, is the chief offender. As this river traverses semi-arid regions (the rainfall over its entire basin is less than twenty inches) it alternates between a millrace and a chain of sand bars. Residents along its shore call the water "too thick to drink, too thin to plow." Each average day 275,000 tons of topsoil swirl by the city of Omaha. In a year the washings of the Missouri total 240,000,000 tons.

In this colossal destruction man has played a dubious role. Overgrazing and "dry farming" have left that vast scar upon the landscape known as the Dust Bowl. In the decade between 1930–40 three hundred thousand settlers deserted the Plains. Certain sections of North Dakota lost nearly a third of their population, while the migration of homeless Okies from Oklahoma provided a national problem and gave John Steinbeck material for that stark portrayal of human degradation, *The Grapes of Wrath*.

To be sure, some upland debris is salvaged in the delta region, which has built up fifty square miles during the past century. But Louisiana's gain is slight compensation for the loss suffered by a score of other states.

Attempts to restrain the temperamental river began in 1717, when settlers at New Orleans constructed the first levees. Since that time these earthen walls have lengthened to 2,130 miles, with a content of more than a billion tons. Raised to an average height of twenty-four feet, their unstable bases will scarcely support a heavier superstructure. According to Frederick Sempich, the great floods of the eighties broke through these levees in no fewer than 712 places. Further problems occur as the river meanders into oxbow loops which show a tendency to pinch off during flood. Within recent years such cutoffs have reduced one 330-mile stretch of channel to 210 miles. Furthermore, the enormous silt freightage tends to build up the river bottom in places higher than the surrounding terrain. The tombs of New Orleans are built above the waterlogged earth!

Along the Big Muddy farmers still protect their caving shore lines with willow mats. Modern engineering methods, however, have largely supplemented the handwork of the pioneer. "Articulated concrete mattresses" are common, formed of jointed concrete matting, sometimes supplemented with screening coated with asphalt. To prevent weed growth salt is strewn beneath them. Exposed shores are reinforced with stone riprap. Engineers, in their battle with the corrosive river, have also enlisted such mechanical helpers as tower machines, draglines, tractors, and trucks. But it is becoming increasingly apparent that the one effective method of flood control is to treat the great river system as a unit. For a sudden influx from any tributary upsets the balance.

As far back as 1820 Congress authorized a survey of the Mississippi and Ohio rivers. The chaining of the turbulent Tennessee by twenty-six major dams is a miracle of modern science. An equal series of barricades impedes the current of the upper Mississippi. Still more ambitious is the project, slowly emerging from the blueprint stage, to harness the Big Muddy. No fewer than 105 dams are contemplated, to cost well over a billion dollars. Eventually the Bureau of Reclamation hopes to integrate every dam. Flood control is the paramount issue, but utilizing waste water is a major consideration. Although the annual rainfall in the Mississippi drainage area averages about thirty inches, this includes well-watered sections like the Appalachian Mountains. Eighty per cent of that vast territory lacks sufficient rainfall to insure crop production. The wastage of the topsoil is but one item on the red-ink ledger. Every cubic foot that mingles aimlessly with the sea could nourish livestock or growing crops in Nebraska or Wyoming.

Maintaining a navigable channel, now purely secondary, was once all-important. The first steamboat to follow the course of La Salle and his Indian canoes left Pittsburgh for New Orleans in 1811. Oddly enough, it passed through the earthquake belt, which caused a vast subsidence of the valley and created Reelfoot Lake. By 1857 river traffic had thriven so amazingly that eleven hundred steamers reached St. Paul, while the number including all the tributaries was estimated at three thousand. Those were the romantic days commemorated by Mark Twain, a river pilot himself, who took his pen name from the droning cry of the leadsman as he plumbed the muddy bottom, "by the mark—twain," or two fathoms. In the valley of the Big Muddy roving bands of Pawnees, Blackfeet, Crows, Gros Ventres, Mandans, Cheyennes, and Sioux Indians sometimes resented the intrusion of the puffing steamboat by a volley of gunfire. Hence pilothouses were made bulletproof.

A special type of river steamer was a moving theater immortalized in *Show Boat*. Innumerable lesser craft also sailed down the Mississippi, while rafts introduced a picturesque river life. Abraham Lincoln once floated down to New Orleans on a raft.

Steamers still go from Pittsburgh to New Orleans, although the peak of such traffic has passed, no doubt, forever. Old Mississippi steamers transported to far-off places now sail such unfamiliar waters as the Congo and the Irrawaddy. The lower river, however, remains a major avenue of trade, and New Orleans, some ninety miles from the sea, is one of the great ports of the world.

Here the Father of Waters has been set the menial task of digging out his own channel. Spur dikes projecting from both banks restrict the width and maintain the depth. In South Pass, most frequently used of the five main mouths, such jetties have compelled the river to plow a channel thirty-one feet deep across a bar that formerly showed an eight-foot depth. The main volume of waters, however, pours through South West Pass. Here for more than twenty miles the current was confined by jetties to a width of one thousand feet, later narrowed to six hundred, with a resultant channel of thirty-five feet. Dredging operations also maintain an even depth. The enormous erosive power of the current was well illustrated in the great flood of 1937, when in one place the swirling waters scoured a thirty-foot channel to a depth of 104 feet.

From the Ohio to the Gulf the width of the Mississippi varies from eight hundred to fifteen hundred yards. This seems unimpressive compared with the Congo or the Lena or the Amazon, whose lower shores blend with the horizon. But the lower Mississippi maintains a pretty uniform channel depth ranging from fifty to one hundred feet.

Americans are proud of their great river. Although it taps no equatorial rain belt with an oceanic volume of waters, its length and drainage area rank it among the three or four greatest rivers in the world. True, it yields in commercial importance to the St. Lawrence, with its fabulous hinterland about the Great Lakes, yields also to the Yangtze Kiang, the "life line" of China, but it is the common prototype of great rivers the world over. Thus the Volga is called the Russian Mississippi, which it resembles, and the Murray-Darling, the Australian Mississippi, a more doubtful comparison. While to millions of persons in North America it remains, what the Indians once called it, the Father of Waters.

THE ST. LAWRENCE AND THE EMPIRE OF THE GREAT LAKES

Extreme length—2,100 miles. Drainage area—565,000 square miles

Unique among the world's great rivers, much of the St. Lawrence drainage area embraces lakes. On many atlases the river rises in Lake Ontario and broadens into an estuary to merge with a gulf of the Atlantic. But a more correct appraisal gives its source as the St. Louis River, winding through the forests of northern Minnesota, to empty into the far extremity of Lake Superior. Then we realize that in length the St. Lawrence approximates twenty-one hundred miles, while its drainage area assumes the imposing dimensions of 565,000 square miles.

Of this area more than ninety-five thousand square miles is lake surface, yet its inclusion is warranted. Geologists tell us that the present beds of the five Great Lakes were eroded by long-forgotten rivers which probably differed little from that of the Ohio today; that they were further sculptured by the continental icecap, while their shore lines were established by tilting rock strata and the heaping up of terminal moraines. For a time much emprisoned water spilled into the Mississippi, but as the ice retreated and order emerged from chaos, the St. Lawrence system, with its ancient river beds now swollen into the grandest lakes on earth, assumed its present pattern.

These lakes maintain a steady river current. Spring thaws may raise its level 7 feet or more, but that is insignificant compared with the upper Mississippi's 50, the Orinoco's 70, or the Yangtze Kiang's reported maximum of 200! Yet the St. Lawrence has important tributaries, such as the Richelieu, which drains Lake Champlain; the Ottawa, some 605 miles long; and the Saguenay, 405, guarded by those stupendous sentinels Capes Trinity and Eternity.

The course of the St. Lawrence is interrupted at Niagara by one of the world's major waterfalls, source of prodigious water power and mecca of countless honeymoons. But this scenic wonder is too well known to need description here. There are other obstructions to navigation, particularly the Sault St. Marie at the outlet of Superior, where an ancient portage is now flanked by gigantic locks; and the Lachine Rapids near Montreal, a minor barricade as steamers navigate the foaming channel, although it halted Jacques Cartier on his first voyage up the river from the sea. The northern Great Lakes area presents many imposing vistas, as does Nipigon cascading downward into Superior. A favorite beauty spot is the Thousand Island stretch of river as it leaves Ontario (the islands really number over fifteen hundred). Beyond the heights crowned by Quebec the river broadens out between the beetling escarpment of the great Canadian shield on the threshold of barren Labrador to the north and the picturesque Gaspé region to the south. Here it attains true Amazonian proportions, for at the big island of Anticosti, where it is supposed to enter the sea, it is quite ninety miles in width, while 150 miles farther upstream it is twenty-six miles wide.

We may gain a clearer view of the picture if we remember

that of all great rivers the St. Lawrence has been most altered by glacial action and the warping of underlying rock strata within comparatively recent geological time. The estuary and the Gulf of St. Lawrence mark a profound subsidence, a drowned valley invaded by the sea, for the river channel etched in underlying rock has been traced all the way to the verge of the continental shelf, the true border of the abysmal Atlantic.

No other river has proved so important in the exploration of a continent. Sagas of the Middle Ages, of doubtful authenticity, have Portuguese and Breton fishermen frequenting the Grand Banks and presumably the Gulf of St. Lawrence. In any case, a Breton sea captain, Jacques Cartier, was the first European of definite record to enter that spacious annex to the sea. In 1534, driven to seek refuge in a harbor over against Anticosti Island, he called the region, in honor of the saint's day, St. Lawrence. Hoping that the river might open up a sea route to the Indies, he ascended to the rapids beyond Montreal. He named his discovery the River of Canada, and for a long time it remained the only important river drawn upon the map of North America, but his maturer choice was overruled, and history, capricious always, has preferred St. Lawrence.

French explorers, dreaming of a vast empire in the New World, found the river a broad highway into the hinterland. In 1603 Champlain established the first French settlement at Tadoussac at the mouth of the Saguenay, and five years later laid the foundations of the fortress city of Quebec. In 1615 he paddled up the Ottawa River and thence by laborious portage to Lake Huron, while young adventurers in his employ, Brulé and Nicolet, later explored Ontario, Superior, and Michigan.

In 1679 La Salle, voyaging from Erie to Michigan on the *Griffon*, the first sailing vessel to navigate the Great Lakes, floated down the Mississippi to the gulf and claimed Louisiana for his sovereign. French *voyageurs* followed natural waterways into the great Northwest, eager to win fortune by trading with the Indians. Fur traders from Montreal competed with those from the Hudson's Bay Company, penetrating westward from that icy indentation of the Arctic. The Sieur Du Lhut built the trading post which was to become Duluth, and La Verendrye, operating from his headquarters on the Lake of the Woods, explored the Saskatchewan Valley, where his followers founded the city of Winnipeg.

The St. Lawrence Valley was long a battlefield of warring Indian tribes. The redoubtable Iroquois dwelling among the Adirondacks and Finger Lakes of New York almost exterminated the Eries and the Hurons, who gave their names to two of the Great Lakes. These hostilities persisted during the French and Indian Wars of colonial days. The struggle between France and Great Britain for world power, which had spread to the Mediterranean region, to the West Indies, and to India, involved Canada also. Quebec, deemed impregnable, was the key of empire, and when the city fell to General Wolfe on the Plains of Abraham the northern portion of the continent acknowledged British dominion. But the embers of warfare merely smoldered, to burst forth afresh during the Revolution. Then Benedict Arnold led his brilliant but rash attack on Montreal, and Burgoyne, thrusting southward from the St. Lawrence Valley, almost split the rebellious colonies in twain. For a time the flames of conflict died away to gain fresh impetus in the War of 1812. Battles raged around Niagara and Detroit, reverses brightened for American arms only by the naval victory of Lake Erie. Thereafter saner counsels prevailed, no fortifications were erected to perpetuate mutual ill feeling and distrust along the border, but the energies of both peoples rather turned to the wise pursuits of peace.

The commercial development of the St. Lawrence area is a more thrilling romance than the lawless era of trapper and explorer. No other valley, save perhaps that of the Yangtze Kiang, has played so prominent a role in the exploitation of a region of continental size. No other compares with the St. Lawrence in the multiplicity or value of its well-nigh countless enterprises and the volume of traffic which utilizes its unequaled waterways. The eight states and two Canadian provinces which border upon this giant river system have a total population exceeding forty-five million. This centers in such American cities as Chicago, Detroit, Cleveland, Milwaukee, Buffalo, and many others, while Canada presents Montreal, its metropolis, Quebec, of storied

history, Toronto, queen city of Lake Ontario, and the beautiful
capital at Ottawa.

The genius of man has assisted nature in the construction of
such canals as the Soo and the Welland, important links in a
gigantic chain of navigation routes. Although the Soo is closed
by ice for five months of the year, more shipping passes through
its giant locks than through the combined Suez and Panama
canals, and the Detroit River has been called the busiest waterway in the world. In a recent season the commerce of the St.
Lawrence lakes and rivers exceeded four billion dollars in value,
while the tonnage involved approached within 10 per cent that
of all American seaports on the Atlantic, the Gulf of Mexico,
and the Pacific combined.

The fisheries of the Great Lakes region have always been important. The forest resources of the river valley are immense.
Among mineral deposits are the copper mines of Michigan and
the fabulous iron mountains of the Mesabi Range in Minnesota.
Down the St. Lawrence Valley passes most of the grain produced in the great Northwest. Meat packing is a major industry.
Manufacturing has thriven enormously. Steel mills and automobile plants are but leading features in a list of enterprises that
would fill a volume.

The one disturbing factor is winter, which grips the north
country when Great Lakes shipping seeks a haven in port and ice
three feet thick forms across the St. Lawrence. Ice palaces are
then erected at Montreal and Quebec, and skiing, hockey, and
snowshoeing usher in a carnival of winter sports.

With all the manifold activities which flourish in the valley of
the St. Lawrence, ambitious plans are on foot to increase its
commerce with the outer world. Ocean steamers ascend the river
to Montreal, which has become one of the great ports of the
world, and they traverse the five Great Lakes. But Niagara and
the lower river rapids are by-passed by canals which limit shipping to a draught of fourteen feet. And so a ship canal has been
advocated connecting Duluth with the Atlantic, a canal which
would furnish hydroelectric power sufficient to defray a considerable portion of the cost. The grain growers of the Northwest and Great Lakes cities favor the project, which is stoutly

opposed by the railways and rival cities on the Atlantic seaboard, which fear such competition. For the St. Lawrence route is some hundreds of miles nearer England and northern Europe than is New York.

So bold a project belongs to the future and may well await a more favorable time. For as things are, the St. Lawrence is the wealthiest, the most prosperous, and in many respects the most remarkable river system in the world.

THE RIO GRANDE—A TURBULENT BORDER STREAM

Length—1,800 miles. Drainage area—232,000 square miles

A rollicking mountain brook, ice cold and fed by melting snows; a torrent foaming between canyon walls sixteen hundred feet high; a sober stream depleted by irrigation ditches; a mere trickle of water choked by sand bars under a withering sun; a tidal current swelling through gardens lush as Egypt's silted by the Nile; then out to its grave in the Gulf of Mexico—such is a voyage in fancy down the Rio Grande.

The cities in its valley—El Paso, Albuquerque, Santa Fe—are reminiscent of Old Spain, when the conquistadors, eager for gold, penetrated north from Mexico or westward from the sea. The river was first sighted by white men when Cabeza de Vaca led his ragged band into hitherto unexplored regions in 1536. Gaspar de Sosa, in 1590, headed a Spanish colony across the Pecos tributary into New Mexico. Santa Fe traces its origin to a settlement by Juan de Oñate in 1598. Jim Pursley, a Kentucky trapper, was the first white man of record to locate the headwaters of the Rio Grande. He was acting for Thomas Jefferson while the latter was negotiating the Louisiana Purchase. Zebulon Pike, whose monument is Colorado's best-known peak, also sighted the upper Rio Grande, though he mistook it for the Red River branch of the Mississippi; while near the same valley several members of John C. Frémont's party froze to death in 1848.

These outskirts of Old Mexico were engulfed in that westward expansion of the United States which its devotees hailed as "Manifest destiny." Theirs was the chief excuse for the war with Mexico; so unpopular at the time, so denounced on ethical grounds ever since. In 1846 Colonel S. W. Kearny led a band of soldiers from Kansas to Santa Fe, where he raised the American flag and declared the territory of New Mexico "Incorporated in the United States." In that same year Zachary Taylor built a fort at Brownsville near the mouth of the river.

The Rio Grande, eighteen hundred miles long, rises in the San Juan Mountains not far from tributaries of the Colorado. Swollen by melting snows, it cuts its way through deep gorges into New Mexico, a stream quite as large as the Connecticut. Here much of its volume is diverted to irrigation canals. Above Albuquerque one may observe hundreds of miles of drainage ditches and levees. Beavers once dammed the upper river, an example followed by engineers for the Department of the Interior. A dam now impounds the Rio Grande Reservoir at an elevation of ninety-five hundred feet. Another dam at Elephant Butte has created a lake forty-nine miles long in a region where lakes were quite unknown. It covers 37,670 acres and impounds 2,210,778 acre-feet of water. The Mesilla Dam, forty-one miles above El Paso, also provides precious water for a region of good soil but scanty rainfall. The city of Brownsville, twenty miles from the gulf, erects protective barricades like New Orleans, while the federal government has constructed a broad canal with reinforced walls to permit an overflow of floodwaters to the sea.

The most noted section of the Rio Grande, some thirteen hundred miles in length, marks the international boundary. To this arid region, with its touch of the Sahara, wild tales of border patrols, of smugglers, cattle thieves, and escaped convicts have given an atmosphere of lawless adventure. In the Big Bend region the river has gouged out deep gorges: the Santa Helena, the Boquillas, and the Mariscal. Much of the surrounding terrain is a sun-scorched waste with a starveling desert vegetation. An odd plant is the peyote, used by the Shoshone Indians as a narcotic. In its early stages it resembles an old leather button. More insidious is the marijuana, a relative of hemp, endowed with some of the properties of the drug hashish, derived from that otherwise useful plant. Marijuana added to cigarettes has a particularly baneful influence on adolescents. There is a proverb along the Big Bend that every wild plant "either sticks, stings, or stinks." Disgusted cowboys call the Rio Grande "the dustiest river in the world," compare it in sulphurous language with another region noted for its heat and general discomfort, and observe that "even the toads have horns." Much of the area is sparsely settled, Terrell County in Texas boasting fewer than one inhabitant per square mile. Wild life includes armadillos, javelinas, and marauding pumas. The latter swim the river to raid flocks and herds. One rancher suffered the loss of six hundred cattle from their depredations. Snakes are numerous, and birds, including quail by the million.

Outlaws fleeing impartially from Texas rangers or Mexican rurales head for that haven which beckons from beyond the Rio Grande. Watchtowers overlook the border, while patrols report that within the past quarter century twenty-three hundred men have been killed on the Texas side of the river alone. Coast Guard planes fly up and down the channel, keeping a sharp lookout for smugglers—a far cry from the camels once employed by Army transports which introduced a glimpse of Bagdad into El Paso. Across the river from this city lies Juarez, with its colorful culture, its carnival spirit, and its bullfights.

Much arid territory is now devoted to sheep and cattle raising, while long-haired alpaca goats are readily acclimated. More interesting creatures are revealed by deep erosion, when the river turns back the pages of global history to the Age of Dinosaurs. Many skeletons of these unwieldy creatures have been thus unearthed, while fossil oyster shells thirty inches long and extinct clamshells four feet across recall an era when the entire valley lay beneath the sea.

The lower Rio Grande threads a different world, the famous delta region built up at the expense of the worn-down uplands. Beginning some seventy-five miles from the sea and broadening to a width of forty, this area comprises two thousand square miles, larger than the state of Delaware. Huge bulldozers root out two acres of tangled jungle in a single hour, uncovering fertile river silt and rotted vegetation accumulated for centuries. Here, in a paradise of truck farming, the growing of citrus fruits has become the major industry. Grapefruit, developed from the wild shaddock of the West Indies, seedy and bitter, thrive amazingly. A pink variety is popular, and a red variety has been developed. According to the National Geographic Society, twenty-nine thousand carloads of grapefruit were shipped from this region in the winter of 1937–38. A by-product is grapefruit wine. Orange, lemon, and lime trees also find the environment congenial.

Although called a delta, the Rio Grande enters the sea through a single muddy mouth across shifting sand bars. The water volume is so depleted by evaporation and by countless irrigation ditches through semi-desert country that the normal outflow is only 5,180 cubic feet a second. In floodtime the mid-channel wanders at will, sometimes carving out a new course through sandy islands in twenty-four hours. These islands, known as bancos, have more than once changed allegiance from the flag of Mexico to the Stars and Stripes, in complete disregard for national obligations. The Treaty of Guadalupe Hidalgo in 1848 defined the boundary as "the middle of the river following the deepest channel." Unfortunately the river was not notified and regarded this covenant as a mere scrap of paper. Several new agreements, ignoring such shifts in the channel, did not solve the problems of riparian ownership. In 1886 a Texas rancher found his real estate greatly enlarged at the expense of a Mexican landowner, a situation many times repeated.

Finally President Cleveland appointed General Anson Mills to study the situation. His solution, adopted by both governments, decreed that all bancos to the right of the channel should be Mexican, to the left Texan, and that they should henceforth be eliminated from future cutoffs. Islands comprising more than 650 acres and 200 inhabitants were not to be considered bancos at all, while the ancient river bed would remain the boundary. Since that day many bancos have been surveyed and markers duly established. But private disputes continue as the great river pursues its way quite oblivious of legal regulations.

II

The Pacific Group

THE COLORADO AND THE GRAND CANYON

Length—1,450 miles. Drainage area—244,000 square miles

AN ABYSMAL gorge gouged in the living rock has made the Colorado famous. Other rivers, notably the Salween, the Mekong, and the Yangtze Kiang, are flanked by loftier heights, but none presents so amazing a panorama of wind and river erosion. Here walls a mile or more in height are built up in benchlike precipices and beetling pinnacles splashed with bizarre color. Neither artists nor descriptive writers can portray the overpowering magnificence of the Grand Canyon. Statistics cloud rather than clarify the picture when they tell us that it is 217 miles long, that it ranges in width from four to thirteen miles, that in places it is quite six thousand feet deep. The color camera, however, has brought to millions of persons fugitive glimpses of this chasm of the titans.

The Colorado is 1,450 miles long. It has its source in northwestern Wyoming, far up the flanks of the Wind River Mountains dominated by Fremont Peak, 13,781 feet high. There it is known as the Green River, a restless stream eroding a narrow valley through chaotic uplands. Not far off are the headwaters of the Snake, chief tributary of the Columbia, while from beyond the range the Wind River flows down to join the Big Horn and the Mississippi. In this restricted watershed spring rains or melted snows may eventually reach the Pacific, the far-off Gulf of Mexico, or the Gulf of California through any one of three great river systems.

The Green River writhes through a series of gorges: Desolation

Canyon, Labyrinth Canyon, and others only less extensive. From the mountains to the eastward the Grand River joins it to form the main current of the Colorado. This cuts through another winding gorge known as Cataract Canyon before attaining its climax in the Grand Canyon farther south. The series of gorges extends more than five hundred miles.

Although the eroded uplands are six thousand feet above the sea with many loftier heights, Major J. W. Powell has estimated that much of the drainage area of the Colorado has been degraded by an equal amount—solid rock more than a mile deep scraped from the face of the earth!

Emerging from the Grand Canyon, the river forms part of the boundary between Arizona on the east and Nevada and California on the west. Much of the dreary region to the sea has been formed by a silt burden estimated at 170,000,000 cubic yards annually. Alluvial deposits carpet the shallow Gulf of California, that probing finger of the Pacific, where the river in former ages has wrested much territory from the sea.

At Yuma, Arizona, another tributary comes winding from the east, the Gila, an elongated stream of little volume, associated in popular fancy with the Gila monster or horned toad, that grotesque child of the desert. That growing metropolis Phoenix is on the Gila.

Leaving American territory, the river crosses a strip of sandy waste to empty through a broad estuary scoured by thirty-foot tides that send crested tidal bores six or seven feet high foaming upstream against the current.

To the geologist the Grand Canyon is the slash of a titan's blade, deep into an ancient volume, revealing pages long since turned by the hand of time. Here the river has cut through layer upon layer of sedimentary rock, the slow accumulations of hundreds of millions of years. More than once the entire region has been submerged beneath the sea to appear again, covered with the wastage of former uplands, in those global heavings and subsidings which have established present boundaries between continents and seas.

The visitor standing upon Yavapai Point and peering down the yawning gulf for five sixths of a mile can trace that story in the multicolored rock strata which are there exposed. A million years ago, in Pliocene-Tertiary time, the river began to gnaw its way downward through the Kaibab limestone, a layer seven hundred feet in thickness which forms the present surface. Beneath this appears red sandstone three hundred feet thick, overlaying a deeper blend of red mud and sandstone eleven hundred feet deep. This in turn conceals a 550-foot layer of limestone laid down in shallow seas during the Carboniferous era when forests of fern-like trees and interminable marshes were forming the first coal beds. Some pages are missing here—those records in stone of the prolonged Ordovician, Silurian, and Devonian eras, when reptiles culminating in unwieldy dinosaurs were wresting the overlordship of the planet from the humbler fishes. These pages have been obliterated by some vast erosion long ago, but more ancient deposits survive in Tonto shales and sandstones to a depth of eight hundred feet. The insatiable river has cut still deeper, excavating a channel from eight hundred to eleven hundred feet in some of the oldest rock on the planet, the Vishnu gneiss of Archean times, thought to be the gnarled and metamorphosed substance of the original continent as it rose above the sea. This simple reconstruction of what transpired during a period of perhaps a billion years is much confused by faults, warpings, and the upsurging of granite dikes from the molten magma underneath.

Far different is the course of the lower river through a region of emptiness, of cactus and wind-swept sands, with its violent tendency to shift its bed. In 1905, when the outlet to the sea became temporarily clogged, the current went foaming into that weird Californian depression known as the Salton Sea, where it threatened to flood the Imperial Valley. Levees and canals finally curbed the lawless river; the surface of the Salton Sea, still much below sea level, has been stabilized, and the Imperial Valley, crisscrossed by irrigation ditches, has become a vast garden.

Far more difficult and costly was the building of the Hoover Dam, a colossal horseshoe buttressed against the canyon flanks. Seven hundred and twenty-six feet high and requiring 3,250,000 cubic yards of concrete, it presents a gigantic barricade against the river to form Lake Mead, which covers two hundred and forty-six square miles and impounds 31,141,755 acre-feet of water. It took the Colorado two years to fill this giant reservoir which has about one twelfth the volume of Lake Erie.

In a single month, August 1939, 108,528 tourists crossed Hoover Dam, where whirring dynamos generate enormous power and surplus waters are piped for 392 miles all the way to Los Angeles.

No great cities flourish in the valley of the Colorado, but mysterious ruins cluster in the canyon of a tributary stream, the San Juan. Among these communal structures two are characteristic ones: the Spruce Tree House and the more imposing Cliff Palace. High up precipitous walls, clinging like eagles' nests to clefts in the rock, these were approachable only by ladder.

The Cliff Palace is 400 feet long by 80 deep and comprises 117 rooms. Roof beams were cut and shaped by stone hatchets, and carved sacrificial stones were ornamented with quaint zig-zag circles and spirals. Conspicuous were the kivas, subterranean chambers, circular, girdled by low benches and supposedly designed for ceremonial purposes. Grain, cultivated by painstaking irrigation, was stored in granaries. Here unknown aborigines who had developed agriculture and adopted settled habits sought shelter from a world that knew no law.

The first white man to sight the Colorado was Francisco de Ulloa, a captain of Cortes, the conqueror of Mexico. The date was September 27, 1539. Caught in the swirl of the tides, his little vessel was stranded on the red mud flats of the estuary which he called the "vermilion sea." Here he found "the sea to run with so great a rage into the land that it was a thing to be marvelled at and with a like fury it turned again with the ebb"; "we did not see a person" he added, "or sign of any. I do not believe that such a land can be inhabited."

The very next year that knightly nobleman, Francisco Coronado, set out from Mexico with a little army of 250 horsemen, 70 Spanish footmen, and several hundred Indians in search of the seven golden cities of Cibola. The pueblos of the Zuni Indians were perhaps the source of this fantastic legend. In conjunction with the expedition, Hernando de Alcarón, following the course of de Ulloa, entered the estuary and sailed up the Colorado for a distance of "85 leagues." The date was August 26, 1540.

That same year a land party under Melchior Diaz reached the upper canyons. Meanwhile Coronado, with the main expedition, advanced into what is now Kansas but found the fabled Seven Cities as elusive as the rainbow's pot of gold. Sadly he turned back to spend the winter of 1540–41 on the Rio Grande and returned to Mexico to share the fate of most explorers, a broken and discredited man.

The canyons of the Colorado long proved an impassable barrier. For five hundred miles the only crossing was the old Ute Ford, some five miles north of the Utah-Arizona boundary. Father Escalantes first led a little group of Spaniards and Indians to this ford after an arduous journey. When provisions failed they were forced to eat seeds, cactus, piñon nuts, and the flesh of their horses. This ford was also crossed in 1858 by Jacob Hamlin, that exploring missionary of the Latter-day Saints or Mormons.

The settlement of California made the valley of the Colorado more familiar territory. In 1867 steamers approaching from the sea established Yuma as a port of call. That same year James White, a prospector, claimed to have descended the Colorado in a boat, through unknown rapids, with death lurking in the shadow of the cliffs, but was largely discredited. In 1869, however, Major Powell accomplished that daring feat as others have done since his day.

President Pierce tried to make the Colorado exclusively American. In 1853 James Gadsden, Ambassador to Mexico, negotiated a treaty whereby for ten million dollars, some fifty thousand square miles in southern Arizona and New Mexico were purchased. Had the southern boundary of this area extended due west, it would have included the mouth of the Colorado, but it was permitted to veer northwest so that the great river remains something of an international problem. At that time much additional territory might also have been obtained, but the project was blocked by northern Abolitionists who feared the extension of slave territory.

On the Mexican side of the boundary the Pattie Basin, with its Laguna Maquata, a former gulf of the ocean, somewhat resembles the Imperial Valley and the Salton Sea. By treaty Mexico is consulted about the diversion of water by our western states for irrigation purposes.

Although the drainage area of the Colorado is 244,000 square miles, most of it lies in a semi-arid belt of light rainfall, while some is desert. Hence the water volume is not only unimpressive but variable. In time of flood the river rises thirty feet or more in the upper canyons; in 1903 it rose twenty-eight feet at Yuma. Its maximum outlet has been estimated at 200,000 cubic feet per second, but its minimum dwindles to scarcely 3,000. The average is 23,300.

This figure may seem meager in contrast with more voluminous rivers, but the Colorado presents other features which challenge comparison anywhere.

THE COLUMBIA—GATEWAY TO THE NORTHWEST

Length—1,270 miles. Drainage area—259,000 square miles

In 1792 Captain Robert Gray, the first American to circumnavigate the globe, was sailing along the Oregon coast. On May 7 he made an entry in the log: "Saw from our masthead a passage in between the bars . . . bore away and ran in north by east . . . having a very strong ebb of tide to stem. Many canoes came along side. At five P.M. came to in five fathoms water sandy bottom with a safe harbour." Thus tersely was announced the discovery of one of the great rivers of North America.

Three centuries had elapsed since Columbus sighted San Salvador. Meanwhile the unknown River of the West had intrigued explorers from Sir Francis Drake to Captain Cook. In 1775 the Spanish Captain Heceta sighted its broad estuary but failed to investigate. The English Captain Meares almost succeeded, but sailed away calling a neighboring point Cape Disappointment. Captain Gray, more successful, entered and named the river for his good ship, the *Columbia*.

The Columbia has its source on the border between Alberta and British Columbia, in one of the strangest regions on the continent. This is a glistening ice field with an area of 150 square miles hemmed in by lofty mountains. According to Lewis R. Freeman, it is comparatively level, lies at an average elevation of eighty-five hundred feet, and may be considered a remnant of the great continental icecap that once crowned much of North America. Sustained by massive glaciers, its melting edges feed the Mackenzie to the north, the Saskatchewan to the east, and the Columbia flowing south and west through superb scenery. Where it crosses the international boundary it is already a great river three quarters of a mile wide with a volume that in flood approaches six hundred thousand cubic feet a second.

It is joined by the even longer but less voluminous Snake River, winding across Idaho from northwestern Wyoming, and trends roughly westward to form the boundary between Washington and Oregon.

The Columbia excels all other North American rivers in potential water power. Although its length is only 1,270 miles and its drainage area, 259,000 square miles, is little larger than that of the Colorado, its volume is eight times as great. The average outflow into the sea, 280,000 cubic feet a second, has risen in floodtime to 1,250,000, or nearly five sixths the recorded maximum of the Mississippi.

The current is accelerated by a rugged terrain. Within a distance of 612 miles from the sea, the river descends 1,288 feet. Many waterfalls interrupt its various tributaries. The Snake River in the Targhee National Forest plunges over upper Mesa Fall, 114 feet high. The Shoshone Fall of southern Idaho is called the Niagara of the West. Its height is forty-five feet greater, and although much of the volume is here diverted to power plants, the great waterfall, in flood, presents a splendid spectacle, particularly at night, illuminated by searchlights of twenty-five million candle power. Automobilists on the scenic highway along the lower reaches of the Columbia are charmed by waterfalls that come tumbling over the precipitous heights; the loftiest of these, Multnomah Fall, though broken near the base, presents a drop of 680 feet.

Such showy spectacles, however, are dwarfed by the now

empty escarpment of the Grand Coulee in western Washington. There a spur of the continental icecap, projecting southward, once barred the river from its bed. The harried stream, diverted across enormous lava beds, gouged out a canyon fifty miles long, eight hundred feet deep, varying in width from one to five miles. It excavated forty cubic miles of rock to plunge at last over a precipice 450 feet high and more than a mile wide in what must have been the grandest waterfall on earth. As the ice field retreated, however, the river resumed its original channel, leaving this jagged escarpment dangling vacantly 653 feet above.

Near this point the federal government, in 1942, completed one of the most gigantic structures ever erected by the hand of man. This was the Grand Coulee Dam across the Columbia, a barricade forty-three hundred feet long, fifty feet thick at the top and five hundred at the base, with a cubic content four times that of the Great Pyramid. Tourists seated in neighboring restaurants now watch the floodwaters foam 330 feet down the great spillway, while beyond the dam the river backs up 151 miles to form a lake with a maximum depth of 350 feet and an area of 126 square miles.

Nor is this all the story. The empty valley, excavated during the Ice Age in the basaltic upland, with its dry waterfall was an open challenge. To fill that depression and create a new lake for irrigation purposes ten great pumps have been designed to lift thirty thousand tons of water every minute a height of 280 feet above present water levels. Working only two and a half hours during the twenty-four, these pumps could supply water for the City of New York. They will utilize the power of the pent-up river, forcing some of its abundant waters to run literally uphill.

Other dams, notably Bonneville, nearer the sea, are either completed or projected in a gigantic program to turn the latent power of this great river to productive use.

Quite as important as such "white coal" is the development of vast irrigation projects. The Snake River Valley is naturally a desert. The stream itself is sometimes lost in subterranean passageways where ice forms in basaltic caves whose upper surfaces blister in the sun, while the topography presents such forbidding features as the Seven Devils Mountains. Irrigation, however, works a magic change. Ditches must be lined with concrete to prevent the dissipation of the water through porous lava rock, but volcanic soil, proverbially rich, produces those garden aristocrats, Idaho potatoes. Thousands of tons of smaller ones, equally nutritious, were once allowed to rot in the fields as shipping costs were prohibitive. Now mills dehydrate them or produce potato flour and plastics. Southern Idaho also grows other crops in abundance, including most of the country's supply of garden seeds. Farther west the Columbia rolls through wheat fields where the yield per acre far exceeds that of the prairie states. Here are cattle ranches and dairy farms, while Hood River apples are shipped in refrigerator holds all the way to Calcutta. The coastal mountains are clothed with those imposing forests of redwood, Douglas fir, and other woodland giants beloved of lumbermen. Freight steamers convey deckloads of such timber as far as South Africa to shore up the galleries of Johannesburg's gold mines.

There was a day when the salmon fisheries of the Columbia were its chief industry. Even now horses wade into the surf off the broad estuary to drag ashore dripping seines two thousand feet long, while at the Bonneville Dam visitors watch salmon surmount artificial runways to their distant spawning grounds.

The valley of the Snake River is rich in minerals. There are great deposits of phosphates, together with copper, lead, zinc, mercury, silver, gold, tungsten, antimony, and cadmium.

The Columbia has long been a natural artery of commerce. Portland, on the Willamette branch of the Columbia, ninety-odd miles from the sea, is an ocean port approached by a broad channel thirty-five feet deep. The only obstruction is the bar off the river's mouth where great combers rolling in from the Pacific once made navigation perilous. Here the government has built jetties miles long to control the current and deepen the channel. The various dams which interrupt the river farther up are equipped with locks to permit the passage of boats all the way to the Canadian border and beyond.

Not the least important of Columbia River products are its scenic beauties. The Selkirks, along its upper reaches, present some of the finest views in the Canadian Rockies. The Snake River has its source in Yellowstone Park, not far from where Old

Faithful leads his brigade of steaming vents in the most picturesque of geyser fields, and flows past the Grand Tetons, which the Rockefeller fortunes have purchased for a national park. Portland, the City of Roses, is also the City of Magnificent Views. From a thousand-foot eminence within urban limits, the visitor may gaze out over a delightful country with distant peaks looming on the horizon. Favored by Oregonians is Mount Hood, 11,225 feet high, but across the border in Washington looms the vast truncated cone of Mount St. Helens, 9,756 feet high, with cloud-capped Rainier in the offing, 14,526.

Yet two early settlers, one from Boston, the other from Portland, Maine, once flipped a coin to determine the name of this city of imposing vistas.

The history of the Columbia River is a romantic one. Meriwether Lewis and William Clark, on their great journey to the Pacific, ascended the upper Missouri, crossed the Divide, and descended the valley of the Snake and the Columbia to pass the winter of 1804–05 at a point near the mouth where the current widens to ten miles or more. Near this spot, a few years later, in 1811, Astoria was founded by John Jacob Astor, whose fur trading in those lawless, pioneering days laid the foundation of the Astor fortune. That profits were large is evidenced by a deal in which a canny sea captain gave an Indian chief an old iron chisel in exchange for two hundred sea otter pelts, rarest and most valuable of furs. Profits were still further swollen when such furs, carried to China and sold to wealthy mandarins, purchased a return cargo of silk and tea. A single round-the-world voyage from Salem or Boston, though beset with many perils, might enrich the owner for life.

In 1810 one William Price built Fort Henry on the Snake River, while not long afterward the advance posts of the Hudson's Bay trading company were established in this virgin territory.

Tales of the Oregon Trail still invest that overland route to the Northwest. Settlers took up rich farm lands, particularly in the sheltered valley of the Willamette, where their presence was decisive in a dispute which later broke out between America and Great Britain. Spain had once claimed the entire coastal region, based upon Balboa's imperial gesture when he appropriated all the shores of the Pacific for his sovereign. Subsequent expeditions had substantiated that claim, but Spain, much occupied with her vast dominions to the south, relinquished all rights to the Northland. Russia, then entrenched in this hemisphere, was a disturbing influence and even attempted to extend her dominions southward into northern California, but this threat was removed with the consummation of the Alaska Purchase on April 9, 1867, whereby the Bear agreed to withdraw to his interminable Siberian wilderness.

Great Britain, however, operating from Canada, was not so easily appeased. Her subjects had settled in the disputed territory, and she presented other claims. Against these were advanced the discovery of the Columbia by Captain Gray, the building of Astoria, and the presence of a preponderant American population. For some years both governments maintained a joint control, but divided authority was little calculated to alleviate friction. The British wished to make the Columbia River the international boundary; extremists in this country demanded the entire coast to the southern limit of the then Russian dominions, 54 degrees and 40 minutes north latitude. These figures provided that aggressive slogan "Fifty-four Forty or Fight" which for a time fanned ill-will. Fortunately saner councils prevailed; President Polk avoided an open break and friendly relations were cemented by the treaty of June 10, 1846, which established a compromise boundary line on the 49th parallel of latitude. Great Britain, however, did reserve the right to navigate the great river.

And so the Columbia, from a potential threat of war, has become the basis of enduring peace, a river whose resources, still but partially developed, have enriched both nations and should insure a growing prosperity to the Northwest.

THE YUKON AN OPEN DOOR TOWARD RUSSIA

Length—2,300 miles. Drainage area—330,000 square miles

Within fifteen miles of Dyea Inlet, one of the many fiords that penetrate Alaska's coast line, the mighty Yukon is born of the seepage of mountain springs, of rains and melting snows. But as the way is barred by the coastal range culminating in such hoary giants as Mount St. Elias and still loftier Logan, whose granite shoulders jostle the clouds at an elevation of 19,850 feet, the great river, like the African Niger, turns away from the nearby ocean to meander for twenty-three hundred miles north in a vast arc across the Arctic Circle, then toward the setting sun to its final resting place in Bering Sea.

Several Alpine lakes swell its headwaters, such as Bennett, twenty-seven miles long, varying in width from half a mile to five miles or more, and Laberge, thirty miles long, its eastern coast a rocky escarpment, its icy waters studded with islands. The Teslin tributary drains a larger serpentine lake of the same name extending further to the south.

The upper Yukon is an impetuous stream fretted by what salt-water sailors call "crooked water." There are perilous stretches such as Miles Canyon, where the precipitous banks approach within 150 feet, and the once dreaded White Horse Rapids. But beyond these troubled headwaters the river pursues its way through a broad valley that fairly bisects the Alaskan peninsula with snowy peaks towering in the distance.

Roughly half its drainage area of 330,000 square miles lies in Canada. There the Yukon receives several tributaries from the Mackenzie area, notably the Pelly and the Stewart. Crossing the international boundary, it reaches its farthest north. A marker in the spruce forest indicates where it pierces the Arctic Circle, but it soon turns west and then southwest through the Yukon Flats, a monotonous region two hundred miles long. Here it broadens out from ten to twenty miles, enclosing many swampy spruce-covered islands.

This dreary landscape ends at the Yukon Ramparts, where loftier banks confine the channel and the scenery is more picturesque. From the north come two large branches: the Porcupine, rising beyond the Canadian border, and the Koyukuk, draining the southern flanks of the Endicott Range beyond the Arctic Circle with lonely Mount Greenough, 4,920 feet high, peering over the horizon's rim toward the Polar Sea. From the south comes the Tanana River, over four hundred miles long, swollen by the glaciers of the Alaska Range, whose loftiest peak, McKinley, 20,300 feet, marks the pinnacle of the continent.

As the Yukon approaches the sea, the terrain increases in grandeur, with mountain peaks glittering in the offing. The delta outlet, which begins about fifty miles inland, embraces a maze of winding channels and marshy islands where spruce forests yield to stunted willows and tundra moss. The frontage of seventy-five miles between Apoon outlet on the extreme north and Kwikluak on the south is being continually extended by river-borne silt. Here local names are often Russian or expressed in the clicking, guttural syllables of the aborigines.

The great river was first made known to the outside world by Lieutenant Zagoskin, in the service of the Czar, who ascended it for some hundreds of miles in the years 1842–43. He built a trading post at Nulato, not far below the junction with the Koyukuk, which was the first white settlement. Here the half-breed Malakoff long maintained a semisavage sovereignty as agent for the Russian Fur Company. Not long afterward, in 1847, Alexander Murray, penetrating the wilderness from Canada, established an outpost of the Hudson's Bay Company at Fort Yukon.

In 1861 Robert Kennicott arrived at this fort from the Mackenzie Valley. He explored much unknown territory while employed by the Western Union on an ambitious project to stretch telegraph wires from North America to Asia, but died at Nulato in 1866. The project came to an abrupt end with the successful laying of the first transatlantic cable, its transmission wires concealed beneath the sea instead of exposed to Siberian blizzards.

Prospects for Alaska brightened in 1867, when the territory was purchased from Russia. To the Czars such remote possessions, separated from St. Petersburg by seven thousand miles of trackless wilderness, were too distant to be more than a perennial expense. Secretary Seward, who conducted the transaction for the United States, paid $7,200,000, or less than two cents an acre. Yet he was severely criticized for lavishing public money on "a dreary waste of glaciers, icebergs, white bears, and walruses." In these days, when governmental squandering of billions has become a commonplace, the acquisition of "Seward's Icebox," as it was once called, ranks with the purchase of Manhattan Island for twenty-four dollars and some gallons of rum as one of the shrewdest bargains on record. For Alaska, having repaid the purchase price a hundred times over, remains an empire of undeveloped riches. Moreover, in the present troubled state of international relations, it is a defensive bastion against Asiatic despotism, and the thoughtful might well ponder what might have happened had it remained in Russian hands.

Unlike many great rivers, the Yukon is navigable for craft of considerable size all the way from the sea nearly to its source. This is the more remarkable since it traverses a region which boasts the loftiest mountains in North America. Salmon swim upstream for more than two thousand miles, clear to Lake Bennett. Caribou cross the river in orderly troops, swimming with shoulders high out of water. Indian canoes, which still paddle along its interminable reaches of thirty-three hundred miles, have been largely superseded by wood-burning steamers. From time to time these stop to "wood up" from supplies gathered by woodsmen from the inexhaustible forests. Winter, rather than shoals or cascades, is the great obstacle to commerce. At Circle City near the Arctic Circle the river freezes early in November to remain a broad avenue of ice until the spring thaws, which occur from May 11–22. The soggy terrain a few feet underground never thaws, while at Dawson the soil remains permanently frozen to a depth of more than two hundred feet. A terrain so permanently saturated permits a greater proportionate "runoff" of surface waters. Hence, although the average precipitation over the Alaskan plateau is only about twelve inches annually, the volume of the Yukon in flood rivals that of the Mississippi.

The Yukon had its hectic heyday when the discovery of placer gold in the Dawson region lured adventurers from all parts of the world. The favored avenue of approach was by steamer to Skagway, followed by the laborious climb over the snowy Chilkoot Pass, the construction of some crude raft or river boat, and the thrilling voyage down the upper Yukon to the peaceful water beyond. Scores of inept boatmen perished in the foam of White Horse Rapids and kindred danger spots.

The grizzled "sourdoughs" who had long pre-empted this

wilderness viewed the advent of such inexperienced outlanders with amazement mingled with contempt. Hardships that tested physical and moral fiber to the breaking point soon weeded out incompetents. As Robert W. Service, the poet of this wild frontier, wrote:

> This is the Law of the Yukon, that only the
> Strong shall thrive;
> That surely the Weak shall perish, and only
> the Fit survive.

In summertime, battling the stinging hell of the mosquitoes that bred by myriads in the muskegs, lucky miners panned out fortunes in gold dust to be squandered at Dawson, the mushroom metropolis of the region. Glamour still invests those "Dawson days, with their sin and the blaze, and the town all open wide," while the "spell of the Yukon" has been graphically portrayed in such stories as *The Iron Trail* by Rex Beach and the *White Silence* by Jack London.

Governmental controls and a wholesome respect for the Canadian Mounted Police established some semblance of order in what had been a lawless chaos, but the days when the glint of gold panned from icy waters repaid months of backbreaking toil have yielded to a Machine Age where huge dredgers sift the river sands with steel-tipped fingers, scar the very landscape, and pile up the ravished soil in great hillocks. And there is much delving for other minerals, such as the operations of the May Lead and Silver Mine which was established many years ago on the Stewart River.

The fisheries of the Yukon have many times repaid with interest the Alaskan purchase price. When the current was alive with moving fins, the Indians toiled with net and spear to gain a winter grubstake for themselves and their dogs. Otters, hawks, and sea gulls joined in the wholesale slaughter, while the great brown bears, hugest of all the carnivora, shambled down to the river brink, scooped out one great fish after another, bit off the head, and threw away the body.

To reap this harvest of the seas, the white man brought bigger nets and seines and invented a new method of fishing, the clumsy but efficient salmon wheel. This device operates automatically from a craft anchored in the current which endlessly rotates the wheel and scoops up the fish. It can be used, however, only where the stream is so muddy that the fish cannot see where they are going.

Split salmon, drying in the sun, are a familiar sight along the Yukon. In the process they not only become cured for future use but lose some four fifths of their original weight.

When the Japanese drove our Navy from the Pacific and seized two of the outlying Aleutians, a feverish attempt was made to open up Alaska from the land. As a result, the Alaska-Canadian Highway, familiarly shortened to Alcan, was projected as a sort of overland canal connecting the three great river systems of the Far North. For months an army of engineers, truck drivers, woodsmen, and road-construction workers, well provided with steam shovels and bulldozers, labored amid spruce thickets and muskeg swamps, laying down a great war road sixteen hundred and seventy-one miles long. One terminus was Dawson Creek in British Columbia, the other Fairbanks in the remote hinterland of Alaska. The road connected with Edmonton on the Saskatchewan, crossed the Peace and Liard tributaries of the Mackenzie River, and terminated on the Tanana branch of the Yukon.

This highway, though passable, is no pleasure speedway, nor designed as such. But it should stimulate the settlement of a vacant wilderness and provide a readily defensible link with Alaska. For the world, though sick unto death of warfare and its senseless destruction, still dreams of some terrific conflict in the future. Should that fateful day ever dawn, it would find Russia and the United States locked in mortal combat, with the destiny of civilization in the balance.

A glance at the map justifies once more the wisdom of Seward's Purchase. The Yukon is a broad highway into the heart of North America, its delta, on desolate Norton Sound, a yawning doorway wide open toward the west. In the distance looms big St. Lawrence Island, and beyond projects the vast shoulder of Asia under the flag of the Hammer and Sickle.

Farther north, at Bering Strait, the two continents approach within thirty-six miles, while in the Diomede Islands they are less than three miles apart! Most Americans think of Soviet Dominions as far off, but Alaskans, remembering how recently theirs was Russian territory, feel no such safe remoteness. Political as well as economic reasons fairly clamor for the development of that great area we purchased for such a pittance, and the utilization of its grand natural highway, the Yukon.

III

The Arctic Group

THE MIGHTY MACKENZIE—THROUGH A MAZE OF LAKE AND FOREST

Length—2,525 miles. Drainage area—682,000 square miles

THROUGH the heart of that mid-continental plain which stretches from the Rockies to the great Canadian shield winds the Mackenzie River. Emptying into ice-rimmed Beaufort Sea, it has been called the Mississippi of the North, for the two, flowing in opposite directions, fairly bisect the continent.

While the Mississippi is indisputably first among North American rivers, the Mackenzie is second, for it stretches 2,525 miles through a drainage area of 682,000 square miles, roughly double that of the Yukon, or the Saskatchewan.

More than most rivers, the Mackenzie has been divided by geographers into sections. From its source in the Rocky Mountains to Athabaska Lake, a distance of 740 miles, it is known as the Athabaska River. Northward from that lake to Great Slave Lake it becomes the Great Slave River, swollen by the Peace River, a thousand miles long, which breaks through the passes of the Rockies to wander across the forests of Alberta. Only from the point of exit from Great Slave Lake does the Mackenzie assume its rightful name. Farther on it is joined from the west by the Liard, 650 miles long, the Peel, and lesser tributaries; from the east it receives the overflow of Great Bear Lake, that huge body of fresh water sometimes called the Arctic Caspian. On the desolate seacoast, little more than a hundred miles from the Alaskan border, it pours a volume of waters that has been estimated at 450,000 cubic feet a second into the Arctic, through an extensive delta two hundred miles long and forty-five miles broad.

Branches of the Mackenzie intertwine with those of the Columbia, the Saskatchewan, and the Yukon, while in the chaos which followed the melting of the continental icecap some of its headwaters spilled over into the Thelon and the Churchill rivers, flowing eastward into Hudson Bay. Essentially, however, the Mackenzie is the Great River of the Canadian Northwest.

Although much of its vast drainage basin suggests the forested monotony of Siberian rivers, in many places the scenery is wild and impressive. The western tributaries are typical mountain streams brimming with melted snows. The upper Athabaska is somewhat impeded by shoals and sand bars, but northward, all the way to the Arctic, the only other obstacle to navigation is the sixteen-foot drop on the Great Slave River known as the Rapids of the Drowned. This sinister name was bestowed in 1786 when two canoeloads of adventurers perished in the foaming waters. Loftier waterfalls interrupt some of the tributary streams. At Virginia Falls the South Nanni River tumbles over a cliff twice the height of Niagara, while Hay River, emptying into Great Slave Lake, catapults over two successive precipices, the first 46, the second 105 feet high, to race onward through a narrow gorge. Beyond Great Slave Lake the Mackenzie sweeps majestically past Great Bear Rock, towering fourteen hundred feet high, and seethes for five miles between limestone cliffs 150 feet high known as the Ramparts. From the air the delta presents a strange mosaic of mingled island and channel clogged with ice, but boatmen find it a perilous region of exposed islets and shallow waters tormented by Arctic gales. It is completely frozen over from November to May, while floating masses drift by even in midsummer.

No other river in the world, save the St. Lawrence and the Nile, drains such extensive lakes as the Mackenzie. Great Bear Lake and Great Slave Lake, each considerably larger than Erie, rank number nine and ten respectively in the list of the world's great lakes. Athabaska, though smaller, has an area of more than three thousand square miles, while Lesser Slave Lake and countless associates would be landmarks elsewhere though lost in a maze of glacial meltings and moraines.

The Athabaska River became known to the outside world in that colorful era of exploration and adventure when fur traders from Montreal challenged the monopoly of the Hudson's Bay Company in many a brawl which sometimes ended in bloodshed. In 1778 Peter Pond, financed by traders from Saskatchewan, led a little expedition of four canoes heaped with trade goods down the Athabaska River, seeking a huge lake which Indians said lay to the northward. Some thirty miles from this lake, now known as Athabaska, Pond established a trading post on the river.

Seven years prior to that date, in 1771, Samuel Hearne, acting for the Hudson's Bay Company, had discovered Great Slave Lake, which he crossed on the ice. In 1787 Pond visited that lake, heard from the Indians of its western outlet, and wondered if this might not be the same river that Captain Cook, exploring the Pacific coast, had observed emptying into that Great Ocean.

In 1788 Alexander Mackenzie, a young Scotsman only twenty-five years old, employed by the Montreal Fur Company, was sent westward to supersede Peter Pond, who had become implicated in the death of two white men. On the southern shore of Lake Athabaska he established a fort known as Chippewyan (later moved to the northern shore). Intrigued by what he learned from Pond and others, he left Fort Chippewyan on June 3, 1789, to follow the river to its outlet. He was accompanied by several Canadians, a German, and a number of Indians with their wives in canoes, one a capacious affair loaded with four tons of trade goods. Avoiding the deadly Rapids of the Drowned, he groped for days through the fog and ice of Great Slave Lake, bailing desperately with an old iron kettle. True, the exit, when found, was eight or ten miles wide but choked with islands, some of them covered with muskeg moss "ten feet deep." Drifting down the river, Mackenzie noted one place in the bank where an exposed coal seam was afire, a wasteful conflagration that has been burning ever since. On a shore excursion his moccasins became mired in oozing petroleum, an episode noted in his journal. Native paddlers deserted and others were reluctant to embark on so hazardous a quest. They feared the Eskimos, with whom a blood feud existed, and even more such unknown terrors as "winged men who killed by the eye." Mackenzie, however, over-

coming such obstacles common to the path of the explorer, penetrated the great delta and at length, through one of the several
mouths, gazed out as through an open window into the Arctic,
where he observed whales, probably belugas, spouting among
the floes. No thrill of achievement was his, however, but bitter
disillusionment. He had hoped that the current would turn westward to provide a new route to the Pacific and the fabulous
Indies beyond. Instead he recorded in his journal, "It was evident that these waters emptied themselves into the Hyperborean
Sea," and called them the River of Disappointment. Fortunately
his own name was substituted by geographers. After an absence
of only 102 days Mackenzie returned safely to Fort Chippewyan
after a journey of over three thousand miles, mainly through an
unknown wilderness.

Mackenzie is believed to have established a trading post on
Great Bear Lake, but the first definite record of anything beyond
a temporary shelter on the shore of that vast inland water was
that of Sir John Franklin, who wintered there in 1825–26. He
made this his base of operations in exploring the not-far-distant
seacoast, early successes which led to his later disastrous expedition into polar waters where he perished with all his company
in the greatest of Arctic tragedies.

Navigation on the Mackenzie was long confined to canoes.
Usually these were of birch bark, but Mackenzie noted among
the Gravel River Indians boats thirty feet long and four feet
broad made of moose hide tightly stretched over wooden frames.
The York boat was an invention of the Hudson's Bay Company,
a stout but clumsy sailing craft. It was designed for lake traffic
and stretches of river unimpeded by rapids. Scows were built
to drift down-river to Lake Athabaska, where they were broken
up for timber. Others, more durable, were dragged upstream
by men sweating at the towline. A 50-foot scow, sturgeon-nosed
to grope its way among rocks, carried a crew of ten. One man
was stationed aft with the long steering oar, another, at the
bow, had to plunge repeatedly into the icy water to shoulder
the clumsy craft away from obstructions, while the other crew
members strung out along a towline of inch rope that might be
five hundred feet long, clung to the bank, or waded through the

shallows. It was tearing work, broken by a brief rest every hour and five hearty meals daily.

Such primitive navigation has largely been eclipsed by steamboats, while air patrols now span in a few hours the space that sturdy *voyageurs* could cover only through weary months. Scattered settlements have sprung up along the valley. Most northerly of Hudson's Bay posts in the region is Fort Arctic River, but visiting whalers have wintered for many years at Herschel Island in desolate Beaufort Sea.

Stefansson, who voyaged down the Mackenzie to his "friendly Arctic," reported that in 1903 one fifth the native population had perished in an epidemic of measles. Food was the ever-present problem. In temperatures that plummeted to 60 below, no amount of lean meat would satisfy a gnawing hunger. Fat was a necessity, hence the Eskimos' fondness for whales' blubber and the white man's tallow candles. Natives sometimes sickened on the flesh of belugas, just as explorers in the Arctic have been made ill by the meat of gaunt white bears, or similar explorers in Antartica from eating an emaciated pony. Fish were abundant in open waters, rabbit a staple food in winter. Fish posts and meat posts (caribou) were common, insuring precious food stocks beyond the reach of wolves or scarcely less savage dogs.

Moose from the Rockies have wandered across the valley, swum the Mackenzie or crossed it on the ice, and now are found in the barren ground all the way to the Coppermine River. A more definite migration of wild life was fostered by the Canadian Government in the purchase of some thousands of Alaskan reindeer which were herded across hundreds of miles of wilderness and the Great River as well to the eastern barrens. Hardy Laplanders, familiar with reindeer habits and inured to Arctic winters, herded the animals by easy stages on a five-year journey which terminated in 1934.

The petroleum seepage first noticed by Mackenzie has interested many later visitors. The tar sands of Athabaska taint the atmosphere with their pitchy odor. Asphalt and coal seams are in evidence in a number of localities. Through faulted rock seams petroleum wells upward to the surface. Some distance from Fort Norman, above the juncture of the Great Bear River, the first oil well was brought into production in 1920. Three other wells sufficed to supply the needs of a vast but sparsely settled region. During the last war, however, in a frantic search for petroleum to supply the Alaskan area, the federal War Department, in co-operation with the Canadian Government, attempted to tap the resources of the Mackenzie. An ambitious project known as Canol, an abbreviation of Canadian oil, involved the laying down of six hundred miles of pipe line extending from Norman Wells, 550 miles above Great Slave Lake, to White Horse on the Alaskan Highway. Bulldozers, derricks, and steam shovels, like grotesque iron monsters, drove through the wilderness to the alarm of wild life. The withdrawal of the Japanese Navy to home waters, however, followed by the capitulation of Japan faced with the horrors of the atomic bomb, removed the pressure of necessity and the costly project was abandoned with the loss of tens of millions of dollars.

Meanwhile the Great River pursues its course through forests and interminable muskegs, while distant peaks, snow-covered, brood over the wilderness. But every year the white man's enterprise becomes more evident in a region once pre-empted by nomadic Indians and marauding Eskimos. The Empire of Furs crumbled long ago, although furs are still an important product. The fisheries which excited Mackenzie's comment are little exploited, the vast forest resources virtually untouched. Much mineral wealth besides petroleum lies undisturbed. Someday the boundless resources of the Great Northwest will be better appreciated in the gradual exhaustion of more accessible reserves. For, after all, the Mackenzie has been sketched upon the map of the world little more than a century and a half, a brief infancy, indeed, contrasted with the venerable age of the Indus or the Nile.

THE CHURCHILL RIVER—A RELIC OF THE ICE AGE

Length—1,000 miles. Drainage area—140,000 square miles

Neither in size nor economic importance does the Churchill rank among the world's great rivers. But it is an interesting type of glacial origin, still in its formative stage, and so recent geologically that it has scarcely developed into a river at all. Rather it is a spillway of surplus waters, the meltings of the continental icecap which still saturates the surrounding terrain.

The Churchill has its source in the Beaver River in Alberta and roughly parallels the much longer Nelson-Saskatchewan to the southward, with which its branches intertwine. Across Saskatchewan and Manitoba it flows for a thousand miles, through a nearly empty wilderness to the vast vacancy of Hudson Bay.

From the north the Churchill receives the Reindeer River, the outlet of Reindeer Lake, one of the lesser known of the world's great bodies of fresh water. Hidden in the heart of the Canadian shield on the rim of the Barren Ground, this lake, through an affluent, receives some of the overflow from Lake Wollaston, which also has an exit westward into the Mackenzie. Hence this queer lake contributes its waters to the far-off Arctic near Alaska and also to Hudson Bay, such is the confused pattern of lakes and rivers in a region but recently emerged from the Ice Age.

The Churchill is also linked with other lakes. For nearly a hundred miles it flows through Southern Indian Lake, a landscape feature elsewhere but here only one of many similar but smaller lakes. In fact, for long stretches the Churchill is little more than a chain of lakes overflowing from one to the other and presenting no clearly defined channel save in the numerous rapids which interrupt the current.

This curious river, only a few thousand years old where others count their age in millions, was named in 1688 for Sir John Churchill, governor of the Hudson's Bay Company and later Duke of Marlborough. But it seems to have been discovered by that rugged Danish explorer, Jens Munc, who spent a terrible winter at its mouth. Henry Hudson, who first entered the spacious bay which bears his name, thought it might prove to be the entrance to the much-sought-after Northwest Passage. He was unable to follow up his discovery, however, as his mutinous followers set him adrift in an open boat to perish of exposure. Munc, arriving later, penetrated to the western shore of Hudson Bay, where winter drove the two vessels under his command to seek shelter in the mouth of the Churchill River. Open fires on deck gave little protection against the paralyzing cold, while scurvy took its deadly toll. When spring at last appeared, Munc, believing himself to be the last survivor, completed the ship's log and philosophically lay down to die. At that hopeless juncture a hail from shore announced the return of two deserters who had cured their scurvy by eating roots and grass. The three men, revived by a gleam of hope, managed to refit the sloop *Lamprey* and by incredible exertion won their way out of that icy deathtrap, around the pitiless Labrador coast, and safe home across the Atlantic, a feat of daring and resolution seldom equaled. Behind them lay the frigate *Unicorn*, tenanted by corpses. Wandering Indians, boarding her, found kegs of wet powder which they attempted to dry out by building a fire. This logical experiment was only too successful, as the ship was blown to fragments in the resultant explosion.

It was not until 1717 that a trading post was established near the scene of Munc's grisly adventures. Here the river, broadening into an estuary seven or eight miles long and two miles wide, opens into Hudson Bay through a half-mile gap between lofty heights. The enclosed waters provide the finest harbor on Hudson Bay, a fact recognized by company officials when they chose it as the site of Fort Prince of Wales. This was designed as the Gibraltar of British Dominions in the West; the guarded gateway to a vast empire of fur and forest.

The fortification, begun in 1731, was forty years in building. A square with a projecting bastion at each corner, it somewhat resembled a four-pointed star.

Walls of masonry, filled with earth, forty feet in thickness and stone battlements bristling with forty cannon were designed to make it impregnable. Samuel Hearne, the first white man in North America who ever traveled overland to the Arctic, the discoverer of Great Slave Lake and founder of Cumberland House, the pioneer company trading post in the remote interior, was placed in command. A neighboring rock bears in still legible characters his signature: "Sl. Hearne, July ye 1, 1767."

But the tides of empire ebbed and flowed in the early history of the northland when war between England and France was almost a normal condition. In 1782 the French Admiral la Perouse suddenly appeared, all unannounced, with several frigates and some hundreds of soldiers. Hearne, who lacked men enough to man the guns, surrendered without firing a shot, while the French did their ineffectual best to demolish the ponderous battlements. This interruption, however, merely delayed the expansion of the Hudson's Bay Company across the continent to the valley of the Columbia River. The victorious La Perouse was given another commission to explore the Pacific, and somewhere among its maze of islands he disappeared with his ships and all on board in one of the greatest marine tragedies of all time.

The Churchill once provided a portage route to the valley of the Mackenzie. Canoes still skirt its forested shores, as they did in the old adventurous days when *voyageurs* and half-breed Indians journeyed all the way to Alaska and the Arctic. But modern science has improved upon such primitive commerce. The wheat and cattle growers of the Canadian Northwest have long turned toward Hudson Bay as a more accessible outlet for their products. The Hudson Bay Railroad from Edmonton, Alberta, now has its ocean terminus at the mouth of the Churchill River. Docks and grain elevators supplant the rude log huts of former fur traders, and the whistle of the locomotive startles the stillness once broken only by the honking of wild geese and the howl of the timber wolf. True, the development of the vast hinterland lies far in the future. Ice impedes navigation on Hudson Bay and its treacherous outlet to the Atlantic. The open season is brief, at best. But the Churchill River may someday justify the dreams of Jens Munc and prove to be a Northwest Passage to an empire quite as alluring as the fabled Indies.

THE NELSON–SASKATCHEWAN—SHADES OF THE HUDSON'S BAY COMPANY

Length—1,660 miles. Drainage area—360,000 square miles

The Nelson-Saskatchewan is one of the great river systems of North America. Through most of its course of 1,660 miles it is also one of the youngest of all rivers, for its drainage area, which comprises some 360,000 square miles, was once buried under the continental icecap. As this ice receded, its melting waters first swept southward to the Mississippi, then northeastward into Hudson Bay. The lakes which now swell the current are remnants of much vaster lakes, while the entire system may be regarded as a gigantic relic of the Glacial Age.

The Saskatchewan rises beyond the Rockies in that geographic curiosity known as the Columbia Ice Field. This region, which occupies some 150 square miles, girdled by mountains, feeds two other great rivers, the Columbia and the Athabaska. The Saskatchewan, turning eastward, sprawls across the Canadian provinces of Alberta and Saskatchewan. Two feeder streams penetrate the United States; the Red River, which forms much of the western boundary of Minnesota, and the Winnipeg, which drains the Lake of the Woods on the international boundary and sends offshoots probing into Ontario to tap a confused lake area.

Some rivers, like the Mississippi-Missouri, are bracketed because of important tributaries; the Saskatchewan-Nelson is cut squarely in two by one of the world's great lakes. This is Winnipeg, 260 miles long, with an area of 9,390 square miles, much larger than Ontario and nearly the size of Erie. From the west into this lake flows the Saskatchewan; toward the east emerges the Nelson, its outlet to the sea.

The Saskatchewan, at first a mountain stream, winds through vast forests mottled with muskeg swamps that yield toward the south to rolling prairies. It has many branches, nor is Winnipeg the only considerable lake to replenish its waters. There are at least three others large enough to be included among the world's major bodies of fresh water: Winnipegosis, Manitoba, and the Lake of the Woods. These are dwindling remnants of colossal Lake Agassiz, with an area of 110,000 square miles, enough to swallow all five of the present great lakes and Winnipeg besides. This inland sea once drained into the Mississippi, but as the icy barrier retreated northward the Saskatchewan pirated the watershed and, from the confused medley of lake and marsh and terminal moraine, wove its present intricate pattern of inland waterways.

Much of the bed of fossil Agassiz now forms the silted wheat fields of the Northwest; much remains a soggy terrain with numberless lakes hidden amid forests of spruce, tamarack, and jack pine with a liberal sprinkling of poplar, birch, and willow.

From the northern sector of Lake Winnipeg the Nelson emerges at an elevation of 710 feet to go hurrying across the great Canadian shield with its ancient rock formations and glacier-rounded hills. Descending this scarred and desolate terrain down a series of cascades, the river broadens through the final ninety miles of its course to a width of three or four miles, increasing to seven or eight in a trumpet-shaped estuary opening out upon the icy horizons of Hudson Bay where it battles fifteen-foot tides.

This bleak seacoast was explored by the British admiral, Sir Thomas Button, in 1612–13. There his mate, Nelson, died and was buried in a lonely grave on the edge of the wilderness, while the great river perpetuates his name. Although this deference of the admiral's to a faithful companion was natural, the entire river system, essentially a unit, might better have retained its Indian name—Saskatchewan.

The river valley is rich in the lore of the Hudson's Bay Company and rival traders from Montreal who once competed with much bitterness and some bloodshed for the great Fur Empire of the Northwest. That picturesque character Pierre Radisson returned to Montreal with six hundred thousand beaver skins, the rich spoils of an excursion into Lake Superior, only to have this fortune confiscated by the French governor. Vainly seeking redress at the court of Louis, the disgruntled Radisson deserted to the British. His rude eloquence so excited the enthusiasm of Charles II that the Merry Monarch issued a charter to "the governor and company of Gentlemen Adventurers trading into Hudson's Bay" and one of history's most romantic chapters was begun. How that great corporation, spreading its conquests over two million square miles, planted the British flag from the Arctic to the Pacific is written in bold characters in the story of North American settlement. At first rude stockades were built on the shores of James Bay at the southern tip of Hudson Bay, but the shallow waters were perilous in storms. Farther north great rivers like the Nelson and the Churchill opened broad avenues into the interior for birch-bark canoes. Hence York Factory was presently erected at the mouth of the Hayes River, which empties into the Nelson estuary, and young Samuel Hearne, just back from a trip to the Arctic and his discovery of Great Slave Lake, was dispatched into the remote interior to establish the trading post known as Cumberland House in the valley of the Saskatchewan.

To Admiral Button goes the credit for discovering the river's mouth, but what white man first gazed upon the Saskatchewan, behind its gigantic shield of Lake Winnipeg, is conjectural. In 1688 Jacques de Noyon from French headquarters on the St. Lawrence, traversing Lakes Huron and Superior, had arrived at the Lake of the Woods which overflows into the Winnipeg River. Two years later, in 1690, Henry Kelsey left York Factory with a party of Indians, followed devious waterways and portages to Lake Winnipeg, and entered the valley of the Saskatchewan beyond. Better authenticated are the later adventures of Anthony Hendry, who accompanied a party of Assiniboine Indians across Winnipeg by canoe and wintered in the wilderness. He seems to have journeyed westward as far as the Great Plains, for he observed Blackfoot Indians on horseback, a story ridiculed upon his return by pompous officials.

In 1732 Pierre la Verendrye built Fort Charles on a forested promontory in the Lake of the Woods and spent some years in that picturesque wilderness. In 1738 a scouting party which he sent into the north country built Fort Rouge on the Red River, the nucleus of the modern city of Winnipeg.

A noted center of the Hudson's Bay Company was Norway House, on an island opening upon Playgreen Lake, which connects with Lake Winnipeg and the Nelson River. Here were constructed many of those clumsy but substantial sailing craft known as York boats.

Several important cities have grown up in the valley of the Saskatchewan and its tributaries. These include Winnipeg, metropolis of the region; Edmonton, capital of Alberta, and Calgary, its most populous city; and Fargo, the largest city in North Dakota.

Pierre Radisson, with all his imaginative vision, never foresaw such activity on waters he navigated only in Indian canoes. Yet the development of this vast area is still in its infancy. While it can scarcely hope to rival that of the St. Lawrence, the Nelson-Saskatchewan Valley, with its four great lakes, embraces an inland empire stretching from the Rockies to Hudson Bay, an empire of far richer possibilities than have yet been realized.

PART NINE

South American Rivers

~~~~~~

ALTHOUGH South America ranks fourth among the great land masses of the globe, it is, due to a favoring climate and topography, the Continent of Giant Rivers.

Wedge-shaped, it tapers to Cape Horn battling Antarctic gales. Down the western edge stretches the ridge of the Andes, its peaks surpassed only by those of Asia. Eastward the great bulk of the continent, crossed by the equator, offers free scope to moisture-laden winds. Except over the rainless coast of the Pacific and semi-arid Patagonia, there is an abundant rainfall, conserved in the valley of the Amazon by the greatest tropic forest in the world. Here drenching showers, a water-soaked soil, and an atmosphere dripping with moisture provide a watery surplus unrivaled elsewhere.

Although the Andes are much loftier than the highlands of Guiana and Brazil, the latter are immeasurably older, the core of the ancient continent, warped and denuded by the climatic wear and tear of uncounted centuries. From this gnarled hinterland rivers radiate to the north, the east, and the south, their channels broken by innumerable cascades and waterfalls.

Two notable rivers drain the northern sector: the Magdalena, Colombia's major stream, whose volume is more impressive than its length, and the mightier Orinoco, which pours into the Atlantic a chocolate-colored flood which exceeds that of the Mississippi.

SOUTH AMERICAN RIVERS

From the Brazilian highlands the São Francisco flows first north then east, a river prominent in the lore of colonial days, draining a region of rich mineral resources and broken by one of the world's major waterfalls, the Paulo Affonso. Flowing southward is the La Plata-Paraná, with its tributaries, one of the great river systems of the globe, its spacious valleys sheltering naked savages and modern cities, its forests resounding to the thunder of unrivaled waterfalls. Lastly, from the icy peaks of the Andes, across the breadth of the continent, flows the Amazon, a resistless tide, its valley an inland Mediterranean of forested waterways, incomparably the grandest river in the world.

THE PEERLESS AMAZON

Length—4,000 miles. Drainage area—2,722,000 square miles

Any account of the Amazon must be penned in superlatives. The rivers of the world fall into two classes: this incomparable colossus—and all the other. The Congo, second in rank, drains 1,425,000 square miles; the Amazon, nearly double that area, or 2,722,000. The disparity in volume is even greater, for while the Congo's current swells the ocean by an estimated 2,000,000 cubic feet a second, the Amazon sends out 7,200,000, or fourteen times the normal volume of the Mississippi. So prodigious is its current that drinking water may be dipped up from the sea a hundred miles offshore, while some discoloration of the ocean surface has been distinguished at a distance of six hundred miles. Nor is this surprising when we reflect that through the Amazon's yawning mouth, widest of rivers, pours forth an estimated one fifth of all the moving fresh waters of the globe.

The area drained by the Amazon is nearly equal to that of the entire United States. Up its main channel ocean liners steam grandly to Iquitos in Peru, a distance of twenty-three hundred miles. Freighters drawing fourteen feet may proceed five hundred miles farther. In fact, the Amazon would furnish a highway nearly across the Atlantic. In floodtime it loses all semblance to a river to become a moving sea whose shore lines broaden in places to four hundred miles.

Eleven hundred tributaries feed this swollen current. At least fifteen of these are thought to be over a thousand miles in length and in themselves would rank among the world's great rivers. They provide a maze of navigable waterways, estimated at fifty thousand miles, that would twice girdle the globe at the equator.

No wonder the valley of the Amazon has been called the Mediterranean of South America. Nor is the allusion farfetched. According to geologists, that valley was once a gulf of the Pacific, shut off by the upsurging Andes. The lowest part of this gulf is now occupied by the great river, whose channel, in places, is one thousand feet deep, while the surrounding terrain, two thousand miles from the mouth, is elevated only ninety-five feet above the sea.

The inner basin of the Amazon is twenty-two hundred miles long by eight hundred wide. The northern tributaries, however, penetrate far into the Guiana and Venezuela highlands, while the southern come foaming down from the tableland of Brazil, the oldest portion of the continent, with its ancient sandstone plateaus and eroded mountains. The main river, with its headwaters, is fed by the snows and glaciers of the Andes, their loftiest peaks rising above twenty thousand feet. The entire drainage area sprawls over much of Brazil and Bolivia, most of Peru and Ecuador, with a generous sector of Colombia, to comprise about two fifths of the entire continent.

The geographical setting for earth's grandest river is well-nigh perfect. From the Andes it sweeps across the width of the continent with no important impediment. It enjoys more elbowroom than any other river. Moreover, it traverses one of the great rain belts of the world. Almost everywhere this rainfall averages from sixty to eighty inches annually; great areas record a hundred inches or more, and some register over two hundred. Nor is this moisture dissipated by deserts or irrigation projects as in so many other rivers, but is conserved by the greatest tropical forests in the world.

Swollen by torrential showers, driven onward by the sheer

weight of waters over a drenched and saturated terrain, the Amazon forces its way across a nearly level plain to the sea. There it battles the very ocean, thrusting back the Atlantic, which presently recoils in tidal bores called pororocas whose foam-flecked crests top fifteen feet. They scour the banks, gouge out great chunks of timberland, and widen the broadest estuary in the world. This battle of the waters, fresh and salt, is sometimes perceptible six hundred miles inland.

The length of the Amazon as usually given ranges from thirty-nine hundred to forty-two hundred miles. The latter figure is probably more nearly correct. The Nile and the Mississippi may be a few miles longer, otherwise there is little comparison. The facts are still further obscured by uncertainty over which of the Amazon's upper branches is the longest. No such accurate surveys as those which delineate the course of the Big Muddy are available. The main river, however, is usually regarded as the Marañón, which rises in the Andes about a hundred miles northeast of Lima, Peru, and still nearer to the Pacific. At first it flows northward through deep canyons, foaming down a series of cascades. In one of these gorges, called Pongos, it vaults over a series of thirty-five rock barriers, creating dizzy whirlpools. Turning eastward through a great arc, the river batters its way through the flanks of the mountains to spread out in broad savannahs studded with islands. The final exit into the great Amazonian plain is through a tremendous chasm five or six miles long whose walls, according to Captain Carbajal, seem "to close in at the top." Here the frenzied current attains a speed of twelve miles an hour. No wonder the natives believe that this rending asunder of the very earth was the handiwork of the gods.

The Marañón, now known as the Solimões, turns eastward across the continent, levying tribute from many branches. Not until its juncture with the Negro is it called the Amazon. Its average depth is 120 feet, its average width from four to ten miles, its average speed perhaps two and a half miles per hour. At Obidos, four hundred miles above the sea, the giant river is constricted between rocky spurs to a width of little more than two thousand yards. Here the current, speeding up to six miles an hour, has dredged a channel 350 feet deep. From this point onward it broadens out until the wooded banks on one shore are scarcely discernible from the other. The swollen waters have carved a maze of channels enclosing numerous islands. One of these, Marajo, which approaches the equator, is twice the size of Massachusetts, a continental tidbit gripped in the jaws of the river, which are here distended to a width of 207 miles.

The Amazon's greatest tributaries join it from the south. First of these as one approaches from the sea, and the most controversial, is the Tocantins. Rising in the rugged tableland of Brazil, it flows for seventeen hundred miles, gaining impetus from numerous branches and broken by roaring cataracts. It is eight miles wide where it empties into the Para outlet of the Amazon. Although some geographers challenge the inclusion of the Tocantins, it is an integral part of the Amazon system.

Next in order is the Xingu (barbaric name), another giant river nearly twelve hundred miles long. Into the wilderness of its little-known headwaters the English explorer Colonel P. H. Fawcett disappeared with his companions in 1925, doubtless murdered by the Indians. Still larger is the Tapajós, which sweeps majestically down a series of tremendous waterfalls to empty into the Amazon through a mouth eight miles wide. Of one of these waterfalls, the Utiarity, Theodore Roosevelt wrote, "I doubt whether, excepting of course Niagara, there is a waterfall in North America which equals it." And there are dozens of other falls on the Tapajós.

Yet these rivers are eclipsed by the far mightier Madeira, so huge that it challenges comparison with the main current of the Amazon itself. This giant tributary, worthy to stand in its own right as one of the major rivers of the world, has a length estimated up to three thousand miles. Natives have conferred upon it the ominous name "River of Death," so difficult is the terrain it traverses, so cursed with tropic fevers. Two hundred miles of its main channel is broken by cataracts. Much of its vast drainage basin has never been visited by white men. When Theodore Roosevelt sailed for six hundred miles down one of its many branches, the Brazilian Government graciously changed its name from the River of Doubt to Rio Teodoro. Another branch of the Madeira, the Beni, approaches within a few miles of Titicaca, loftiest of the world's big lakes. La Paz, capital of Bolivia, is situated upon this river. But it would require several pages to catalogue all the streams that pour their surplus waters into the Madeira.

Still further westward the Purus, one of the crookedest rivers in the world, winds for eighteen hundred miles through the Amazonian forests, followed by the Jurua. But the most interesting of the Amazon's tributaries, next to the Madeira, is the Ucayali, which penetrates into the heart of the ancient Inca Empire. Cuzco, the capital, was situated upon a branch of that river, while another branch, the Urubamba, skirts tremendous precipices crowned by Machu Piccu, the deserted city explored some years ago by an expedition of the National Geographic Society. It has been conjectured that this was a city of refuge in a maze of almost inaccessible mountains, or perhaps a relic of an older civilization destroyed by the Incas, but no one knows. Upon the map the Ucayali looks longer than the Marañón and may prove to be the true headwaters of the Amazon.

From the north the Amazon receives several tributaries whose sheer size demands recognition. Most westerly are the Putumayo and the Yapura, which drain the mountainous terrain of southern Colombia. The far mightier Negro, in places twenty miles wide, with its jet-black surface like polished ebony, contrasts sharply with the yellowish, silt-laden waters of the Amazon. Reaching northward through that strange natural waterway called the Casiquiare Canal, the Negro has captured some of the headwaters of the Orinoco in the most impressive example of river piracy known anywhere.

The story of the Amazon is one of incredible hardship. It was discovered by the Spanish explorer Vincente Pinzón in 1500. Sailing up its broad estuary, he called it Mar Dulce, the freshwater sea, for he had tasted its waters while the seacoast still lay beyond the horizon. Marañón, however, was preferred, a name still applied to its headwaters. In 1539 Gonzalo Pizarro, brother of the Conqueror of Peru, set out from Quito on Christmas Day to explore a fabled region called "the Land of Cinnamon." His little army of 350 Spaniards and some four thousand natives crossed the snowy Andes to plunge into a steaming wilderness of almost continuous rainfall. Reaching the Napo, one of the many giant tributaries of the Amazon, they were astonished at the velocity of its current and the roar of its waterfalls. One of these they estimated was twelve hundred feet high. They were forced to cut a path through the rope, like creepers of the equatorial forest. Their garments rotted in the dampness and were eaten by ants. Their provisions failed until they were reduced to devouring their hunting dogs and roots and berries. At their wits' end, they decided to build a vessel to search for supplies. Timber was no problem, but tatters of their clothing sufficed for oakum, and they wrought nails from the shoes of horses that had perished of starvation. Francisco Orellana was made captain, with a crew of fifty Spaniards. Sailing for some days down the swift Napo, he entered the main channel of the Amazon. The silent forests offered no sign of provisions anywhere, while return became increasingly difficult, perhaps impossible. And so he abandoned his former companions to their fate. These were left with no alternative save to fight their way back to Quito. In a straight line the distance was some five hundred miles; through the wilderness and across the mountains it was nearer twelve hundred. Gnawing their very saddles and belts, they dropped in their tracks one by one. Finally, after more than a year of heartbreaking exertion, some eighty Spaniards, mere tattered scarecrows, with fewer than half the native contingent that had originally accompanied them, staggered back to civilization.

Meanwhile Orellana drifted down the ever-broadening current to the sea. At one place he fought with Tapua Indians who were aided by their women. This minor brush with Amazons in the wilds, by a perverse twist of history, gave its name to the world's greatest river.

Arrived in Spain, Orellana related a tale of wonders that needed little embellishment. Although Pizarro branded his former lieutenant as a traitor, he was entrusted with a return expedition but perished amid the maze of waterways he had been the first to traverse.

Meanwhile, after a lapse of more than four centuries, the exploration of the Amazon progresses with vast areas still awaiting the advent of the map maker. Governmental investigation has been furthered by many scientists—Humboldt, Agassiz, Bates, and others—as well as obscure rubber hunters and butterfly and orchid collectors.

The most impressive feature of the Amazon, next to its oceanic maze of waters, is the vast forest that clothes much of its drainage area, a living labyrinth which Brazilians call the Green Inferno. This forest would cover the United States from the Appalachians to the Rockies. Much of the undergrowth is killed out by towering trees, but one may easily get lost in the cloistered gloom, often silent and seemingly destitute of other life. A distinction should be made, however, between the dreadful *igapo*, or marginal forests, which are annually inundated, and the ocean of vegetation on higher ground beyond. Most human settlements, unfortunately, are in the former region, where vegetation welters in a perpetual bath of moisture as in a gigantic hothouse. The natives have coined a proverb: "Man and the river are always going, but the forest remains." Here jungle roads called *picadas* are mere tunnels in the verdure, while deserted settlements are swallowed up in a single year. The trees are interlaced with lianas hundreds of feet long and perhaps centuries old, which possess a tensile strength greater than that of sisal rope of the same diameter.

Among a veritable profusion of tropical trees whose species, according to Dr. Huber, number more than twenty-five hundred, the ceiba towers forty feet above its fellows. Another giant is the Brazil-nut tree (*Bertholletia excelsa*). The trunk of this monarch of the upland forest is sometimes forty feet in circumference, while the pods, hard as iron, may weigh forty pounds and contain as many as twenty-two of the familiar nuts. But there are hoary giants that grow to even greater dimensions. Gonzalo Pizarro encountered one in the valley of the Napo, which Prescott estimated from the Spaniard's description must have presented a girth of ninety-six feet.

Much valued is that wonder tree, the babassu palm. From its leaves are woven hats and baskets; its tough fiber is twisted into ropes; its oily nuts supply a substitute for olive oil, lard, and margarine and are utilized for firing boilers on river steamboats.

The assai palm grows a purple fruit whose juice provides a drink refreshing in hot climates. Cashew nuts grow wild. One species of laurel supplies an inflammable sap; from the heart of the jupati palm natives brew a liquor so fiery that white palates require a dilution with five volumes of water.

Amid the profusion of mahogany, ironwood, and other hardwood trees are some of definite medicinal value. Quinine, the standard preventative of malaria, is obtained from the bark of a tree native to the upper Amazon. There also flourish the coca plants, whose leaves endow Peruvian porters with unnatural endurance. A product of these plants is the useful though sometimes misused cocaine. Other plants less advertised have been disclosed by native experiment and will no doubt prove additions to the world's medicine chest.

In contrast with such friendly herbs are others of evil reputation: the sinister assacu, with its poisonous sap; the curare, used by natives to tip their poisoned darts; and the even more fearsome *mata calado*, or "silent death," which slays and leaves no trace.

Among innumerable flowering trees and plants, orchids flourish beyond all counting. More conspicuous, however, are the giant water lilies, *Victoria regia*, whose leaves, upturned around the edges, are sometimes eight feet across and buoyant enough to support a small child.

A staple article of food is farina, made from the root of the manioc plant. This root, which resembles a parsnip, is poisonous. The Indians shred it in a rude trough of flints set in hard pitch. The fluff is then packed in woven mat tubes, suspended from a branch in the river, and repeatedly squeezed by a tourniquet. This extracts the poison and leaves a residue of coarse, rather tasteless meal that is made up into cakes a foot in diameter and half an inch thick. These queer "loaves" are current everywhere. Rice, plantains, and fish are also prominent food items.

Cotton flourishes in the valley of the Amazon, while Indian jute, imported from the banks of the Ganges, finds here a congenial environment. But prized above all other plants is the rubber tree, whose importance in modern manufacture has sometimes renamed the Amazon the Rubber River.

This unprepossessing gum of magic properties is obtained from the juice of many plants, but the original and far the best source is the latex of the *Hevea brasiliensis*, a hundred-foot giant that originated in the forests of the Amazon. This latex, almost ninety per cent pure caoutchouc, forms the Para brand, still recognized as the finest in the market.

Columbus, on his second voyage to America, observed natives playing with a heavy ball of black gum. Here, all unrecognized, was a richer product of the New World than the gold which fired his acquisitive soul. Rubber, introduced into England, was first used to erase pencil marks, hence its common name—rubber. As its uses multiplied, rubber-bearing trees were much sought for in the valley of the Amazon, a quest that was renewed during the late World War. Meanwhile the seeds, packed in moist charcoal, had been introduced into the Far East, where great plantations in Malaya and the neighboring islands were destined to supply most of the raw rubber of the world. In such plantations trees are set out in regular rows ninety to the acre. A mature specimen yields four to five pounds of latex annually.

The Amazon swarms with animal life. Sea cows, or manatees, bluish gray in color, invade the river from the sea to be caught in nets or harpooned by the natives. Dolphins have lived so long in these fresh waters that they have developed a definite species called botos. The anaconda, that breasts the current, is perhaps the longest of all snakes; Bates credits one specimen with a length of forty-two feet. Other forms of reptilian life include huge turtles whose flesh and eggs are an important article of food. Caymans, or alligators, grow to a larger size than their North American cousins. The muscular tail of a small species, known as jacaretinga, is sometimes eaten.

Agassiz once estimated that the fresh-water fishes of the Amazon numbered two thousand species. A recent revision downward lists 748, one third more than inhabit the Congo. Ocean vagrants swell the list: sharks, skates, and giant sting rays with poisoned blades three inches long. Indigenous is the pirarucu, called the beef of the Amazon and largest of all strictly fresh-water fishes. Ernest G. Holt mentions one specimen 15 feet long that weighed 410 pounds.

Better known is the piranha, or caribe, which Theodore Roosevelt familiarized as the "man-eating fish." Chunky like a perch and seldom more than a foot long, its ferocity is unbelievable. To trail the hand behind a canoe is to risk having a finger bitten off, while a school of piranhas maddened by the taste of blood will strip the flesh from any animal unfortunate enough to swim or wade among them. A piranha will bite through two strands of wire upon a hook; out of water, he grunts savagely and grips a knife blade so hard as to crush his own razor-edged teeth. Another aquatic curiosity is the electric eel, whose touch paralyzes small animals.

Unlike Africa, big game is rare in the uplands. The largest native animal is the tapir, a relic of former ages. Although he bears more resemblance to a pig, his flesh suggests beef. Largest of predatory types is the jaguar, or American tiger. His spotted coat resembles a leopard's, but he is much larger, attaining a weight of 250 pounds. His fur, coarse and sparse, is quite valueless. Fierce javelinas, or peccaries, range the woods, and giant anteaters whose curved claws can demolish an anthill of almost bricklike hardness. Capybaras three feet long are the largest of the rodent family. Sloths, most sluggish of animals, hang pendant from the branches, which also harbor arboreal anteaters. Here, too, congregate howler monkeys, whose raucous concerts echo through the woods for two miles or more. A throat formation endows these small creatures with a volume of sound that rivals the roar of a lion. Armadillos and other grotesque creatures abound, including an arboreal frog that glides from tree to tree by extending its legs. Among the legions of bats, big and little, is one species that catches fish. More gruesome is the vampire bat, that loathesome spirit of the night which hovers noiselessly about to leave his victims weak with lassitude from loss of blood. Lewis R. Freeman mentions a strange creature, a species of skunk called the yacca, which is domesticated by the natives for a singular purpose. Tossed overboard from a canoe, it is swallowed alive by a cayman with astonishing results. The yacca, resorting to its natural weapon, so bloats the cayman by the discharge of gas that sheer buoyancy forces the latter to the surface to be speedily harpooned.

Poisonous reptiles are another hazard of the Amazon. Tree vipers lurk in the branches, but most varieties are ground dwellers. Much dreaded is the bushmaster, or sururucu. Freeman observed one nearly eleven feet in length. The fer-de-lance of the Caribbean is here known as the jararaca. Coral snakes, smaller but equally deadly, are common.

A reptilian Judas is the mussurana, harmless to man and often kept as a pet. This interesting creature, which may attain a length of seven feet, feeds upon poisonous serpents. Immune to the venom of the bushmaster or the fer-de-lance, he swallows them alive, but is said to fall victim to the coralline serpents.

The valley of the Amazon is the paradise or rather the inferno of insect life. Here the ceaseless warfare between man and insect has so far witnessed the triumph of the latter. Ants swarm in inconceivable numbers and a bewildering variety of species. Travelers complain bitterly of ants big and little, black, white, and red, in everything, including the food. They gnaw a garment to shreds in a single night. Fire ants, whose bites blister the skin, coat the very vegetation. The sauba, or leaf-cutting ant, perhaps our first agriculturist, so strips vegetation that agriculture in certain areas has proven impossible. Another species, the tangaranga, is over an inch in length. H. G. Wells chose this region as the setting for one of his weird romances, *The Empire of the Ants*.

Ticks of various shapes and sizes are an abomination and are thought to spread certain diseases, while explorers in the uplands mention caterpillars whose bristles are tipped with stinging venom.

Winged insects are quite as annoying. Mosquitoes, carriers of malaria and yellow fever, find here a natural habitat. A tabanid fly, with a proboscis half an inch long and sharp as a needle, makes the natives howl with pain. The bite of the motuca leaves a stream of blood. Tiny gnats, or piums, invade protective mosquito netting and inflict itching bites which must not be scratched lest they form ulcers. W. L. Schurz mentions a curious insect called the traffic bug which bears a red light on his head, a green light on his tail. The beetle *Titanus giganteus* attains a length of six inches. One species of spider is so huge that it captures and devours young birds. Most detestable of all are the berni flies, which deposit their eggs beneath the victim's skin. These develop into twisting, hairy grubs which cause torment for days until they emerge. A lancet gash may relieve humans from this affliction, but animals get no such relief.

Into this world of swarming and malignant life, animated by a savagery softened by no trace of pity, other insects project a vision of almost unreal beauty. Such are the dragonflies with iridescent wings and the butterflies that flit about like animated blossoms. Within an area half a mile square Agassiz counted 117 species, while Bates collected 770 around the city of Belém on the Para. There are only 321 species in all Europe.

Huge yellow butterflies collect around salty surfaces, and great morphos and agrias drip with color like changeable silk.

Strange birds are also numerous, such as the grotesque jabiru stork. In the upper valleys of the Negro the hoatzin presents a lingering glimpse of the Age of Reptiles, when the family of the birds diverged from the forerunners of the dinosaurs. Young hoatzins have claws upon their wings to climb with and are excellent swimmers. Their odor, however, is reptilian, and their characteristics note a snakelike hiss. Parrots are almost infinite in number. Their brilliant plumage brightens the forest gloom and their chattering relieves its deadly silences. The cock of the rock is called the most beautiful bird in the world, with its flame-colored coat topped by a double crest from neck to beak like the plume of a Roman helmet. But beauty and ugliness are inextricably commingled in this region of continental size, where life, both vegetable and animal, riots in chaotic profusion.

In vivid contrast is the sparse human population. Here, as Buckle affirms, nature's prodigality has become a burden. The headwater streams were embraced in the empire of the Incas, but these masterful builders never ventured far into the steaming lowlands. Elsewhere the valleys were thinly settled by wandering bands of savages in ceaseless warfare with their environment and with one another.

Some of these aborigines were among the most primitive of humans, wearing no clothing and erecting only temporary shelters of branches little better than those of a chimpanzee. Civilization peered within only to pause upon the threshold. And yet these Indians, often athletic and finely proportioned, have succeeded in adjusting themselves to a hostile environment, in itself no mean achievement. Doubtless by painful trial and error they had learned to transform the poisonous manioc root to a staple article of food, had learned also to tip with lethal poison the darts of their deadly blowpipes. They had discovered the curative values of herbs, particularly quinine, and had developed a relative immunity to that most formidable of all diseases, malaria. In a region cursed with insect pests, they had manufactured a crude type of rotenone, now employed with excellent results by farmers of the north. Dugout canoes bore them about their endless waterways, while by harpoon and net they conducted a crude fishery. Nor should it be forgotten that they presented the world with one object of almost universal use which neither Greece nor Rome could evolve—our common hammock.

The white man, however, has made little progress in the valley of the Amazon. There are few important cities. The metropolis of the region, Para, or Belém, near the mouth of the river, although founded in 1615, before the landing of the Pilgrims at Plymouth, showed a population, according to a recent census, of only 330,000. Manaus, on the Negro, is a city of 67,866 people. Here docks are built upon pontoons to allow for a sixty-foot rise in flood levels, but the million-dollar opera house is rather a reminder of that day when the city was the Rubber Capital of the world than a forecast of future prosperity. At the mouth of the Jurua lies the island called Ilha da Consciencia, where, according to cynical observers, rubber prospectors bound farther inland left their consciences. Iquitos in Peru is a modern city, though it numbers only 34,231. The inhabitants of the Amazon's drainage basin have been estimated at 1,600,000, less than one per square mile, fewer, in fact, than the population of the Sahara. This contrast presents an arresting picture: two regions of comparable area, with the world's best watered region more sparsely settled than its greatest desert.

Following our Civil War, a group of southern irreconcilables emigrated to the Tapajós, where they tried to establish a colony. Within a generation, however, this settlement had dwindled to a few squalid huts on the edge of the jungle. Similar projects, though employing the most advanced methods and backed by unlimited resources, have proven dubious ventures at best. On this same river, the Tapajós, Henry Ford obtained from the Brazilian Government a princely grant of 703,700 acres for a rubber plantation. Later he exchanged this tract in part payment on a much larger area of 2,500,000 acres, called Fordlandia, some eighty miles farther up the river. Here he planned a model town with dwellings for ten thousand persons and provided with hospitals, schools, and all the other communal buildings of modern civilization. But up to the time of his death this too had proved a costly failure.

Water, so welcome elsewhere, is here a burden. In many places garden seeds must be planted in boxes, as they would rot in the saturated soil. Of the Amazon, Colonel E. G. Church writes, "There are probably not over twenty-five square miles of its basin under cultivation."

Tropical diseases are also a menace: malaria, leprosy, yellow fever, beriberi, dysentery, and less common disorders. A type of African sleeping sickness, doubtless borne by airplane, has recently invaded the valley. Yet in some districts malaria is unknown, while medical science learned how to cope with an unhealthy environment when it transformed Panama from one of the worst pestholes in the world.

So vast a region as the Amazon Valley presents many varieties of soil and climate. The temperature is not unduly hot, compared with other densely populated regions, while intervals of a month or more are free from rain. Cattle raising prospers in the lower valley, particularly on the island of Marajo, where, however, it encounters unique difficulties. During the annual inundation cattle stand up to their knees in water for weeks on end. At such times they fall victims to the caymans, which are lassoed and slaughtered by the cowboys. Tributary rivers penetrate highlands rich in minerals. Among less familiar products are quartz crystals. W. Robert Moore mentions one such crystal that weighed five tons!

The forests of the Amazon would supply the world. The potential water power of the upper river and its branches has never been estimated, but it may surpass that of the Congo. And all this incalculable wealth is made readily accessible by the grandest system of natural waterways in the world.

Bolivia and Peru have made some effort to avail themselves of these waterways. A railroad has been constructed with infinite labor around the two-hundred-mile stretch of rapids that impedes the Madeira. This has been called the costliest railroad in the world, for although quinine was imported literally by the ton, hundreds of laborers died in its construction.

Native dugout canoes are supplemented by rude rafts. One such drifted down the Purus from Peru, bearing a little settlement of seventeen families with their poultry and livestock. But steamers and launches are becoming more numerous. Five-thousand-ton freighters can proceed all the way from the sea to the Xingú through broad and deep side channels without even entering the main current.

Incomparably the greatest river in the world, the Amazon remains a challenge to the engineering genius of the future. Humboldt long ago forecast thriving cities on its banks. In 1853 Alfred Russell Wallace wrote, "I fearlessly assert that here the primeval forest can be converted into rich pasture and meadow land." W. L. Schurz, who observed only six poisonous snakes in exploring an extensive area of its basin, said, "By far the greatest part of it is entirely habitable by white men." Mankind, half desperate from self-inflicted evils, might better turn from dabbling in such hellish forays into black art as atomic bombs to consider that major item of unfinished global business, the conquest of the Amazon.

THE LA PLATA–PARANÁ—GREAT CITIES AND GIANT
WATERFALLS

Length—2,450 miles. Drainage area—1,198,000 square miles

In 1516 Juan de Solis, Pilot Major of Spain, while probing the South American coast line for a route to the Indies, entered a broad gulf which he found to his astonishment was fresh water. Landing, he was murdered by the Charruan Indians, but his surviving followers returned to spread strange stories of a fresh-water sea on the Atlantic's western edge. That fresh-water sea known as La Plata is the estuary of one of the great river systems of the world.

La Plata has been called the river broader than it is long, a pardonable exaggeration since its length is 170 miles, its width at the mouth 138. Its depth varies from ten fathoms to two and one half, but the nearly tideless waters heap up dangerously before violent blasts known as pamperos. Near its upper extremity, even there forty-five miles broad, it receives the Uruguay, ten miles wide, and the much larger Paraná, which empties through a delta nearly forty miles across.

Steamers leave New York bound for the "River Plate," although it is only a section of one great system better called by its native name, Paraná, or "Mother of the Sea." The total length, usually given as 2,450 miles, is not particularly noteworthy, although some estimates raise the figure to three thousand. But its drainage area, 1,198,000 square miles, only slightly under that of the Mississippi, ranks it fourth among the great rivers of the world. Still more impressive is its volume, so enormous that it may surpass the Congo and yield only to the Amazon. According to E. L. Corthell, records show a discharge of "608 cubic miles in a year," or approximately 2,800,000 cubic feet a second; more than five times the normal outflow from the Mississippi.

Magellan, on his voyage around the globe, entered the Plata in 1520. Six years later Sebastian Cabot, co-discoverer of North America, first ascended the Paraná to about the latitude of Asunción, a thousand miles from the sea. From the natives he obtained silver ornaments which so enthused the Spaniards that they named the estuary Rio de la Plata, or the Silver River.

The drainage area of the Paraná and its many tributaries embraces much of northern Argentina, southern Brazil, most of Uruguay, a sector of Bolivia, and all of Paraguay. The scenery through so vast a region is of the most varied character. The northern shore of the La Plata estuary is a wooded upland stretching into southern Brazil, blessed with a healthful climate and rich in potential resources. The southern shore, relatively low, merges on the west into the treeless pampas, those endless prairies of South

America. Far to the north this region blends into the Gran Chaco, the scene of bloody strife between Bolivia and Paraguay. In the Quichua tongue *chaco* means "hunting ground." Geologists consider it the bed of a vast fossil lake or ocean inlet—the Pampean Sea. At present it is a relatively flat region of mingled swamp and upland. Theodore Roosevelt, a visitor on his expedition into the valley of the Amazon, thought it excellent cattle country. From the highlands of Bolivia flows one of many tributaries, the Pilcomayo, a thousand miles long, which, like the Nile, gropes its way through a vast swamp called the Estero Patiño. Though known to the Incas, this river has but recently been surveyed. From the north comes the Paraguay, a huge river nearly as voluminous as the Paraná itself, its muddy waters draining from the far-off highlands of Matto Grosso, not far from the headwaters of those giant tributaries of the Amazon, the Tapajós and the Xingú. In the Corumba territory it sometimes inundates an area of thirty thousand square miles.

The clear waters of the Paraná flow down from the northeast across Brazil, penetrating the coastal range almost to the sea. Its tributaries, like those of the Amazon and the São Francisco to the north, are slowly eroding the tough tableland and weathered mountains of eastern Brazil, the core of the continent, exposing some of the most ancient rocks on earth.

The Paraná is pre-eminent among rivers for its tremendous waterfalls. Most spectacular is the Iguassú, often compared with Niagara and Victoria Falls on the Zambezi. The Iguassú River rises in the coastal range hardly thirty miles from the sea. Turning inland, it traverses the Brazilian uplands for 430 miles until, within twelve miles of its juncture with the Paraná, it plunges headlong over an escarpment more than two miles wide with a maximum height of 230 feet. In floodtime its volume exceeds that of Niagara; in drought no fewer than 273 separate waterfalls have been counted along its rugged verge. At one point the descent is an abrupt fall, but through most of its width this fall is broken into two sections each slightly more than a hundred feet in height. The greatest volume roars down the Devil's Throat on the Brazilian side, shut off from the Argentina sector by the island of San Martin, for, like Niagara, this waterfall is also on an international boundary. Less lofty than Victoria, less torrential than Niagara, the Iguassú presents a panorama of varied features that excels them both.

Not so well advertised or spectacular, but far more stupendous, are the falls of La Guayra, 120 miles north at the head of navigation on the Paraná. Here the vast river, three miles wide, becomes constricted between canyon walls scarcely three hundred feet apart. Foaming downward for more than a hundred feet over a series of eighteen separate cataracts, it goes tearing through a gorge some miles long, excavated mostly from ancient red sandstone, for a further descent of over two hundred feet. In floodtime a torrent more than eight times the volume of Niagara rages through this gigantic trough with a clamor that fairly deafens the beholder. Nowhere else on earth is there so tremendous a display of water power. Edward C. Rashleigh, writing in the *Journal* of the Royal Geographical Society, says, "it exceeds the combined mean volumes of Niagara, Paulo Affonso, the Iguassú Falls, the Grand Falls of Labrador, the Victoria Falls of the Zambezi, and the Kaiteur (of Guiana) rolled into one." Other notable waterfalls adorn this great river system, but they are eclipsed by the magnificence of the Iguassú and the titanic fury of La Guayra.

Plant life in the Paraná basin varies from treeless plains to matted jungles. In the São Paulo area of Brazil alone are to be found over four hundred species of cabinet wood. Some are so hard they dull a chisel. Along the Paraguay grows the quebracho tree, called the axbreaker because of its flinty hardness. Not only the bark but the wood itself is rich in tannin for dyeing leather. Each trunk, so massive it will not float, is sandwiched between two lighter logs when rafted down-river. A characteristic shrub is the yerba maté, which grows wild in northern Argentina, Paraguay, and southern Brazil. A member of the holly family, it somewhat resembles an orange tree in appearance. Workers break off small branches, hold them over a blazing fire, beat the dried leaves to fragments, then pack them for shipment. Natives prefer to sip the tea from a gourd through a long tube. An odd plant of the Chaco region is the unwit, or ground watermelon. W. H. Grubb describes it as larger than a thirty-gallon pot and providing a fluid substitute for water. Along the river shores dense masses of aquatic vegetation break away in floating islands called camelotes, which frequently bear snakes and the much bulkier capybara. Such islands sometimes hamper navigation, even in the harbor of Montevideo, before drifting out to sea on the muddy current which is perceptible two hundred miles offshore.

From immemorial times natives have eaten of the manioc root, better known to the Northern Hemisphere as tapioca. Forests are often gay with flowers, while in southern Brazil more than four hundred species of orchids are cultivated.

Among the profusion of native flora many imported species flourish. Cotton and tobacco have become important crops. In the grassy *pampas* transplanted poplars and Australian blue gums cast a welcome shade, while it has been estimated that the coffee trees of the São Paulo region number a billion and a half.

River life ranges from tiny mandi, no bigger than sprat, to huge catfish said to reach an extreme length of ten feet. Mud flappers sprawl about, and there is a plentiful supply of the bloodthirsty piranhas, or man-eating fish. Alligators abound and sting rays venture inland from the sea. Among numerous bird species grotesque jabiru storks, five feet high, wade about the Chaco lagoons, while the fleet rhea, or South American ostrich, races across the plains. Big game includes tapirs, jaguars, ant bears, peccaries, and in more open country pumas or mountain lions. Of evil repute are loathsome vampire bats which gorge themselves on the blood of sleeping victims. Their lancetlike teeth inflict a painless but debilitating wound. Serpents vary from poisonous species to the huge anaconda, or water snake. Insect life includes most of the biting, stinging pests that abound far more abundantly in the valley of the Amazon. But most of the drainage area of the Paraná is no such chaotic wilderness but a naturally healthy region that might well become one of the most prosperous in the world.

Sharp, indeed, are the contrasts in human life along the great river. While naked savages hunt their game with blowpipes along jungle tributaries, the La Plata-Paraná might well be called the river of great modern cities. For miles along the Plata's southern shore stretches Buenos Aires, metropolis of the continent, called the Paris of the New World, a city nearly as populous as Chicago and rapidly expanding. Founded in 1536 by Pedro de Mendoza, that knightly adventurer, with fifty other grandees, 150 Germans, and twenty-five hundred Spaniards, its mud stockades proved ineffectual safeguards against sickness, starvation, and hostile natives. But Mendoza's judgment was more than justified in the future growth of this amazing city.

A similar energy animates São Paulo, the great city of southern Brazil, located on the Tiete, one of the headwater streams of the Paraná. This river rises in the Sierra do Mar, where the annual rainfall varies from 180 to 240 inches. São Paulo, twenty-seven hundred feet above the sea, only thirty-five miles distant, pumps water from the Rio Grande Reservoir over the intervening ridge whence it catapaults downward more than half a mile through five great pipes, generating 380,000 horsepower. By this ingenious method some of the headwaters of the Paraná are diverted to the sea near their source instead of following the circuitous journey of nearly twenty-five hundred miles by river.

In 1948 São Paulo boasted a population of 1,600,000, which was increasing at a phenomenal pace. Known as the coffee center of the world, ten million bags of coffee, each weighing 132 pounds, is a normal annual shipment from the neighboring seaport of Santos. Professional coffee samplers, seeking the choicest blend, taste as many as six hundred cups of coffee daily, spitting out the liquid, as swallowing blunts the nerves of taste. A feature which never fails to interest tourists is the snake farm where ten thousand snakes are annually received. Of the four hundred species native to Brazil, only thirteen are poisonous, but these number some of the world's worst offenders. At this farm, in a single forenoon, as many as nine hundred of these killers have been milked of their venom—orange, milky, or transparent, but deadly. From this venom serums are prepared which have saved many human lives.

Montevideo, across the La Plata from Buenos Aires, is the third largest city of the system. Capital of the small but prosperous republic of Uruguay, its population exceeds half a million. Though better located than Buenos Aires, it lacks the boundless hinterland which has given that rival city its millionaire wheat growers and cattle kings.

Older than the others and once more important is Asunción, capital of turbulent Paraguay. It was founded in 1535 by Juan de Ayolas, or rather by his associate Iralá, as Ayolas was killed by the Indians on an expedition up the Pilcomayo River. Site of an ancient university, this city was a Spanish center in the New World when São Paulo was not even a village. And so the Paraná, with all its wide stretches of wilderness, may be called the River of Great Cities.

More representative, however, are those more sparsely settled regions which stretch into the remote hinterlands. In 1552 the Portuguese brought over seven cows and one bull, the ancestors of the vast herds which now range over the Paraná valleys. Many strayed away across the rolling *pampas* where thousands were formerly slaughtered merely for their hides and tallow. Later highbred bulls were imported and the era of the cattle kings began. Cattle thieves who infested this expanding industry were first branded and upon a second offense were hanged. Fence posts were brought down from the Chaco and thousands of miles of barbed-wire fence were erected. Windmills provided reservoirs; swine, fattened on alfalfa, throve enormously, and sheep multiplied by the million. From a half-vacant emptiness Argentina became one of the great meat-producing countries of the world.

Cattle raising requires cowboys, a picturesque breed the world over. In Argentina they are called gauchos; in Paraguay, chacreros. From the wild freedom of their environment, they acquire a certain reckless lawlessness. Babies are said to be born with knives in their hands, for a knife is quite as essential to a gaucho as a beak to a heron. Bloody fights are all too common, and so adept are the gauchos at knife throwing that a keen blade is considered a better weapon, up to a distance of thirty feet, than a loaded revolver. The familiar lariat of Arizona or Wyoming is supplemented with the native boleadoras, terminating in two thongs, once weighted with stones but now with lead, which trips the fleeing steer or rhea by twining about the legs. The usual gaucho costume comprises a broad sombrero, wide-topped boots, a foot-wide leather belt called a tirador, and the customary poncho, which, deftly wound about the free arm, offers some protection against knife thrusts. These roving spirits of the wide-open spaces are fond of roast mutton washed down with draughts of cana, a fiery liquor brewed from sugar cane. From gaucho dances to the tune of strumming guitars was evolved the Argentine tango.

On the trail of the cattle herders came the more settled agriculturists, destined to become the wealthiest of farmers. Seas of billowy wheat and Indian corn now undulate endlessly across far horizons in one of the great grain-producing regions in the world.

The Paraná system is woven into the very pattern of South American nationalities. Its various component parts, the La Plata, the Paraná, the Paraguay, the Uruguay, the Pilcomayo, and the Iguassú, form portions of the boundaries which separate Argentina, Brazil, Uruguay, Paraguay, and Bolivia. Uruguay owes its independence to its geographical position, for, coveted both by Argentina and Brazil, it remains a buffer state between them. Paraguay has had a stranger history. Though among the first to be settled, it has remained the most isolated of South American states, its only access to the outer world the great river system of which it is essentially a part. This aloofness has bred a pride of race and a martial spirit fostered by able but reckless dictators who first raised the country to eminence and then plunged it into ruin. From 1864–70 Francisco López, the most ambitious of these dictators, waged a war against the combined armies of Argentina, Brazil, and Uruguay that became one of the most sanguinary on record. The Paraguayans, hopelessly outnumbered, fought with the frenzy of despair. Whole regiments were composed of boys from twelve to fifteen years of age; many women entered the ranks, and others became little better than beasts of burden. Whole regions were almost depopulated, and when the fratricidal struggle ended with the death of the dictator the ratio of men to women was only one to seven. Yet this insensate frenzy to expand national boundaries, ill defined at best and spacious enough for many times the present population, has led to more recent conflicts. True to their warlike traditions, the Paraguayan armies have defeated those of Bolivia and appropriated most of the Gran Chaco, which neither nation needs or is prepared to develop.

Since the days when Sebastian Cabot sailed in his caravels up the broad current of the Paraná, that river has been a highway of commerce. Steamers, both freight and passenger, maintain regular schedules on the Paraná, the Paraguay, and the larger tributaries, while Buenos Aires, on the La Plata, is one of the great ports of the world.

Of the eleven major outlets of the Paraná, one shows a minimum depth of thirty-six feet, allowing ocean liners to ascend freely to Rosario, 222 miles above Buenos Aires. The river often widens to three miles or more, with an average current of two and one half miles per hour. A twelve-foot rise in floodtime converts the valley to an elongated lake thirty miles broad.

The Paraná presents few such problems as confront the pioneer along the Amazon. Much of its valley, though sparsely settled, is healthful when drained and brought under control. South America has well been called the Continent of the Future, and in that future this huge river seems destined to play a prominent role. Nature made it a natural highway to the heart of the continent; endowed it with that inexhaustible fertility revealed from the coffee groves of São Paulo to the wheatlands of the Argentine; enriched it also with forest products and enormous potential water power.

The cities which now mark its course herald that larger population and greater prosperity when the Paraná takes its rightful place among the foremost rivers of the world.

THE ORINOCO—A BROWN HIGHWAY THROUGH A GREEN INFERNO

Length—1,700 miles. Drainage area—570,000 square miles

Although the Orinoco was the first big river of the western world to be noted by European explorers, it is the least developed and the most imperfectly known. Few white men have ever visited its remote headwaters, while its broad current, flowing for long stretches through dense forests, suggests Bryant's Oregon which "hears no sound save its own dashings."

Potentially one of the richest of river valleys, it remains largely a wilderness, for the population—nomadic Indians and scattered white settlements—is probably less numerous than when the Spaniards arrived upon the scene more than four centuries ago.

The Orinoco, the great river of Venezuela, also drains a large section of Colombia. Surveys which are fragmentary and embrace many estimates give its length as seventeen hundred miles, its drainage area as 570,000 square miles. These figures show but an inadequate picture of the tremendous sweep of the current, for, bearing the surplus moisture of a heavily forested region drenched by tropic downpours and swollen by 436 considerable tributaries, it pours into the ocean a volume of waters that few of the world's great rivers can equal.

Columbus noted this fact in 1498. Sailing through that strait he named the Serpent's Mouth, which separates the big island of Trinidad from the mainland of South America, he found the waters of the nearly enclosed Gulf of Paria freshened by the Orinoco delta, although the main outlet lies some distance to the south. Strangely enough, the admiral, with a new continent at his feet, did not pause to investigate, but passed outward through another constricted waterway that he named the Dragon's Mouth.

Schoolboys will remember how one of their favorite fiction characters, Robinson Crusoe, alone on Tobago Island beyond Trinidad, battled dangerous currents that he ascribed to the Orinoco.

What Columbus failed to do was attempted by the Spaniard, Diego de Ordaz, who in 1531–32 ascended the river all the way to its juncture with the Meta, an important affluent approaching from Colombia. In this expedition many Spaniards fell victim to tropical fevers, the hardships of the wilderness, and battles with hostile natives.

They were lured onward by a magnificent dream, a native legend that beyond the gloomy forest was Manoa, the shining City of El Dorado, its emperor robed in plates of gold.

On April 5, 1800, Alexander von Humboldt, with a companion in a small boat, beat his way from the ocean fringed with white-caps into one of the many mouths of the Orinoco, two and a half miles wide. He proceeded far up the river, adding greatly to the scientific knowledge of his day, but found the region quite as forbidding as his predecessors had done.

He was astonished at the extent of the inland waterways and wrote, "The Junction of the Guarico, the Apure, the Cabullare, and the Arauca with the Orinoco forms a kind of interior delta of which hydrography furnishes few examples in the Old World."

Among the profusion of species in the vast Venezuelan forests, Humboldt found the cow tree, which he called the *palo de vaca*, the most singular. Although the branches might appear dry and withered, the sap was like thickened milk. Natives drank it by the bowlful, while analysis revealed chemical properties similar to cow's milk. The coagulated sap suggested "butter" in con-trast with the tough "cheeselike" constituency of the sap from rubber trees. In his memoirs he wrote, "Amidst the great number of curious phenomena . . . few have made so powerful an im-pression on me as . . . the cow tree."

The Orinoco drains a lofty tableland that occupies most of southern Venezuela and extends into Colombia on the west and Brazil on the south. This mountainous mass appears like an island between the valley of the Orinoco and the far larger basin of the Amazon. Few explorers have penetrated the region. E. An-drep, ascending the Caura branch of the Orinoco, was continu-ally dissuaded by his native paddlers with tales of malignant gnomes and demons. The wilderness proved, indeed, rather frightening, with violent storms whose lightning bolts and crash-ing thunders were "terrific." Nonetheless, Andrep climbed a rugged peak known as Turagua and found that it exceeded six thousand feet in height. Cerro Duida, ascended later, is 7,860.

The Orinoco delta is usually given an area of seven hundred square miles, but including the territory comprised within the outlets stemming farther up the main channel, it really covers several thousand. No fewer than thirty-six mouths have been traced, but the principal one, known as Boca Grande, is some-thing of an estuary choked by islands little above sea level and periodically inundated. This region is inhabited by Guarauno Indians who dwell in palm-thatched huts elevated upon stilts. Beebe describes it as "the land of a single tree," the mangrove, which luxuriates in the sodden ground and even wades out into the shallow sea.

The lower Orinoco is a broad, muddy current with savannahs stretching on either side. Some 228 miles above the sea, however, the river, narrowing between spurs of higher ground, has gouged out a channel 335 feet deep, its floor 226 feet below sea level. This is the site of the city of Ciudad Bolívar, founded by the Spaniards in 1764 as San Thomé. The Venezuelan constitution was drawn up in this city and its name changed in honor of Bolivar, the George Washington of South American independence.

Above these narrows the river broadens again to an average width of three and a half miles until, some seven hundred miles above the sea, it comes tumbling down a series of foaming rapids. Through one series known as El Fierno the current boils at a speed of twelve miles an hour. Boats are dragged up-current by floating towropes made of palm fiber which are nearly as tough as hawsers.

World-famous is the so-called Casiquiare Canal, which unites the upper Orinoco with a branch of the Negro, chief northern tributary of the Amazon. This unique waterway is no canal but a battleground between two great rivers in which the more powerful has won the victory. It was first made known to the world by the missionary Padre Acuña in 1639 and described by Father Roman, who ascended the Orinoco in 1744. Humboldt investigated this phenomenon of river evolution in his voyage of scientific research. Since that time it has frequently been traversed. The town of San Carlos now stands upon the banks of the Negro nine miles below the juncture, while there is a settlement called Capibara on the canal itself. A. Hamilton Rice, in 1921, reported to the Royal Geographical Society the results of a voyage through the canal. He found its length slightly over 227 miles. At the Orinoco end it was 758 feet wide and 283 feet above sea level; at its junction with the Negro 2,150 feet wide, its altitude 212. This gradient of seventy-one feet caused a continuous current from the Orinoco into the Negro as though the Amazon, hugest of rivers, not content with the most spacious drainage area in the world, was reaching out for new conquests. The muddy brown waters of the Orinoco may be clearly distinguished as they blend with the ebon blackness of the Negro. Through this strange sluiceway, it has been estimated, one third of the waters of the upper Orinoco are drained away into the Amazon.

That enough remains, however, is evident by the swirling floods which swell the normal channel of the mid-Orinoco to a width of seven miles, rise sixty feet or more at Ciudad Bolívar, and sweep over the low-lying islands of the delta to battle with the tides. The burden of silt and decayed vegetation imparts a characteristic color. As Lady Dorothy Mills observed, "The Orinoco is the greyest river I have ever seen—it never looks clear or dark like other rivers."

Fish are abundant and the repulsive caymans or alligators. Great numbers are slaughtered as upward of two hundred thousand of their skins have been exported. Their eggs are also eaten by the natives but are too oily to please European palates. River otters are common, but most conspicuous are the turtles which once swarmed in myriads. On three sand bars in mid-channel Humboldt estimated that no fewer than 330,000 repaired to lay their eggs.

The eggs of the larger species were the size of pigeon eggs, with leathery shells so tough that Indian children tossed them to one another. The "nests" excavated in the sand were commonly two feet deep and contained upwards of a hundred eggs. From these eggs the natives manufactured an oil which they used both in lamps and for cooking. Humboldt estimated that thirty-three million eggs a year were utilized in its production. The wastage was appalling, while jaguars killed many adult turtles, tearing the soft body from its shell. Since that time the industry has suffered much from overfishing.

Humboldt noted some quaint notions among the natives. Those of the Casiquiare region thought the morning dew was "the spittle of the stars." Along certain sections of the river dwell the Guahibos Indians, who wear clothing of pounded bark. Scarcely less savage are some white men of this hinterland beyond the pale of the law. In 1913 a desperado named Funes, a river trader, gathering about him a kindred group of cutthroats, murdered most of the other white men of the district and set up a despotic rule which lasted for years. The bullets of a firing squad ultimately terminated his bloodstained career.

The name Orinoco is derived from the Carib Ibironoco. The wealth of its drainage area has hardly been tapped; its forests serve merely to discolor the too-abundant waters; agriculture has scarcely begun; fisheries are wasteful and inefficient, while the steamers that ascend readily from the sea for seven hundred miles could handle a far greater commerce. Even the mineral wealth that lured the conquistadors may yet justify the legends of El Dorado. Sir Walter Raleigh, seeking to retrieve his shattered fortunes, calked his ships from the famous Pitch Lake in Trinidad and wrote, "There is that abundance of stone pitch that all the shippes of the world may be therewith laden from thence, and we made triall of it in trimming our shippes to be most excellent good, and melteth not with the sunne as pitch of Norway, and therefore for shippes trading south portes very profitable."

Millions of dollars' worth have since been extracted from that weird lake and millions remain. But Sir Walter sailed away, battled fever-ridden jungles, and returned a broken man to be emprisoned in the Tower and later beheaded.

The gold that early explorers sought may still glitter in undiscovered veins in the remote highlands. But greater riches lie unclaimed in the vast potential resources of the Orinoco and its maze of waterways.

THE SÃO FRANCISCO—GOLD, GEMS, AND IRON MOUNTAINS

Length—1,811 miles. Drainage area—252,000 square miles

To most Americans the São Francisco is scarcely even a name. Yet it is one of the most fascinating of rivers and in the development of Brazil has proved more important than the Amazon.

A glance at the map of South America reveals that prominence like an elephant's forehead which would fit so snugly into a corresponding indentation in the African coast that Wegener, visualizing a single land mass which had split asunder, advanced his audacious theory of "drifting continents." Be that as it may, this intrusion of the Western Hemisphere into the mid-Atlantic has changed the course of history and made Brazil alone, among Latin-American Republics, Portuguese rather than Spanish.

In 1499 Vasco da Gama returned from his voyage to India to unfold a vision of empire which embraced the Orient and half the world besides. His delighted monarch, yielding to delusions of grandeur, assumed the title "Lord of the conquest, navigation, and commerce of Ethiopia, Arabia, Persia, and India," and commissioned Pedro Alvares de Cabral to investigate this route to world power and riches.

And so, in March 1500, the latter sailed from the Tagus as admiral of a fleet of thirteen vessels, manned by over a thousand eager adventurers. Following Da Gama's instructions to bear well out to sea and thus avoid coastal gales and currents, and driven westward by what proved to be fortunate winds, on April 22 he sighted the South American coast. Here history presents one of its many speculative *ifs*, for had not Columbus sailed from Palos but eight years before, Cabral might have gained immortality as the discoverer of the New World. As it was, he dispatched one of his vessels homeward with the news, and the king promptly sent out exploring parties. One of these, under Amerigo Vespucci, whose name, by another caprice of history, was destined to be bestowed upon both continents of the hemisphere, investigating the coast line, entered a broad river a mile wide and thirty feet deep which he named in honor of St. Francis. Sailing some distance upstream and finding neither gold nor silver, he reported the region as "of little value." As the river traverses territory whose wealth in minerals rivals that of South Africa, this appraisal must rank with Daniel Webster's dismissal of all lands west of the Mississippi as fit only for prairie dogs, or the later arraignment of the Alaskan Purchase as Seward's Folly.

Cabral's discovery had far-reaching results, for it led to the famous line of demarkation whereby Pope Alexander VI divided much of the world outside Europe between his two loyal "sons," the monarchs of Spain and Portugal.

According to the Brazilian Hydraulic Commission, the São Francisco is 1,811 miles in length and drains an area of 252,000 square miles. Through most of its course it flows in a north-easterly direction roughly parallel to the ocean, then bends in a great arc southeastward. Its upper tributaries compete with branches of the Amazon to the north and the Paraná to the south and west. Sandwiched between two such colossal river systems, it has been largely ignored. Even history neglects it, although it formerly directed Brazilian settlement straight to the heart of one of the richest mineral-producing regions of the world.

Into this hinterland penetrated those hardy prospectors known as bandeirantes, equally ready to exploit surface mining or to despoil the aborigines. Their paths led into the uplands of eastern Brazil, an area of fabulous antiquity, of worn-down mountains and eroded valleys. Here lies the oldest part of the continent, where are exposed some of the most ancient rock surfaces of the globe. Three mountain ranges cross it: the Serra do Mar and Mantiqueira, both relics of the ancient Laurentian formation, and the more recent though immeasurably old Espinhaço of Huronian time. Itatiaia, 9,283 feet high, was long regarded as the loftiest peak in Brazil, though it seems to yield to Pico Bandeira, 9,462. Both gnarled giants had battled the clouds for untold millions of years before the parvenu Andes had risen from their abysmal ocean trough.

As this remote frontier lay beyond the pale of the law, it became infested with escaped convicts, runaway slaves, and other human tatters on the fringe of society. Bands of outlaws terrorized a region where tales of gold and gems nevertheless continued to attract new adventurers. Mining operations were but little improvement over those of the unfortunate natives who were promptly enslaved, but the crumbling rocks exposed gold and diamonds which awaited only the enterprise of the collector.

From the headwaters of the São Francisco now flowed a golden stream which maintained the showy splendor of the Portuguese court long after the collapse of its ill-assembled empire. The source of this wealth was concealed from the rest of the world behind an iron curtain which neither permitted outsiders to enter nor the inhabitants to leave. Meanwhile oppressive imposts reduced the miners to virtual peonage. Ignorance was their lot, as well, for throughout this region not a single school was maintained for a hundred and twenty years. No wonder such repressive measures spawned a breed of defiant smugglers.

Most of this territory is now incorporated in Minas Geraes, which, according to a recent census, is the most populous of all the Brazilian states. Nearly as large as Texas, it boasts even more inhabitants, while its capital, Belo Horizonte, in one of the upper valleys of the São Francisco, has become a thriving metropolis.

The French geologist Gorceix, in a burst of Gallic rhetoric, endowed Minas Geraes with a "breast of iron, a heart of gold." This figure of speech is but a slight exaggeration. Throughout the eighteenth century Brazil produced 44 per cent of the world's output of the yellow metal. The crude washings of the bandeirantes, however, have been replaced by more efficient methods, and the ancient gold mine of Morro Velho claims the deepest shafts in the world, shafts which penetrate to a depth of over eight thousand feet.

Still more glamorous is the story of diamonds. These costly pebbles were exposed in river gravel. Even now they are usually collected by independent prospectors called garimpeiros, a system in sharp contrast with the abysmal excavations at Kimberley. In 1938 fortunate individuals found the blue-white Getulia Vargas, third largest solitaire on record, weighing 726.6 carats, and appraised in New York for three quarters of a million dollars.

Other precious and semiprecious stones are fairly abundant. Occasional sapphires, rubies, and emeralds are found, while aquamarines, tourmalines, and garnets are common. Here was unearthed the largest topaz crystal in the world, 350,000 carats, while a quartz crystal exported to Rochester, New York, weighed sixty-three pounds.

There is even richer store of other minerals: silver and platinum, bauxite, the ore of aluminum, lead, zinc, manganese, and rarer metals. But iron eclipses them all, for here, so geologists believe, are to be found the largest deposits in the world, culminating in the famous Itabira do Campo, a mountain of almost pure ore.

As the overworked supplies of the Mesabi Range in Minnesota diminish, the Empire of Iron, the basis of our mechanized prosperity, may yet pass from north to south of the equator.

The São Francisco and its tributaries afford nearly four thousand miles of navigable waterways. Steamers ascend the lower river for nearly a hundred and fifty miles from the sea, the only impediment a sand bar at the river's mouth which shows a twelve-foot depth of water. The upper courses, though broken by rapids, have one clear stretch of nearly a thousand miles. Native boatmen, or barquieros, battle with shoals, erratic currents, and the other hazards peculiar to river navigation. Smaller boats, roofed with leaves, are poled along the shallows with patient labor. Not unnaturally these sweating boatmen invest the river with whole legions of malicious spirits.

Seeking an outlet to the sea, the river forces its way through the coastal range down a series of foaming cascades. In one stretch of 79 miles it descends 643 feet. The climax is reached at Paulo Affonso, one of the world's major waterfalls. Vera Kelsey describes it as "motion gone mad." Between canyon walls colored "brass, bronze, iron, red, yellow, and black" gleams the "unearthly white of the waters" until, "divided momentarily by monstrous boulder spines . . . they crash together . . . explode, boil, vaporize in foam, mist, fog and at terrific velocity leap 260 feet." No wonder, in this chaos of gorge and spray, the bats which issue from wet caves underneath are looked upon by superstitious natives as the "demons of the falls."

This frenzy of a mighty river is thought to generate potential water power greater than that of Niagara. A prodigious mine gushing white coal, someday it will still further refute Vespucci's lack of appreciation.

Along the upper valley great estates are devoted to cattle raising, the owners assuming the lawless liberty of former days by raids upon rival cattle barons. Agriculture is still in its infancy, although the rainfall is abundant throughout most of the drainage area, though only eight to twelve inches in the region of the Great Bend. Farina, called the "meat of the sun," is the staple food of the more humble Brazilian, while fish and huge turtles abound in the river. The climate is generally healthful.

A railroad flanking the Paulo Affonso now connects river traffic with the interior. Someday, when the fitful glitter of gold and diamonds has grown dim, a more enduring prosperity will doubtless arise upon the firm foundation of iron and aluminum, of stock raising and agriculture, and the wasted water power of the Paulo Affonso. Then the São Francisco, too long neglected, may take its rightful place among the most productive rivers in the world.

PART TEN

River Types and Problems

~~~~~~

SOME CHARACTERISTIC RIVERS

RIVERS are our most efficient archaeologists. The Colorado, slicing through layer upon layer of sedimentary rock, cuts into the original crust, now greatly modified, of the primordial continent as it rose dripping from the seas perhaps a billion years ago. Many another river has turned back one by one the pages of the story of life upon this planet so that we may contemplate the footprints of huge dinosaurs as they lumbered over the mud flats; reconstruct from bones and shells innumerable species of animal life long since extinct, and in our oldest limestones detect the traces of minute algae and more rudimentary plants as life itself awoke from inorganic chaos.

In 1891 Professor Eugene Dubois exhumed from the gravel beds of the Solo River in Java the thighbone and part of the skull of a primitive being which he burdened with the name *Pithecanthropus erectus*, an apelike man that thrust back the dawn of human history perhaps half a million years. Other discoveries were quite as startling. The hairy mammoth, *Elephas primigenius*, etched on bone by men of the Stone Age, followed the trail of the dinosaurs to oblivion long ago. Yet Siberian rivers occasionally uncover the body of one of these uncouth monsters. E. W. Pfitzenmayer, commissioned by the Russian Government, reported no fewer than twenty-one specimens from the valleys of the Yana and Kolima rivers. Some, the veins still swollen with coagulated blood, were so well preserved that dogs and even natives fed upon their flesh. Stomach contents revealed a summer forage of grasses, sedge, beans of the Oxytropis, and an Arctic variety of crowfoot, while winter browsings were of withered leaves and twigs. The shoulder hump seems to have stored fat like that of the dromedary. As protection against the piercing cold, the body was covered with wool up to an inch and a half deep, draped with coarse brown hair hanging nearly to the ground. A companion beast, the woolly rhinoceros (*Rhinoceros antiquitatis*), whose body resembled the rare white rhino of Africa, was also clothed in golden-brown hair above an undercoat of wool. To observe these grotesque creatures, resurrected from their prehistoric sleep, is to step at a single stride into the smoky caverns of Cro-Magnon man.

Four great rivers provided a favorable environment for the development of racial groups and cultures: the Nile, home of the Hamitic race, remembered in ponderous temples, tombs, and monuments; the Euphrates, where Babylonian and Assyrian empires rose upon Sumerian ruins; the Indus and the mysterious people that dwelt there before the irruption of the Aryans; and the Hwang Ho, where flowered the political institutions and venerable philosophies of China.

Many rivers have been reverenced and some even deified. The God Osiris was the personification of the Nile, and one of the earliest of all hymns apostrophizes the great river: "Hail to thee O Nile who . . . cometh to give life to Egypt." Nor is such respect a thing of the past. When that saintly character Mohandas Gandhi fell victim to an assassin's bullets, his ashes, at his request, were scattered upon the Sacred Ganges, and Tibetan monks, regarding the source of every river as holy, mark the spot with commemorative monuments or shrines.

Rivers have been haunted by legions of lesser spirits, some evanescent as the mist above cascades, some perilously seductive, some fiendishly malignant. Egyptian priests sought to pacify their unclean crocodile gods; African natives people the gorge of the Zambezi with frightful demons, while Chinese boatmen risk collision by crossing the bows of an oncoming vessel in order to divert pursuing devils. The Lorelei who combs her golden locks above the dark current of the Rhine is akin to the sirens who enticed Odysseus, and the natives of Cambodia invest the Mekong with similar river sprites which drag unwary swimmers to their death.

Many a stream has inspired artists and poets with its picturesque loveliness. The Rhine flows through a landscape of song and legend, while other rivers offer grander views, such as the breath-taking gorges of Asia and the Grand Canyon of the Colorado.

In the utilitarian field smaller rivers are often sources of water supply, as their currents, impounded by dams, provide reservoirs for New York and many a lesser city.

Rivers, once the only means of transportation through such wild regions as Siberia, Central Africa, and the forest of Canada, retain much of their former usefulness. The Yangtze Kiang is still the great highway to interior China, while the St. Lawrence, with its cluster of Great Lakes, has developed a commerce that is well-nigh oceanic in its dimensions. Such rivers are continental waterways.

Many rivers are valued chiefly as aids to agriculture. The Nile and the Euphrates were primarily garden rivers, as are the Indus and the Rio Grande today.

Some rivers are noteworthy as harbors, tidal indentations of the sea. Such is the Mersey, with its great port of Liverpool, and Boston, at the mouth of the Charles River.

From immemorial times rivers have turned water wheels and other rude contrivances to irrigate the crops or grind the grain. But harnessing them to the production of hydroelectric power is a modern episode in the great drama of man's conquest of Nature, which deserves separate treatment.

SOME STRANGE RIVERS

Greek legends which personified even trees and rocks had the river divinity Alpheus pursue the water nymph Arethusa beneath the ground. This merely clothed fact in poetry, for the Alpheus, flowing for seventy-five miles through the mountainous Morea, has excavated hidden passageways and so become the prototype of subterranean rivers the world over. Coleridge, in opium dreams, roamed through a fantastic oriental landscape:

> Where Alph, the sacred river, ran
> Through caverns measureless to man,
> Down to a sunless sea.

His "sunless sea" was also authentic, for deep in the earth lie vast saline reservoirs, the imprisoned remnants of vanished seas.

Tourists in the White Mountains pause to explore Lost River; the Tipitapa, which unites Lake Managua with larger Nicaragua in Central America, flows through deeper channels, and limestone caves the world over have been excavated by water action. The Natural Bridge in Virginia is thought to be a remnant of a collapsed terrain that once roofed hidden waters.

Even surface-flowing streams are sometimes masked in curious guise. In Ecuador, I have observed the Guayaquil River so covered with aquatic vegetation that it resembled a living current of greenery. I have also noticed similar phenomena among the lesser African rivers, while the mighty Nile in the famous sudd region is arched over with vegetation firm enough "to bear up an elephant." The Androscoggin River in New Hampshire, like other northern streams, becomes so choked with pulpwood logs that little or no water is anywhere visible. Ice, snow-covered, so veils many a winter stream that only the flatness of the treeless surface betrays its presence.

More curious are Siberian streams, which congeal clear to the bottom to thaw in summer heats, and most curious of all are frozen rivers that remain so, the glaciers which etch mountain valleys deeper than liquid currents.

Such rivers are the great landscape sculptors in mountain districts and polar regions. Grasping flinty rocks, they gouge out deep V-shaped trenches which they widen to U-shaped valleys. They move slowly onward under enormous pressure. Usually they are but a few miles long, but their melting fringes are the source of many a river, such as the Indus and the Brahmaputra. Formerly the Karakorum Range was thought to have the longest glaciers in the world, and the Biafo Glacier is thirty-seven miles in length. But Admiral Byrd, in his explorations in Antarctica, that riverless continent crushed beneath the ice, observed one glacier eighty miles long.

Glaciers occur only in high latitudes or altitudes. In nival regions the snow becomes compressed into ice and is forced outward or downward by gravity and backed-up accumulations. The rate of movement of many glaciers has been measured together with the depth of ice and its effect upon local topography. In the Glacial Age frozen rivers swelled into oceans which mantled millions of square miles of earth surface as they do today in Antarctica and Greenland. Such ice may have accumulated to a depth of ten thousand feet or more. Spreading outward from focal centers, it scraped the face of the earth, leveling mountains and filling valleys, grinding even solid granite to "rock flour." Such enormous abrasion is inevitable when we note that ice a mile in depth exerts a pressure of three hundred thousand pounds per square foot. Ice still covers parts of Greenland to a depth of more than a mile and a half! Although the Glacial Age is thought to have terminated some eleven thousand years ago, it lingers in the polar regions, as navigators are reminded when icebergs drift into sea lanes to imperil shipping. Collision in the night with one of these ghostly white mountains sent the *Titanic* to the bottom in the most appalling of modern marine disasters. Ice fields still warp the pattern of ocean currents and chill the climate of the globe.

Mountain glaciers seem relatively unimportant, but they have sculptured many an Alpine lake and feed many a river. The Oxus and Jaxartes, for example, traverse the deserts of Turkestan sustained by the glaciers of remote mountains. Sir Aurel Stein thought the gradual dwindling of such glaciers had hastened the dry-out process which has made so much of that region an arid waste.

Glaciers are most spectacular when associated with mountains of fire. Those which drape the flanks of Hecla are lighted by volcanic glow. One of the most arresting of these weird rivers is the Weyprecht Glacier, which winds downward from a frozen lake in the burnt-out crater of Beerenberg, looming more than eight thousand feet above lonely Jan Mayen Island in the Polar Sea.

Rivers of solid earth seem fantastic, yet there are such rivers. Anderson, exploring Bear Island, that isolated bit of terrain which Barents discovered centuries ago far north of Norway, measured one such river, thirty-five meters in width and over two meters in depth, creeping slowly toward the sea. The whole mass was sodden with moisture, and from the edges seeped semi-liquid mud. This process has been observed in various localities and has been give a name—solifluction.

More curious still are the stone rivers of the Falklands, that lonely archipelago far down the southern Atlantic, nearly in the latitude of the Straits of Magellan, which has been a recent bone of contention between Great Britain and the Argentine. From the sea these rivers look like glaciers filling mountain ravines, from a few hundred yards to a mile in width, but closer inspection shows great masses of quartzite, roughly diamond-shaped and sometimes twenty feet long by ten broad. Piled one above the other in a confused tangle, they present a streamlike outline and once moved, if indeed their motion be even now arrested, onward toward the sea. Weathering evidently broke up surface strata, water action ate out connective tissue, and the huge blocks, thus released, went lumbering down a slippery gradient impelled by gravity. There is something almost uncanny in such rivers of fractured rock in that remote setting.

Yet earth movements on a far more impressive scale are not uncommon. In 1903 the top of Turtle Mountain in Canada slid forward two miles or more, destroying the settlement of Frank, while loftier mountains show even more terrifying spectacles. In 1348 an earth-and-rock slide in the Villach Alps buried no fewer than thirteen villages. In India, I once met an excellent lady who had lost six children when a moving hillside at Darjeeling swept them into the valley. Kipling wove a dramatic story about a holy man of India who lost his life in warning a village of such impending doom.

A mountainside in the Himalayas, undermined by rains and gushing springs, once collapsed, hurling eight hundred million tons of earth and rock across a branch of the Ganges. The resultant dam, nearly a thousand feet high, created a new lake called Gohna. But this dam, loosely thrown together, eventually gave way, and the flood that roared down the valley swept away all life for a hundred and fifty miles.

Natives speak of occasions "when the mountains walked," an apt description of such convulsions. Yet they are less colorful than the molten rivers with which volcanoes swallow up whole villages. Pouring into the sea they "make the deep to boil like a pot," to employ Biblical language. The island of Hawaii has arisen from the ocean floor upon successive lava intrusions, and the crater of Kilauea, the "house of everlasting fire," sometimes sends an incandescent river raging through crags of crumbling scoria.

Such rivers may seem minor, but lava flows have buried millions of square miles of upland and remain a prominent feature of global topography.

RIVERS IN LAW AND POLITICS

Plato discussed the ownership of fresh waters with his usual clarity. "Neither soil, sun nor wind which, jointly with water, supply nourishment to the products of the soil, are easily tampered with by poisonous substances, diversion or theft but water is by nature liable to all three." This problem which Greek thinkers recognized long ago has been complicated by the conflicting requirements of modern enterprises both private and public.

Tampering with poisonous substances is too well illustrated in that pollution by sewage and the waste products of manufacturing which have converted many a stream of "living waters" into a river of death, while water diversion for irrigation or other purposes has alienated friendly communities, caused endless bickerings among the states, and compelled the federal government to intervene when Chicago, by opening a drainage canal from Lake Michigan connecting with the Mississippi, endangered harbor facilities in Cleveland, Buffalo, and other Great Lake ports.

Clashing interests have bred clashing laws. In general, however, the riparian owner has been conceded the right to a reasonable use of the waters immediately bordering his holdings, while streams really navigable have been regarded as open to the public. Moreover, the state has assumed the privilege of erecting levees or building bridges, reimbursing the riparian owner for property damage.

Shifting channels have caused much argument. One owner's loss is another's gain, for the farmer who watches his fertile acres engorged by the Big Muddy may later have them increased when that rapacious river builds out instead of tears down his water frontage. But in cases of wide divergence, such as the Indus or the Hwang Ho, such jurisdiction cannot always be established.

Rivers, from the viewpoint of the map maker, are ideal boundaries. We read in the Old Testament (II Samuel 8:3) how "David smote also Hadadezer, the son of Rehob, king of Zobah, as he went to recover his border at the river Euphrates," which marked the farthest limit of Hebrew empire. The Ural River has even been recognized as a part of the division between Europe and Asia. For centuries the Rhine was the boundary between Roman dominions and barbaric tribes and has remained the scene of bloody strife between France and Germany. The Rio Grande, for thirteen hundred miles, separates Mexico from the United States, while in the northwest Great Britain tried, though unsuccessfully, to have the Columbia recognized as the international border.

Unfortunately, whatever their advantages as boundaries, rivers are prolific breeders of dissension. Our word "rival" stems from the Latin *rivus*, or river, and sprung from a partnership of riparian privileges. But its very etymology reveals how neighbors became competitors and even antagonists, which "rival" now connotes. A common jurisdiction causes inevitable disputes which touch upon national honor and lead to war. Hence, even when recognized as international boundaries, rivers have sometimes remained under the control of one riparian power or the other. The Romans, while they recognized long stretches of the Rhine and the Danube as limits of empire, nevertheless controlled both river valleys. The Manchu emperors, conceding that the Amur River separated their dominions from those of the Muscovite czars, long retained jurisdiction over the valley.

It has been said that global features are delineated in water rather than in land. The leaders of the French Revolution, seeking to sweep away a jungle of restrictive customs and regulations, attacked the problem of river control. The Government, in its decree of November 16, 1792, declared, "No nation can, without injustice, claim the right to occupy exclusively a river channel." This noble declaration is in sharp contrast with the cynical Russian appropriation of the Danube which now conceals that great natural highway across central Europe behind the Iron Curtain.

The French decree, however, has been challenged by other powers. Holland protested against the Free Rhine proposed by the French Government in 1797, nor was it until 1868 that the last toll was abolished on that important waterway. In 1851 Brazil claimed the right to bar the Amazon to foreign shipping. In 1883 Portugal raised a similar question about the Zambezi. The great powers, in granting Belgium its vast empire in Central Africa, insisted that the Congo should remain an open doorway for the commerce of the world. In the development of the American Commonwealth friction with Great Britain over the Columbia River basin led to threats of war, while frequent disputes with Mexico have arisen over the Rio Grande and the Colorado.

Even the oceans have become involved in nationalistic claims and counterclaims. The Turks made the eastern Mediterranean a Moslem lake. Venice and later Mussolini did the same with the Adriatic Sea. Portugal, in the days of her greatness, attempted to control the commerce of the Indian Ocean, as did Spain the approaches to the New World. England fought this oceanic monopoly under the leadership of those doughty sea kings, Drake, Hawkins, Morgan, and other adventurous buccaneers, while Queen Elizabeth protested to the Spanish ambassador, "Neither can a title to the ocean belong to any people." But how quickly this policy changed when England inherited the watery despotism of Portugal and Spain, and Elizabeth's courageous challenge was superseded by the proud boast "Britannia rules the waves," a policy veiled in normal times but boldly assumed in war when British warships blockaded the whole world against Germany, seized and searched neutral shipping, and indulged in all the high-handed acts which led to the War of 1812.

The morality, not to say common decency, which controls the

acts of individuals has been sadly absent in the dealings of one country with another, where might alone has usually determined international policy.

Nations still exercise certain privileges over neighboring waters, levy tribute upon passing shipping for the maintenance of lighthouses, charge harbor dues and the like. The result has been a patchwork quilt of legislation which has varied with the locality and since World War II has become more clouded than ever by nationalistic suspicion.

That splendid but pathetic dream, Universal Freedom, can never become a reality until international law is recognized and enforced, until the freedom of the seas has become an established fact, and with it access to the world's great rivers.

PART ELEVEN

Revising Our Global Economy

~~~~~~

MAN, THE BUNGLER

MAN strides the earth and deserts follow in his footsteps" is a dramatic arraignment of Man, the Bungler. Too often has he intruded upon the scene to upset within a few brief years the wise checks and balances nature has established during long millenniums. It has been estimated that in the United States an inch of topsoil is the accumulation of more than eight hundred summer seasons. Yet that irreplaceable legacy may be swept away in a single spring freshet, a single autumn dust storm.

Virgin forests which once clothed millions of acres and provided an equable volume to innumerable streams have been destroyed. China is condemned to periodic floods and the wastage of her uplands by the removal of forests which once covered much of her territory. The ancient Chinese character for morning depicts the sun's disc peering through the trunks of trees. The disc remains, but the trees have gone from much of coastal and central China. Forest cutting by the natives of Africa has imperiled the levels of Tanganyika and Victoria Nyanza and struck at the very roots of such rivers as the Congo and the Nile. In this country the splendid stands of first-growth timber which greeted colonial settlers have largely disappeared. No band of Tartars ever ravaged a smiling countryside more wantonly than many a logging camp. The resultant jungle of scrub and dead branches is a fertile field for forest fires. A land robbed of its forests is exposed to widespread denudition. Only within recent years has the science of forestry attempted to halt this inexcusable wastage of our resources and begun to repair a little of the damage already done.

Unwise cultivation of the soil is an even blacker mark upon the record. It has been said, "the most destructive weapon ever devised by man was the steel plough." A peril overshadowing Greece, more fundamental than the raids of mountain brigands or the red tide of Communism, is a soil impoverished or ruined by centuries of unwise cultivation. To this tragic blunder once fertile fields gashed by raw gullies or rocks swept bare of topsoil bear eloquent witness.

In India, where millions subsist upon the verge of starvation and poverty is chronic, records show 115 tons of priceless topsoil swept in a single year from a single acre of growing sorghum. But this spectacle of ignorance or folly may be brought nearer home. The soil in certain parts of colonial Virginia was long ago robbed of its fertility by excessive tobacco culture. Failure of such tobacco lands drove many a settler beyond the Appalachians to the virgin fields of Kentucky or Ohio. Persistent cotton growing has impaired the fertility of great areas of the southland. In upper New England abandoned farms are melancholy milestones along the route of land destruction. Had not the Chinese learned about bench farming and crop rotation centuries ago, they would have starved.

In 1930 H. H. Bennett wrote, "In Oklahoma of 16 million acres under cultivation 13 million was subject to excessive washing while 6 million had become so deeply gullied that it was no longer subject to the plough."

The "home where the buffalo roam," or once did so in countless numbers, has been largely ruined by unwise cultivation. Breaking up the protective turf has uncovered soil that disintegrated in violent clouds or was swept into silt-burdened rivers. Every year in America, so estimate has it, five hundred thousand acres are desurfaced, an annual loss of one billion dollars. Nor is this a tax which may be made up in more profitable seasons, but a permanent impairment of national capital. The delta shore line of Louisiana is advancing at an accelerated rate as the Mississippi sweeps the wreckage onward to the sea.

Even excessive grazing is destructive. Major C. S. Jarvis, discussing lands that border the Arabian Desert, writes, "The Arab with his camels and goats has destroyed nearly all the fertility in places that formerly supported thousands of inhabitants."

A graphic picture of arid British Somaliland in Africa is drawn by A. Veeby Thompson in the *Journal* of the Royal Geographical Society. The rainfall, which "varies from .05 to 27 inches but is sporadic and unsatisfactory," finds animals by the thousands milling about the dwindling water holes where "every edible particle has been devoured and the surface converted into a dust bowl. . . . Reduced to skeletons by starvation, the emaciated creatures, covered with sores and moving in clouds of dust, become an easy prey to the hyenas, jackals, and even carnivorous birds, while flies in swarms perpetually worry them." Here life in the raw appears in stark realism against a pitiless background. A similar desiccated terrain was discussed by Dr. R. S. Troup, Professor of Forestry in Oxford University, who observed, "It is reported that the women in upper Nigeria are refusing to bear children fearing that the further encroachment of the Sahara will cause starvation."

But perhaps the severest indictment of man's misuse of nature's bounties was made in 1933 by Mr. Swinnerton, Director of Tsetse Fly Research in Tanganyika. Of this insect, carrier of the dread sleeping sickness which has almost depopulated great regions of Africa, he wrote, "The Tsetse Fly has been, in certain directions, one of the greatest benefactors of the country. Two thirds of Tanganyika has been preserved by the fly from erosion and ruination at the hands of the natives."

Can nothing less than such a visitation, suggesting the Black Death of the Middle Ages, arrest the depredations of Man, the Bungler?

MAN, THE BUILDER

Primitive man took rivers as he found them. He could no more hope to control them than to control the frosts or storms.

Attracted to river valleys by a fertile soil and abundant water supply, his cultivated fields were first confined to narrow strips along the banks. As population increased, however, remoter areas appealed and a wider distribution of the waters was effected by the digging of irrigation ditches.

These muddy sluiceways are older than recorded history. That cruel despot, Sennacherib, paused from gloating over the torture of innumerable prisoners to inscribe upon a tablet a pet project of his: "To make the orchards luxuriant I cut and erected a canal with iron pickaxes from the borders of Kisiri to the plain about Nineveh through mountains and lowlands." The word "erected" implies that portions of this waterway were aqueducts.

Herodotus adds his descriptive touch: "The land of Assyria is but little watered by rain and that little nourishes the root of the corn . . . the grain grows to maturity by being irrigated."

Babylonia was a checkerboard of ditches. Not until the ferocious Mongol invasion completed their destruction in the thirteenth century did this former garden spot of the world degenerate into a mingled desert and morass.

But the advantages that river dwellers enjoyed were shadowed by the menace of impending floods. From seeking to appease the malignant spirits of the waters by incantation and sacrifice, man early turned to more practical methods, such as embankments to restrain the swollen current. In A.D. 69 the Emperor Ming Ti commissioned one Wang Chin to repair breaches in the banks of the Hwang Ho, that roistering demon among rivers, and to expedite the work presented him with the earliest recorded map of all China. Since that day thousands of miles of similar levees have been constructed as strait jackets on many turbulent rivers. Often they are reinforced by more resistant materials. In China mats of kaoliang, a reed resembling sugar cane, reinforce caving embankments. Similar mats of woven willow along the Mississippi are now supplemented by concrete mattresses. The aid of living vegetation has also been enlisted. Willows and poplars define many a river channel and help reclaim swampy areas.

But such barricades may prove ineffective when a great river, swollen by rains, goes upon a rampage, as innumerable valley dwellers have learned to their sorrow. Hence necessity long ago suggested diverting surplus waters into side channels or reservoirs. Perhaps the earliest mention of such a practice was mysterious

Lake Moeris, in ancient Egypt. Although modern research questions Herodotus's claim that Moeris was wholly "man-made," it was evidently enlarged and utilized for storing floodwaters from the Nile. Herodotus wrote: "By canal . . . the Nile . . . flows out into the lake and six months back into the river." Evidences of the locks and floodgates which regulated this alternate ebb and flow have been unearthed by recent excavations.

By similar methods the current of the Yangtze Kiang was stabilized by utilizing the shallow lakes in the valley of that great river, particularly Poyang Hu and Tung Ting. The latter, a favorite resort of mandarins and poets, is, in floodtime, a beautiful sheet of water, larger than Utah's Great Salt Lake. River connections are supplemented by canals which receive floodwaters only to restore them in time of drought.

Where similar storage reservoirs are lacking, short cuts to the sea are sometimes adopted as a last resort. In the great flood of 1927 New Orleans was saved only by dynamiting the levees below the city and allowing the pent-up waters to sweep across the lowlands to the gulf.

Rivers first navigated by rafts, by balsas of bundled reeds, by dugout canoes, and by coracles of hide have remained the great natural highways of the globe. Unfortunately they were not always located where most needed. Hence man, having learned that he could broaden a river's normal current by digging irrigation ditches, made further progress in more ambitious waterways or artificial rivers. To quote Herodotus again: "The Babylonian territory, like Egypt, is intersected by canals, and the largest of these is navigable stretching in the direction of the winter sunrise, and it extends from the Euphrates to the Tigris."

Doubtless the most impressive undertaking of this type was the Grand Canal of China, the work of many emperors. Begun some twenty-five centuries ago, it connected the Hwang Ho with the Yangtze Kiang and was eventually extended in both directions to the sea. Nearly twelve hundred miles in length, it provided the main artery of commerce between those dissimilar sectors, North China and South China, where the great rivers run from west to east. A picturesque waterway, crowded with junks and lesser craft, crossed by many arched bridges, and adorned with gaudy pagodas, it probably did more to unite the discordant political and economic segments of that great country than the most powerful central governments at Nanking or Peiping.

The glittering Moslem empires that flourished about Samarkand and Bokhara in Turkestan were nurtured by similar canals from the Oxus and the Jaxartes. In Russia both travel and commerce depended largely upon canals easily excavated in that low, flat terrain and linked with existing river systems. More familiar to the western world are the canals of Belgium and Holland which have so expanded the natural waterways of the Rhine and neighboring rivers that the Low Countries have been for centuries a veritable beehive of industry. Even in Java the Dutch have transplanted a bit of Holland's landscape to the Orient. For cities such as Batavia, built some distance inland to avoid the fever-ridden coast, are connected with the sea by canals.

In America, although irrigation and drainage ditches have far outstripped navigation canals in importance, New York owed much of its early prominence to the Erie Canal which made it the natural outlet for the recently opened Northwest.

Indians paddling birch-bark canoes, in dread of sudden storms, once hugged the forested shores of the Great Lakes. But the Soo Canal unlocked the gateway to Superior, while the Welland Canal gave access to the sea to the inland empire of the St. Lawrence.

The Suez Canal was the belated fulfillment of a Pharaoh's dream. The dredging of that waterway across the sandy isthmus changed the trade routes of the world and largely eliminated that perilous trail around the far-off Cape of Good Hope that Vasco da Gama's caravels followed to the Indies. Almost immediately it became the recognized life line of the British Empire, of such vital importance that unfortunately it proved a factor in the World Wars which have imperiled our civilization.

A more formidable engineering feat, the Panama Canal, severed the rocky spine of the Western Hemisphere. This, too, had its political repercussions in that revolution which established the new state of Panama. The voyage around Cape Horn, which long tested the endurance of "iron men in wooden ships," has been largely eliminated, and the course of freezing topsails, furious winds, and thunderous gray beards has been rerouted through tropic vegetation. How those doughty navigators Magellan, Sir Francis Drake, and Schouten would have welcomed this short cut to the Orient, and what human suffering might have been avoided in that age-old search for the Northwest Passage which cost the lives of Henry Hudson, Sir John Franklin, and many others.

More rudimentary but more fundamental is mankind's belated repenting of past follies and his resolve to avoid similar blunders in the future. Having ravaged his forests and depleted vast areas of fertile soil, he now seems bent upon turning over a new leaf.

To be sure, the Chinese long ago learned to avoid soil erosion by contour plowing, pebble mulching, and the like. The Incas and their unknown predecessors in Peru flanked the precipitous Andes with terraced gardens nearly to the snow line. Similar laborious embankments climb the slopes of Java, Luzon, and elsewhere in the Far East. Although such works were designed to provide additional space and better irrigation, they were also conservers of the soil.

In 1813 Thomas Jefferson wrote, "We now plough horizontally following the curvature of the hills and hollows . . . however crooked the rows may be . . . at present we lose none of the soil." That his wise example was not more widely followed is revealed in depleted farm lands everywhere. But there are encouraging symptoms that Americans, notorious for their prodigal wastefulness, are beginning to realize that such spoliation must be arrested.

National forests have been set apart, green oases in a desert of denudition, while reforesting is now widely practiced by great lumbering interests. Farmers are being instructed in the benefits of crop rotation, in contour plowing, and other methods of preserving the perishable topsoil. Cattle raisers and sheepherders have learned that overgrazing can kill the grass and cause disastrous dust storms. Trees have been planted in our western states, in Central Africa, and many other places as windbreaks to prevent the formation of other Dust Bowls.

All this, though only a beginning, is an encouraging augury of a saner approach to global problems.

TAMING WILD RIVERS

One of the most inspiring chapters in human achievement is the taming of great rivers.

Neanderthal man watched stupidly as maddened floodwaters uprooted great trees and undermined the banks. Rather would he face a charge of enraged aurochs than brave such a torrent.

In the first crude efforts at flood control, man's purpose was purely defensive. He wished to enjoy a river's bounties without suffering its ungovernable frenzies. His attitude was that of the African lion hunter, who yet builds thornbush shelters and keeps the watch fires blazing at night.

Long ago man learned how to compel wild animals to work for him: the ox, the donkey, the horse, the camel, the buffalo, and even the elephant. But only now is he beginning to domesticate wild rivers.

True, the ancients occasionally played at this dangerous game. Legend has it that Cyrus and his Persian cohorts diverted the channel of the Euphrates to expose passageways beneath the walls of Babylon. The body of that despoiler of decadent Rome, Alaric the Goth, was concealed beneath an Italian stream forced from its bed to provide a grave. A similar story has De Soto buried beneath the Mississippi, his monument the Great River which he had discovered.

Such engineering feats would now be commonplace. When Hoover Dam was erected in the gorges of the Colorado, the river was rerouted through a new channel blasted out of the living rock. Within recent years Russian savants have even suggested swerving the Oxus from its Aral outlet into the Caspian, to arrest, if possible, the subsidence of that greatest of inland seas.

In such projects man has enrolled a weird array of mechanical monsters, such as steam shovels, bulldozers, dredgers, and the like. The ancients could enlist no such robot toilers with metallic fingers and sinews of steel. Their machines were of the crudest type. Herodotus tells us that the valley of the Euphrates was "irrigated by hand and by engines," but the latter were such clumsy well sweeps or creaking water wheels as one may still observe along the upper Euphrates or on the Hwang Ho. Some glimmer of modern hydraulics is discernible, however, in the Hanging Gardens of Babylon, kept fresh and blooming by water raised through tubes by rotating screws.

The ancients also experimented with rough dams of little better workmanship than those the beavers erect athwart many a forested stream. These barricades were installed to raise the waters for irrigation. As craftsmanship improved, more elaborate pools and reservoirs appeared. But it is within the past century, mainly during the past few decades, that man has begun in earnest the taming of major rivers.

Earliest of these great projects was the Assuan Dam across the Nile, completed in 1902. This structure, 172 feet high, near the site of the first cataract, has accomplished more to water the farm lands of Egypt than the wisdom of all the priests of Pharaoh could compass through thousands of years. Similar structures now impede the current of other impetuous rivers. An even larger dam, the Mettur, impounds the floodwaters of the Cauvery, in southern India, a river little known to the western world, although, when swollen by the monsoon rains, it pours a torrent into the Bay of Bengal greater than the normal discharge of the Mississippi. The Bolshevist campaign to industrialize Russia embraces the construction of several huge dams. The one across the Dnieper, which Hitler's bombers damaged, is two hundred feet high and was built mainly to produce hydroelectric power. A more ambitious project would dam the Volga where that great river winds through limestone gorges in the Samara Bend. Australia, whose capricious and inadequate water supply is a problem, has already erected several dams across the Murray River. Tributary streams are also being barricaded. The Burrinjuck Dam across the Murrumbidgee is 247 feet high. Dr. John L. Savage, who made the blueprints for the Hoover and Grand Coulee dams, advocates a similar attempt to tame the spirit of the Yangtze Kiang. As reported in the *National Geographic Magazine*, he believes that such a project would provide irrigation for ten million acres, develop more than ten million kilowatts of power, and permit ocean-going vessels to proceed to Chungking and beyond. He says, "The Yangtze Gorge project is unquestionably the most important hydro project ever conceived, when considered in relation to the untold benefits that will accrue to ancient but undeveloped China."

America has made the greatest progress in controlling great rivers. The Colorado is now partially subdued by the Hoover Dam, 726 feet in height, a miracle in reinforced concrete. Still larger is the Grand Coulee Dam across the Columbia, where that great river is forced to perform stranger tricks than a circus elephant. But the colossus of such structures is the Fort Peck Dam across the Missouri, 250 feet high, nearly four miles long, with a material content of 128,000,000 cubic yards.

Most thoroughly domesticated of all big rivers is the Tennessee, whose stubborn temper is curbed by no fewer than twenty-six dams. But an even more complicated framework, comprising 101 of these restrictive structures, is being forged for the Big Muddy.

Flood prevention was the first problem on the agenda, and dams are ideal devices to stabilize river currents between varying extremes of flood and drought. To this end rivers must be treated as units, tributaries surveyed, and their temperamental caprices noted. For floodwaters in the Tennessee once spelled disaster at New Orleans.

Flood avoidance, however, is but one of the benefits of river control. Irrigation projects stem from the man-made lakes that back up beyond these barricades, projects designed to transform millions of unproductive acres into farm lands. Navigation is assured by flanking locks, where sufficient depth is now maintained over once impassable shoals. Many lakes thus formed in regions where lakes were previously unknown are beauty spots and favorite recreational centers. Still more engrossing is the creation of electric power.

Man learned long ago to compel many a minor waterfall to turn the millstones which ground his grain. The city of Rochester grew up about a waterfall in the Genesee River, while those twin metropolises, Minneapolis and St. Paul, arose from the wilderness about the Falls of St. Anthony on the upper Mississippi. Such natural mines of white coal, however, have been exploited but sparingly the world over. Many are located in remote or inaccessible regions where power is not required by the sparse population. High-tension wires have partially solved that problem by permitting the transmission of power to great distances. The energy that foams over Niagara's white precipice sets many a dynamo whirring and many an electric bulb aglow in faraway cities.

There is something akin to wizardry in such enterprises which lessens not a whit the other virtues of the waters. They will continue to irrigate as many acres, supply the needs of as many people, provide navigation for as much commerce, remain sylvan retreats, their beauty unimpaired; in short, suffer no loss whatsoever from the extraction of that vital but invisible essence—hydroelectric power.

Huge dams which provide artificial waterfalls in regions where they may be more readily utilized often justify construction costs which otherwise might prove prohibitive.

Water power! What a challenge to man's audacity, his courage and his enterprise! For his achievements to date are only a beginning. The toil-bowed shoulders of all the coolies in China cannot equal the power that goes to waste down the gorges of the Congo. But the man who would place a bit in the white teeth of that giant river has probably not yet been born.

Great rivers, as their spirits are more thoroughly broken, are assigned more menial tasks. The Father of Waters, though he chafes and rages, has been compelled to dredge out his own channel. Similar jetties and cutoffs force the Volga to narrow and deepen its approach to the Caspian. And other rivers, broken like fractious colts, are employed in similar labors.

In some cases even gravity has been defied. At the Grand Coulee Dam the power of the chastened Columbia elevates water more than two hundred feet beyond the beetling escarpment above. Here part of the current is forced literally to run uphill. Rivers still go berserk and occasionally rend their shackles, but more and more they are yielding to the spell of the surveyor's transit and the engineer's blueprint, are being restricted and even rerouted; in short, transformed from irresponsible forces to fit into the orderly pattern of the future.

Man has evoked the demoniac frenzy which lurks in the atom, although its control may await that superintelligence with which imagination endows the Martians. Fortunately a less dangerous power is latent in the flowing fresh waters of the globe, ready to be made available by the taming of wild rivers.

THE RIVERS OF THE FUTURE

River valleys which sheltered our earliest cultures have lost none of their appeal; for they still provide the most favorable environment for those political, commercial, and manufacturing centers which are the focal points of modern civilization.

If this statement be doubted, a glance at the global map should prove instructive. Just as those ancient capitals, Memphis and Thebes, once flourished along the Nile, while Babylon and Nineveh rose beside the Euphrates and the Tigris, modern cities cluster in similar river valleys the world over.

The European array is particularly impressive. London on the Thames heads the list, with Glasgow, second city of the British Isles, on the Clyde. Of the foremost cities of continental Europe, Moscow is on a branch of the Volga, Berlin on the Spree, and Paris on the Seine. Among lesser but still populous centers, Leningrad is on the Neva; Kiev on the Dnieper; Vienna, Budapest, and Belgrade on the Danube; Hamburg on the Elbe; Bremen on the Weser; Rome on the Tiber; Milan in the valley of the Po; Madrid in that of the Tagus; Antwerp on the Schelde; Rotterdam, Cologne, Strasbourg, Frankfurt, Essen, Düsseldorf and other important centers in the valley of the Rhine, while the list might be greatly extended.

The largest city of continental Asia, Shanghai, is on a branch of the Yangtze Kiang, while Chungking, the war capital, Nanking, the seat of Ancient Empire, Hankow, the Chinese Pittsburgh, and many other cities are in the same great valley which nurtures an estimated population of two hundred million people. Only less numerous are the multitudes which swarm in the valley of the Ganges. There stands Calcutta, once the second city of the British Empire; Delhi, the ancient capital; Benares, the holy; Agra of the Taj Mahal, and others. Rangoon, queen city of Burma, is on an outlet of the Irrawaddy; Mukden, metropolis of Manchuria, on the Hun Ho; Harbin on the Sungari, while the growing cities of Siberia are all of river origin.

The largest city in Africa, Cairo, overlooks the Nile, while Johannesburg, the mining center of the south, is on a branch of the Orange.

In the New World river valleys have maintained their perennial lure. New York, greatest of all, is on the Hudson, Philadelphia on the Delaware, while the valley of the St. Lawrence is fairly studded with populous centers. Among them are Montreal, Toronto, Buffalo, Cleveland, Detroit, Milwaukee, and Chicago. The Mississippi Basin also has its coterie of great cities: New Orleans, St. Louis, Minneapolis, St. Paul, Kansas City, Louisville, Cincinnati, Pittsburgh, and others. The founders of America chose the banks of the Potomac for the site of Washington, while Canadians placed their capital overlooking the picturesque Ottawa River.

The chief city of South America, Buenos Aires, is on the Plata, a river system which also boasts that energetic Brazilian center São Paulo, Montevideo, capital of Uruguay, and Asunción, capital of Paraguay. Other South American cities follow the pattern laid down by Pizzaro when, upon the ruins of the Inca Empire, he established his capital, Lima, beside the Rimac River.

Few of the world's great cities are *not* located upon rivers, and those few are usually seaports, such as Tokyo, Rio de Janiero, San Francisco, Marseilles, and Istambul. Even Los Angeles, once inland, has spread out to secure a window upon the Pacific at San Pedro, just as ancient Athens extended its long walls to include the seaport of Piraeus.

The popularity of river valleys is fundamental. Proverbially fertile both in farm lands and forest resources, such valleys offer an unfailing water supply and convenient transportation. Neither graded highways nor railroads, nor fleet-winged airplanes can obscure the fact that the cheapest shipments are by water. This is particularly true of bulk freight, such as coal, ore, grain, and building materials.

Rivers offer other advantages also: the scenic charm which abides in watery foregrounds and shores both undulating and precipitous, and lastly, that water power which has run to waste for centuries.

The industrial centers of the western world have developed

about great deposits of iron and coal: mid-England, the Ruhr Valley in Europe, the Pittsburgh and Great Lakes area in North America. Coal, and more recently petroleum, has furnished the power and steel the framework of the Mechanical Age in which we live.

But the scene is shifting. Our petroleum resources are approaching exhaustion. Coal, though more abundant, once burned is lost forever. Iron-ore deposits are dwindling. The development of new power sources and new metals is impending. Unlike combustibles, the water power of our rivers is continually replenished. Moreover, new metals, aluminum and magnesium, lighter and more abundant than iron, offer alluring possibilities.

The dams of the Murray River are expected to increase Australia's population by at least a million persons. The Tennessee, now harnessed to productive work, has raised the standard of living of several millions who inhabit its valley and doubtless will provide homes for many more.

British enterprise, attracted to Victoria Falls and the lesser-known rapids of the Zambezi, now visualizes a new prosperity in the valley of that great river. The development of the Niger River Valley holds similar prospects. In such favored areas Great Britain may yet restore her crumbling world empire.

Earth's grandest rivers are even more attractive. The Congo is a mine of living waters, a natural highway to a vast interior of fabulous forest, agricultural and mineral resources. The La Plata-Paraná, with its unrivaled waterfalls and rich hinterland, is another challenge to the future. But the project that most invokes the fancy is the conquest of the Amazon. No one will ever subdue that moving ocean of fresh waters as the Tennessee River has been subdued. The clearing of those fever-ridden jungles is no such program as confronted engineers at Panama when modern sanitation transformed that onetime pesthole. The task is too formidable even for the concerted efforts of border countries, although Brazil, Bolivia, Peru, and Ecuador have recently combined upon a study of the Amazon. Surely that inland Mediterranean, with its unrivaled network of navigable channels, its boundless resources in forests and water power, will not always be abandoned to the ants and other swarming insects, man's rivals for the mastery of the globe.

Elsewhere science has advanced in seven-league boots. Consider the strides medicine has made in combating disease and promoting health; the mechanical conquest of the air, and the dizzy speeding up of communications through such media as the telegraph, telephone, radio, and radar. How completely chemistry and physics have reorganized our knowledge of matter from the wreckage of discarded theories once revered as axioms. How deeply giant microscopes peer into the mysteries of cell life to reveal those deadly viruses once deemed invisible. How far our telescopes range outer space, thrusting back the boundaries of the universe to an immeasurable remoteness while astronomers speak glibly of starry distances and rates of motion that benumb the very senses.

No less spectacular has been our development of the infernal mechanisms of war, so that we have far outdistanced all the butchers of history and made even Genghis Khan appear a piker in bloodshed and human misery.

Meanwhile we forge blithely along the highroad to global destruction with our atomic bombs, our jet-propelled planes, and our death-dealing rockets guided by invisible rays; devices that would sober a medieval Satan himself. And all the while our knowledge of geography is neglected and our appropriation of nature's powers for useful purposes largely ignored.

Yet war has taught one salutary lesson—the essential unity of our world, whose problems are common to all. That fact is nowhere more evident than in the need for saner utilization of global fresh waters; to avoid floods, eliminate soil erosion, irrigate our fields, foster our commerce, and provide inexhaustible power to offset depleted coal and petroleum resources that once expended can never be restored.

Astronomers tell us that upon our neighbor planet, Mars, the meager moisture collects in snows about the poles, whence it trickles feebly toward the equator through waterways that some claim were constructed by superior intelligence. However that may be, the picture thus starkly drawn may one day be our own. The date may lie too far in the future to impress the improvident and wasteful present, yet its approach seems inevitable. As a grim finale we may, with profit, contemplate that burned-out celestial cinder, the Moon. Among the ghostly shadow patterns upon its surface we search in vain for markings familiar to our happier sphere, such valleys as embrace Earth's Grandest Rivers.

THE THIRTY RIVERS WITH THE LARGEST DRAINAGE AREA

	River	Drainage Area Square Miles	Continent
1.	Amazon	2,772,000	South America
2.	Congo	1,425,000	Africa
3.	Nile	1,293,000	Africa
4.	Mississippi-Missouri	1,243,000	North America
5.	La Plata-Paraná	1,198,000	South America
6.	Lena	1,169,000	Asia
7.	Ob	1,000,000*	Asia
8.	Yenisei	1,000,000*	Asia
9.	Amur	787,000	Asia
10.	Yangtze Kiang	750,000	Asia
11.	Mackenzie	682,000	North America
12.	Volga	592,000	Europe
13.	Niger	580,000	Africa
14.	Orinoco	570,000	South America
15.	St. Lawrence	565,000	North America
16.	Zambezi	513,000	Africa
17.	Ganges	432,000	Asia
18.	Euphrates	430,000	Asia
19.	Murray-Darling	414,000	Australia
20.	Hwang Ho	400,000	Asia
21.	Orange	400,000	Africa
22.	Indus	372,000	Asia
23.	Brahmaputra	361,000	Asia
24.	Nelson-Saskatchewan	360,000	North America
25.	Mekong	350,000	Asia
26.	Yukon	330,000	North America
27.	Jaxartes	320,000	Asia
28.	Columbia	259,000	North America
29.	São Francisco	252,000	South America
30.	Colorado	244,000	North America

*Rough estimates, probably understatements.

THE THIRTY LONGEST RIVERS*

	River	Length in Miles	Continent
1.	Nile	4,053	Africa
2.	Amazon†	4,000	South America
3.	Mississippi-Missouri	3,986	North America
4.	Yenisei	3,553	Asia
5.	Yangtze Kiang	3,400	Asia
6.	Lena	3,000	Asia
7.	Congo	2,900	Africa
8.	Amur	2,900	Asia
9.	Hwang Ho	2,700	Asia
10.	Ob	2,600	Asia
11.	Niger	2,600	Africa
12.	Mekong	2,600	Asia
13.	Mackenzie	2,525	North America
14.	La Plata-Paraná	2,450	South America
15.	Murray-Darling	2,345	Australia
16.	Volga	2,325	Europe
17.	Yukon	2,300	North America
18.	Zambezi	2,200	Africa
19.	St. Lawrence	2,100	North America
20.	São Francisco	1,811	South America
21.	Rio Grande	1,800	North America
22.	Salween	1,750	Asia
23.	Danube	1,725	Europe
24.	Orinoco	1,700	South America
25.	Indus	1,700	Asia
26.	Euphrates	1,700	Asia
27.	Jaxartes	1,700	Asia
28.	Brahmaputra	1,680	Asia
29.	Nelson-Saskatchewan	1,660	North America
30.	Ganges	1,540	Asia

*According to the latest available statistics.

†Estimates of the Amazon's length range up to 4,200 miles.

EARTH'S GRANDEST RIVERS

1. The largest river—the Amazon
2. The longest river—the Nile or Amazon
3. The most important river—the Yangtze Kiang
4. The most commercialized river—the St. Lawrence
5. The most venerated river—the Ganges
6. The most romantic river—the Rhine
7. The most dangerous river—the Hwang Ho
8. The most copied river—the Indus
9. The most historic river—the Euphrates
10. The most spectacular river—the Colorado
11. The most mysterious river—the Mekong or the Oxus
12. The river richest in farm and grazing lands—the Mississippi
13. The river of the most extensive forests—the Amazon
14. The rivers of richest mineral resources—the São Francisco, Orange, and St. Lawrence
15. The rivers of greatest potential water power—the Congo, Amazon, and Paraná
16. The river with the most extensive waterways—the Amazon, 50,000 miles
17. The least important of great rivers—the Salween
18. The least developed of great rivers—the Orinoco
19. The most interesting river—the Nile
20. The river of greatest prospects—the Amazon

THE FIVE LARGEST DELTAS

1. The Ganges-Brahmaputra	20,000	square miles
2. The Niger	14,000	" "
3. The Lena	12,000	" "
4. The Mississippi	8,600	" "
5. The Irrawaddy	8,500	" "

THE FIVE BROADEST ESTUARIES

1. The Amazon	207	miles wide
2. The La Plata	138	" "
3. The St. Lawrence	90	" "
4. The Yangtze Kiang	50	" "
5. The Yenisei	40	" "

Index

Date Due